PRAGUE,
MY
LOVE

Hilary
A. James

Jiří
P. Musil

PRAGUE, MY LOVE

An unusual guide book to the hidden
corners of Prague!

Crossroads of Prague Ltd,
Lodecká 2, Prague 1

Copyright
© Hilary A. James, Jiří P. Musil,
1992
All rights reserved

© Illustration Zdeněk Mlčoch,
1992

Design Miloslav Fulín

ISBN 80-900009-9-1

Printed and bound
in Czech and Slovak Federative Republic
by Polygrafia a.c.
Prague

DEDICATION
FOR
DEAR JOY KOHOUTOVÁ

CONTENTS

PROLOGUE

ALICE GOT THROUGH CUSTOMS and passport control quickly and stood in the inconspicuous modern hall of Prague's Ruzyně airport. It seemed tiny and quiet after the bustling vastness of Heathrow. She saw an ordinary-looking man of about thirty with untidy black hair. He was holding up a card with the name of his agency,

HAPPINESS IN PRAGUE.

He bowed to her and introduced himself, "Blažej Kohout!" Taking her shoulder bag he led her to what seemed the smallest car in the world, a minute Fiat. She looked at it in astonishment.

"Our agency's car."

"How many people work for your agency?"

"Only me! A one-man agency."

It was raining and everything was rather blurred and indistinct. She made out lines of ugly little houses and a few concrete apartment blocks. She was travelling on her own for the first time and her parents had insisted on a professional guide. Blažej glanced at her furtively. He saw a very pale girl with short fair hair. She was wearing a neat white blouse and a grey pleated skirt. Regrets! he thought. It always starts like this. She's been saving up her money and now a whole week in such an out-of-the-way place."

"I'll never fly again!" she burst out angrily, "We had engine trouble and the plane was lurching all over the place. Cups of coffee and beer bottles were falling everywhere. People were shouting and laughing hysterically and rushing to get to the toilets. They wouldn't stay in their seats. The old man sitting next to me asked me if it was 'the End!'. The pilot told me we would have to make a forced landing in Germany. It was horrible! Never, never again!"

"But you're safe!" he said, swerving to avoid a taxi, "Imagine the feelings of the first aviators."

She frowned. He's not a proper guide and the car's like a beetle. I can't even stretch my legs. I could have gone to Paris, she thought.

"Prague airport is the biggest in Central Europe with

57,000 aircraft belonging to 24 companies landing here every year and handling nearly two million passengers."

"But let me tell you about the first man to be airborne in Prague," he continued, turning a corner so sharply that she gripped her seat, "It was October 1st 1790. A Frenchman, an 'aerial sailor' François Blanchard, went up in a balloon. A year later, Karel Enslen made colossal painted hot-air balloons in human and animal shapes. A gigantic flying boar appeared above some Prague riflemen at target practice. A huge flying stag fell down in front of a bakery in Votice, south of Prague. The baker nearly had a heart-attack and dropped a tray of fresh rolls."

Alice turned from her window and looked at Blažej in surprise.

"The figure of a bearded man, three metres high, flew into a barn on the outskirts of town and fell on two lovers embracing in the straw. The girl shouted, 'My father!' They were both stiff with fright and had to be carried out wrapped in blankets!"

She smiled reluctantly.

"We're driving through the Šárka district now. Mammoth hunters once lived here."

The little car bumped over the cobble-stones, as Blažej drove through Vokovice into Dejvice district.

"A statue of Lenin stood here once, he looked as though his bees had emigrated. One morning people went to work and found that his statue had disappeared. Only the pedestal remained. He had left Prague! Maybe he was angry."

"Where did he go?"

"No one knows. His statue was offered to the Soviet Ambassador who declined the generous gift. Perhaps Lenin's sleeping somewhere in a cellar waiting for a Western beauty to awaken him with a kiss."

Alice stared at Blažej's profile. He seems a bit crazy, she thought.

"Primeval people lived here. The Slav people had to struggle against waves of invaders. Fierce tribes fought their 10 way across Central Europe. The recurring threat of invasion left its mark on the Slavs — a dread of the unexpected. Also the feeling that history is a tortuous business."

"I hope you're not going to give me lectures! I can't work up any interest in ancient tribes. I want to know what's happening now."

The car joined a slow-moving line of traffic. Suddenly the spires of the Cathedral and then the whole Cathedral, appeared on their right. Blažej knew that this view acted as a tuning-fork.

Alice leaned forward in her seat.

He began to recite,

"...I read the duties of the arising day
Which appeared in front of me like unfinished kisses,
So that I should colour them with your eyelids'burning brush,

St Vitus' Cathedral

Half-closed to dream forever of what you've seen,
While I walked through the awakening streets of the town
In the middle of Europe..."

The car groaned and rattled as they turned down a narrow cobbled street. She saw tall walls marked with damp and decay, metal-studded doors, wooden house-signs, blackened statues and grey scaffolding blotched with lichen.

She turned to Blažej. "If I'm really going to dream about Prague forever, I need an unusual guide. I don't want someone who's going to rattle off dry facts or read me things from official guide-books. And I don't want to see the usual places with a crowd of tourists. I want..."

"Our agency is different," he interrupted gently.

"All I know about your country is that there was a Defenestration somewhere or other. Also, I've read Kafka and I've seen President Havel on TV. I can't remember what he said, though. I'd like to know a bit about the history of Prague to understand what's happening now. I'd like to know how people here really lived and felt. I'd like to see places most tourists don't see. I'm in Central Europe and I want to see..." She laughed suddenly, "Well, I don't really know what I'm looking for but maybe you'll help me find it! I've heard that people come to Prague because there's some special feeling in the air. Is it true?"

"I think so. We're no longer afraid. There's hope in the air." He drew up in front of Alice's small hotel near Náměstí Republiky. "You'll be here for six days. If you agree, I'll show you my city in a different historical setting each day and I'll try to tell you what happened to the people of Prague. And I'll tell you about our recent past, the time of communism. We've had a turbulent history. We've come through many years of darknes. I'll show you some unusual places and I've some stories to tell you. Do you like stories?"

"Very much! Will they be true stories?"

"Perhaps," he replied, as he carried her bag into the lobby.

"I'd like to know what you think and feel about things,"

she said, as she searched for her passport. "I'm sure a lot of tourists never know what Czech people are thinking. I'd like to know your thoughts about your city, your Revolution — everything!"

Blažej looked at her with interest for the first time since leaving the airport.

THE FIRST DAY·PRIMEVAL

EARLY MORNING

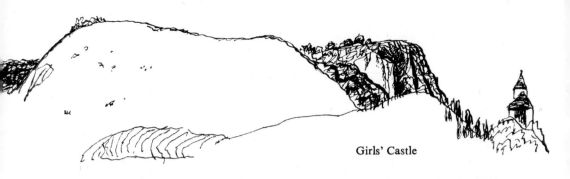

Girls' Castle

ALICE'S FACE WAS STONY as she got into Blažej's car.
She had slept badly and the drive from the airport left an
impression of a decaying town — scratched walls, crumbling
plaster, broken pavements. And today, everything was
shrouded in grey mist.

"I hope you've recovered from your journey."

She yawned, "I'm tired. I'm not quite sure if I'll be able
to stay here a whole week..."

Blažej nodded. A professional guide, he was used to grumpy
tourists and poor starts. "Over four thousand million years
ago," he began, "Pre-Cambrian Prague was under the sea.
There were giant glaciers nearby and under Prague there was
an enormous volcano, the Butovice volcano, churning out hot
lava. The sea covered the territory of Prague three times.
In the wild ocean there were rocks as big as Stonehenge!
When the ocean receded there were swamps with huge lizards.
Imagine a landscape of colossal horse-tails and club-mosses
and glaring through them a huge red sun. Eventually, these
swamps became savannas with mammoths, tigers and apes,
and finally... the first human being."

She rubbed her eyes, "This car's too small, I can't stretch
my legs!"

He parked the car in a narrow street.

"Are we in a village?" she was astonished that they could
be out of Prague so quickly.

"No, we're still in Prague. This is a quiet suburb."

They climbed a steep path through woodland and came out
onto high cliffs.

15   "This place is called 'Girls' Castle'. You're walking on

prehistoric land. From the dawn of time, through immeasurable ages, this cliff, Hammer's Cliff, was at war with the turbulent sea. The cliff survived! Down there in the valley, hidden in a copse, is all that remains of the ocean, a tiny lake." He stooped and handed her a stone. "A prehistoric pebble!"

The mist was clearing and Alice felt the hot sun on her face. She was looking into a deep wooded valley. Far away to her right she saw the apartment blocks of Barrandov and below her, the glint of the River Vltava.

"You can see why primitive people settled down there. They had the protection of natural cliff walls," he said.

"And they had the Vltava. Fishing and trade..."

"Water," he pointed out, "And this place was a cross-roads for East-West trade."

"I wonder if there were sharks in the Vltava?"

"Who knows? Sharks have been around for 94 million years whereas humans have only existed for seven million years."

She looked at the encircling cliffs. The lower slopes were sprinkled with sparse grass and yellow flowers but the gleaming blue-grey peaks were bare. She glanced down at her feet, "My shoes are soaked," she said indignantly.

"There's heavy dew. We'll return to the car. You're looking down on the territory of the early settlers. Countless tribes lived down there. Settlement pits have been discovered and trepanated skulls."

"My feet are cold!"

"After the hot jungle came the ice-age. The valley tribes had to survive ice-storms for eight long months of winter. And they had to fight off ferocious bears; reared on their hind legs, they were three times taller than a man."

"This is agony!" she gave a small shriek as she got into the car.

"What's the matter?" he asked in alarm.

"I filled my pockets with stones and now they're sticking into me!"

Šárka Valley

"Please, throw them away! They're useless!"

"But they may be precious fossils."

"No, just stones. We may find fossils later, we're on our way to Šárka Valley."

* * *

"Now, we're in Šárka," he told her.
"This is said to be the oldest settlement, the territory of the first Praguers — the Stone Age people."

They walked down a flight of wooden steps to a charming open air swimming-pool, fringed with willows. Swans sailed by. They climbed up onto the high cliffs. Alice looked down into a sheer wooded ravine. To her right, in the distance, stood a solitary apartment block.

Blažej pointed to it: "Dejvice district!"

"It's bizarre! We're only a few steps from town and yet we're in the heart of the country among corn-fields. She took a deep breath, "Beautiful, pure air! It smells of dry grass and trees."

She scrambled to the edge of the ravine starting a small avalanche of rocks which cascaded to the ravine's edge and into nothingness.

"Stop!" he shouted, "Stay where you are!"

"Why? I'm not going to fall."

"Never mind!" he said sharply, "I don't want a corpse on my hands, I'm a professional guide, you know."

She scowled at him.

"I'm sorry," he said more mildly, "I didn't mean to give you orders. It's just that I'm concerned about your welfare."

She smiled faintly, "I appreciate your concern. I must admit, when you talked about Lenin's bees yesterday I thought you had a few bees in your bonnet."

"Maybe I have. I belong to an amateur archaeological society and we come here every weekend to be primeval hunters. We change into skins, start fires by rubbing flints together and catch small animals with primitive slings. We've made an artificial mammoth which slides rapidly down this sheer cliff. We attack it with flint darts and bows and arrows."

She looked at him warily.

"The Stone Age Praguers made their homes in caves," he continued. "Near here, in the former brick factory at Jenerálka, weapons and tools of Stone Age hunters have been found and remains of their fires. For the primeval hunter, the cave was their refuge, their home and their grave."

They descended the cliffs and, skirting a car-park, walked back into the woods and along a gorge. There was a trout stream on their left, great cliffs towered above them and the birch trees on the high crags on either side of the gorge almost touched each other above their heads.

She knelt by the stream and stared into the clear water, "It's a fabulous place. Just the spot for tired tourists after a long morning in town and hot pavements."

Blažej nodded, "Most tourists would never find this place, though it's only a tram ride from Dejvice Square.

"I keep looking out for caves! Where are they?"

"These cliffs were riddled with caves in ancient times. If you want to go inside a cave, I'll take you to a cave town."

* * *

"Your car's making strange noises!" she said, as they drove through the little town of Beroun with its Gothic gateways.

"It always does," said Blažej cheerfully, "although it's a Polish Fiat, I've decided it's a Slav. I've christened it 'Šemík' after a legendary flying horse."

"This car's never going to fly!" she interrupted crossly. "I'd christen it 'Dying Wheelbarrow.' I thought guides had to have proper cars."

"If I could afford a better car, my neighbours would be envious. They'd probably creep out at night and scratch the bonnet. Please look at my beautiful countryside! This is the Bohemian Karst, a protected area."

They were driving through wooded country with rolling hills and small streams.

"I'm thinking about the contrast between the English countryside and yours," she said thoughtfully. "I think the contrast lies in colour. England is greener — there's every possible shade of green."

"It always rains in England. When I think of London, I think of Piccadilly Circus with pattering rain bouncing off top-hatted men."

"How ridiculous!" she said scornfully, "My feet are still damp". She took off her shoes.

"We'll be in Koněprusy in a few minutes. You'll see the biggest caves in Bohemia."

With a grinding of gears the little car struggled up the steep road towards Golden Horse Cliff. Blažej pointed to a pine-covered hill on their right.

"That hill contained a miraculous horde of treasure, chests overflowing with silver and gold. But the hill would only open and reveal its riches for someone with an iron hand and golden hair!" He pointed to a derelict cottage, "Over there lived a vain and greedy woman. Desperate to enter the hill and seize its treasure she went to Prague and engaged a famous smith to make her an iron hand..."

"How did she fix it to her arm?" asked Alice quickly.

"It was a glove of iron. She also purchased a great metallic wig with golden strands. When she came to the hill it opened for her. She descended into its depths and disappeared." He pointed to a small copse, "A poor young couple lived over there. They talked endlessly about the hill and their neighbour's strange disappearance. One day, the girl looked thoughtfully at her lover's hands,

'In a way, you've got iron hands.' she said, 'You tame wild stallions. And my long hair is bright gold! Come! We'll go to the hill!' The hill opened for them and they were greeted by an old man who pointed to chests brimming with gold and silver. 'Help yourselves, my children. You may take as much as you can carry.' 'But where's our neighbour?' asked the girl anxiously. 'She was last seen climbing this hill!' 'Who knows,' said the old man, 'Liars always disappear from view!' The young couple left the hill with their pockets bulging with gold."

"I suppose they lived happily ever after?" said Alice derisively.

"Yes," Blažej replied, "They bought a private farm."

* * *

They descended cautiously down winding ice-coated steps into a world of caves.

"We've got many wonders here in Bohemia which are often unknown in the West," Blažej explained. "This cave labyrinth takes us back 60 or 70 million years to the Tertiary Age. These strange caves and their bewildering corridors sheltered people in the Ice Age."

They were moving in a world of fantastic shapes and colours. Great stalagmites glittered far above them and

20

stalactites seemed to sprout from jutting cliffs. Icy drops of water fell on their heads.

"Watch out for ice-drops! A stalactite might grow in your hair. There are 40 metres of stone above us. We're in the bowels of the earth, in the homes of my ancestors, the Stone Age hunters." He pointed to the dim forms of two bulls high above their heads: "Their paintings!"

Alice forgot about her damp feet, "It's incredible! A landscape by Salvador Dali."

Koněprusy
Caves

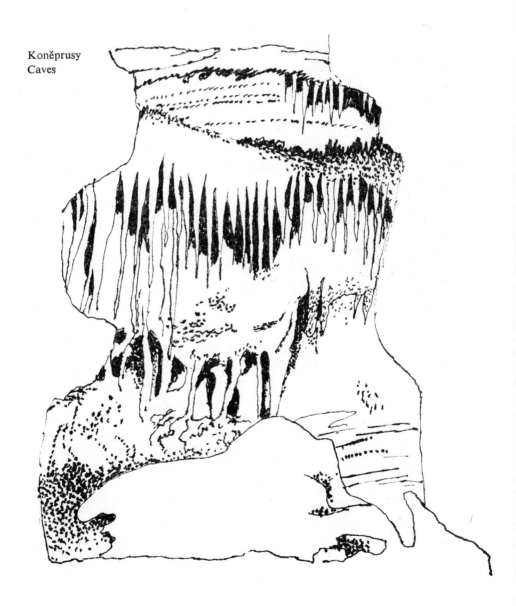

21

She looked in wonder at the weird colours of the rocks — virulent green, yellow ochre and rose. Around them were dreamlike, gorgeous shapes of cave-castles and above them unending twisted chimneys of stone.

"This limestone dissolves and reappears in a never-ending succession of grotesque forms." He pointed to a rock in the shape of a gnarled human face and a giant stalactite looking like a city with innumerable towers.

"It's Prague!" he announced.

She peered between two gnome — like stones guarding the entrance to one of the caves.

"That's a bear-cave. Many bones have been found here and a rhino's jaw. Imagine the Stone Age family surviving in darkness huddled in these icy depths, at the mercy of ferocious rhinos and savage bears."

"I expect they had some kind of know-how we don't have. They must have moved in this darkness like bats." Leaning over the stair-rail, she looked down at a ring of stones and replicas of tools.

"A medieval forgers'den." he said. "These caves were a hide-out for all sorts of crooks." They entered an enormous cave. In its centre was a hill of stones like a giant's chair.

Alice looked round in wonder. "It's like a royal hall," she said, "with a throne of kings."

* * *

"We're now standing above the cave-world on Golden Horse Hill," Blažej explained. "The ancient Celts used this hill as a place of worship. They worshipped the horse. If you're not tired, I'll take you to a Celtic site. It's not far from Prague. But first we'll have lunch in Zbraslav."

They sat near the river in an old restaurant with a vaulted ceiling. "I like walking in woods," Alice told him, "but I thought you were going to show me Prague."

"This is all Prague territory," he replied, waving his arms expansively. "We're in Prague 5. The chateau round the corner, a former abbey, houses one of our greatest collections

Golden Horse Hill

of nineteenth and twentieth century sculpture. What will you have to eat? Pork and dumplings?"

Alice shuddered. "I'm a vegetarian. Anyway, I'm not hungry, I had a huge breakfast."

He smiled, "I'm a vegetarian, too. That makes two odd people."

She frowned, "I don't think we're odd. It's only crazies who eat meat."

The waiter brought them coffee and poppy-seed cakes. "You may not approve of the crazy Celts," Blažej took up the tale, "they ate horses in their rituals. It was the custom for a new chieftain to copulate with a mare in full view of the tribe. When the mare gave birth, the baby horse was cooked and eaten. After the feast the tribe was filled with magical strength."

* * *

They crossed the Vltava River and following a winding path through plantations of young birches they climbed an ancient hill.

"What an extraordinary light! One side of the wood is purple-grey and the other a mellow gold."

"You've got an eye for colour!"

23

"I want to be a landscape painter," she replied shortly.

"This must have been the palace," she said, looking with interest at the stone outlines of rooms and fortified walls on the crest of the hill.

"This was a town. Thousands of Celts lived up here. Their remains have been found in Bohemia dating from 300 B.C. and one of the Celtic tribes, the Boji, gave Bohemia its name. They built their towns deep in the forests. Some of the tribes ruled large territories and controlled important trade-routes from their strategic fortresses. Here in Bohemia they were a vulnerable frontier people staving off attacks from hostile tribes. They flourished for about a thousand years until Germanic tribes drove them to the fringes of Europe. I call myself a Slav," he continued, "but I may have a few drops of Celt in my veins!"

"We're all a hotch-potch," she said. "My father's a Welsh-man so I'm partly Celt. And I've got Saxon in me, too. I could even be Roman if I didn't have such a ridiculously small nose!" She glanced at Blažej but he was looking intently at the site and seemed to be lost in thought.

"A thousand years of Celtic history," he murmured, "and we know so little about them. They didn't leave written records, but excavations here and in Switzerland show that in secure times they produced fine artists who made exquisite objects — clasps, drinking cups, beautifully painted vases and decorative chariot-fittings. They loved gold objects decorated with flowers and animals. Their bards sang of nature and feasting and their Druids taught ritual and worship and foretold the future of the tribe."

Alice sat silently in the sunshine feeling the strange remoteness of the site. "I've read about the Celts," she said at last, "Caesar's 'Gallic Wars'. The Romans looked on them as mysterious barbarians from the North."

"The Romans tell us that the Celts were tall, fair, muscular people," he replied, "Caesar said that they loved liberty and hated slavery. The Greeks also thought them brave. Aristotle said they had no fear of earthquakes or the raging seas."

24

"I thought Caesar despised them."

"He thought they were hopeless organizers and far too fond of riotous feasting. The Romans found them ferocious in attack but pathetic in defeat. Livy said that a defeated Celt was less than a woman."

"What male prejudice!" she said indignantly. "They had amazing women chiefs. Look at Boudicca!"

"Yes, their women fought in war with long spears alongside the men."

"I think the Celts have got lost in a cloud of Roman

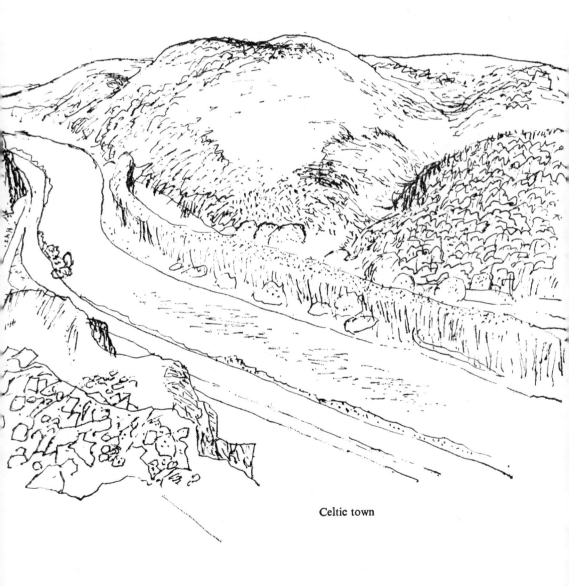

Celtic town

propaganda," she got up, brushing stone-dust from her skirt. "The Romans were boring road-builders and central-heating engineers. The Celts were mystics who loved the forests and the seasons and singing to the trees. I think I'll excuse them for eating young horses."

* * *

They drove along a road between lowering wooded cliffs and then climbed to a rocky headland, an area of wild grassland dotted with fir trees, overlooking the Vltava.

"This is Levý Hradec. In the 9th century, the Slav Prince Bořivoj of the Czech tribe became a great ruler in Central Bohemia and he built his hill-fort here. It was the first residence of our Přemyslid dynasty."

Levý Hradec

Alice stretched out on the grass. Almost submerged in tall grasses, she smiled up at the blue sky, "Where did the Slavs come from?"

"The Slav tribes probably came here from Central Asia in   26 the 5th or 6th centuries A.D. From the very beginning they had to fight for their independence against hostile tribes, the Avars in Hungary, the Franks in the West and later, German tribes. To survive they needed bravery and cunning. They resorted to all kinds of tricks, set traps for their enemies and even used trained birds of prey. Our playwright, Josef Topol, refers to the first Slavs as the 'Midnight Wind' — tough, resourceful, weavers of brilliant strategies..."

"What kinds of tricks and traps?" Alice interrupted quickly.

"I'll tell you about 'Figs from Buttocks'" Blažej began.

Alice sneezed mightily, "I've got grass-seeds up my nose and I haven't got a handkerchief. "Sorry, please go on about the buttocks."

"The Emperor, Henry II, had decided to besiege the Italian town of Medulan and he sent a messenger to Czech King Vratislav to ask for manpower. The Czechs preferred to use cunning rather than lose lives, so they began to circulate terrible stories about Czech atrocities in Medulan. It was rumoured in the town that the Czechs ate children! The Czech warriors made images of babies out of dough, stuck them on spits and around their campfires at night they baked and ate them. The horrified Italians watched them from the ramparts. Two Czech warriors got into a single garment, sat on a horse and galloped round the fortifications. The Italians saw one body with two heads looking in different directions. They thought a fearful devil had come, and panicked. The Czechs seized their opportunity, put on black masks, climbed the town fortifications with long ladders and captured the town — by this time in the grip of hysteria — without the loss of a single life..."

"Did the Czechs kill the Italians?"

"The Czech cronicler Dalimil tells us that the Czechs were in a merry mood. They told the Italian forces that all they had to do to save their lives was to pull a fig from a horse's arse with their teeth. The Czechs carried away a lot of booty including a marvellous candlestick which shines to this day in St. Vitus'Cathedral."

"At the beginning of the 10th century," Blažej continued, "the Slavs actually established the first Western Slav state of Great Moravia but this fell to hostile tribes and the future would lie with the Přemyslid dynasty. They were Czech princes who gradually united Bohemia and this was their first stronghold. By the end of the 9th century they had moved to Prague..."

"Why?!"

"Because of its position at the crossroads of Bohemia." Blažej stretched out on the grass beside her. "Slav legends are amazing. Would you like to hear another?"

Her eyes were closed but she nodded sleepily.

"Czech chroniclers like Cosmas of Prague tell us about the wondrous Princess Libuše. She was a soothsayer and standing on a high cliff above the Vltava surrounded by her thanes, she prophesied the future giory of Prague. 'I see a city whose splendour shall reach to the stars.' However, her tribesmen grew restless under petticoat government and they put great pressure on her to find a husband..."

"Typical male prejudice, again! ' Alice murmured.

"Wait! You haven't heard the whole story. Pointing to the dense forests and the distant hills, Libuše told her envoys to travel to the village of Stadice where they would find a young farmer called Přemysl ploughing a field with spotted oxen. She gave the envoys her beautiful white horse telling them that he would lead them to Stadice. 'You will recognise your future Prince if he eats with you at an iron table.'"

"The messengers set out and after travelling through the forests they saw a handsome, muscular young man. He was ploughing with spotted oxen near Stadice village. When he saw them he stopped ploughing and thrust his switch into the ground where it shot up into a tall nut tree. Libuše's white horse sank onto its knees before him but Přemysl didn't look at all surprised. He unhitched his oxen, saying, 'Be off with you!' Amazed, the envoys saw the oxen rise into the wind and disappear in a nearby cliff. Přemysl invited them to have breakfast with him so they sat down on the ground and

28

he turned over his plough and set out bread and cheese on the iron table of the shining ploughshare, saying: 'This table is the sign that my family's rule over you will be as hard as iron'. The envoys arrayed him in the fine clothes of a Duke and splendidly attired, seated on the white horse, he rode into Prague. At Vyšehrad his marriage to Princess Libuše was celebrated and they founded the Přemyslid dynasty which ruled my country for six hundred years. Before leaving Stadice, Přemysl had put his bast peasant shoes into a bag as a reminder of his origin, saying that the Přemyslid dynasty must never grow too proud, for everyone is equal in the eyes of the gods. According to some accounts Přemysl's shoes could still be seen in the castle in the 12th century."

"How clever Libuše was," said Alice dreamily. "I'm glad she got her Mr. Right."

She turned towards Blažej and began to remove grass-seeds from his hair. He got up and brushing the grass from his trousers, sat down on a large boulder.

"The Slavs produced powerful, tough women. They even waged war on men!"

She got up eagerly and perched herself next to him on the boulder, "A war of the sexes?"

"Exactly." he said.

"Please tell me the story."

"But perhaps you're tired?"

"Not in the least!"

"Well... when Libuše died, her court maidens dressed her body in beautiful clothes, placed a purse containing five gold coins in her right hand to pay the unknown guardian-god of the netherworld and placed two silver coins in her left hand to pay the ferryman who would row her across. These maidens had held a very special position at court while Libuše was alive but after her death their influence declined. Vlasta, the leader of the girls, realized they might be expelled from Vyšehrad so she called them together for a consultation and one of the girls, Stratka, Vlasta's closest friend, came up with the idea of sending a delegation to Prince Přemysl and his closest adviser, Hynchvoj, with a marriage proposal. Vlasta would marry Přemysl and Stratka, Hynchvoj. When the men heard the proposal they scornfully rejected it and fell about laughing. Vlasta accused Stratka of giving her stupid advice and she swore vengeance on the men. 'Woe to the men who only mock us. They will witness our revenge! We shall show them no mercy!' Then Vlasta ordered the maidens to prepare for war so that when she summoned them they would be armed with a sword or a bow..."

"Did she get her revenge?" Alice asked.

"At first the men laughed when the girls secretly led their horses from the stables and sitting astride them, fled from Vyšehrad. However, their laughter turned sour when the six hundred girls built their own hill-fort called Děvín — after the word 'děva' meaning 'girl', mastered the art of war and hunted game in the forest. The girls struck fear into the whole region. They would lie in wait for the men, set traps and kill them. One of the girls, the beautiful Šárka, trapped the warrior Ctirad. Drawn into the forest by her sad cries and desperate pleas for help, he found her tied to a tree. When Šárka lied to him saying that she'd been forcibly abducted from Vyšehrad, Ctirad unbound her. Embracing him, Šárka offered him a jug of mead which just happened to be there! Overwhelmed by her loveliness he gulped it down and when he was half-drunk she persuaded him to blow on her hunting-horn. The horn summoned the armed maidens who had been hiding in the forest. They fell on Ctirad, tied him up and threw him in front of the castle-gate at Vyšehrad..."

"Is that the end?" she asked.

"No! The men managed to entice a group of girls to Vyšehrad and raped them. To Vlasta's great sorrow, the pregnant girls lost all heart for war. She ordered a great attack on Vyšehrad and in the fury and confusion of battle, she became separated from her warriors. The infuriated men captured her, cut her to pieces and fed her to the dogs. On that day, two hundred girls were killed."

"What happened to Šárka?"

"When Ctirad saw Šárka among the warriors he captured her and buried her alive." Blažej stood up, "And so ended the War of the Bohemian Maidens. An early example of women's lib!"

"You're a great story-teller but you've got some funny ideas about women's lib! I mean funny-peculiar," she added.

* * *

"You'll need to rest, eat something and have a shower," he said, as they drove into town. "But if you agree, I'll call for you in a couple of hours. You only have a few days here and I would like to show you Romanesque Prague today."

Alice was silent a while.

"May I ask you a personal question?"

"By all means!"

"Have you got a girl-friend?"

He nodded.

"Do you see her as an equal?"

"She's very clever," he replied.

"May I ask you another question?"

"That's what I'm here for, to answer your questions," he replied with a smile.

"Why do you call the car Šemík?"

"Because he was a noble creature and saved Horymír's life at Vyšehrad by flying over the castle battlements and conveying him safely across the Vltava." He drew up in front of the hotel.

Alice got out of the car, groaned and stretched her legs. She turned to look at Blažej, a rather disheveled figure as he stood beside his little car. His black hair stood up in tufts. She smiled suddenly. "My feet have dried out!"

ROMANESQUE

LATE
AFTERNOON

ALICE ADMIRED the sweeping view of Wenceslas Square as they stood beside the saint's bronze equestrian statue. She blew his horse a kiss.

"Why is Wenceslas so important to the Czechs? All I know is the English carol. He 'looked out' somewhere on the Feast of Stephen and then struggled through snowdrifts to gather winter fuel for the poor."

St Wenceslas

Blažej laughed, "The Feast of Stephen is in August! St. Wenceslas was a Bohemian Prince, born early in the 10th century. It is said he built a rotunda where St. Vitus' Cathedral stands today. He built it over a pagan shrine where the Slavs sacrificed black cocks to their fertility god, Svantovit. Wenceslas had his wits about him! Guessing that the rotunda would upset his half-pagan subjects, he adopted the cock as a Christian symbol. Wenceslas promised to rule with 'justice and mercy' but the years of his reign were thorny ones."

"Why did he become a saint?"

"He was assassinated! It was probably the first political assassination in Central Europe. A bitter quarrel developed between Wenceslas and his brother, Boleslav. Wenceslas, who wanted the approval of Emperor Henry I of Germany, was accused of draining Bohemia of its wealth by selling out to the Germans. He paid them an annual tribute of five hundred sacks of silver and one hundred and twenty oxen. He became extremely unpopular with the Czech nobility who saw him as the Emperor's stooge. His death was dramatic and bloody. Do you want to hear about it?"

She smiled, "You've whetted my appetite. Lectures send me to sleep but I like gory tales."

They sat down on a bench near the statue.

"This tale is the earliest Slavonic legend about St. Wenceslas, written by an unknown Bohemian priest. On the fateful morning, when the bells for Matins were ringing, Wenceslas knelt down and prayed. 'Thank you, Lord, for letting me live to see the morning light!'"

"Then he rose and walked towards the church. Boleslav, hurrying behind, caught up with him at the church gate and Wenceslas looked round saying: 'Yesterday you did me a good turn...'"

"However, the Devil appeared and whispered in Boleslav's ear, clouding his heart. He drew his great sword, saying: 'I want to do you a better one!' And with a mighty blow he struck Wenceslas on the head with the flat of his sword.

"Wenceslas, a powerful man, shouted: 'Brother! Why are

you attacking me?' He rushed towards Boleslav and seizing him by the shoulders, hurled him to the ground. Then he threw himself on top of Boleslav and pinned his arms to his sides."

"'Calm yourself brother! God be with you!' At that point, Tuza, one of Boleslav's accomplices, ran forward and struck Wenceslas a terrible blow on the hand. Wenceslas released Boleslav and ran like the wind to the door of the church, but two of the villains, Cesta and Tira, were waiting for him. They leaped at him in a fury and beat him to the ground with their swords. Then, as Wenceslas was still struggling, Hnorysa, another accomplice, rushed forward and thrust his sword deep into Wenceslas'ribs. His blood spurted out staining the oak door of the church. As the last breath of life was leaving his body, he murmured: 'I place my soul in thy hands, O Lord!'"

Blažej paused and glanced at Alice, "After his death, Wenceslas became a martyr and the patron saint of the Czechs. He became a magnet for legends! Miracles happened at his tomb and his church became a place of pilgrimage. Only last week, the Archbishop of Prague held a solemn Mass in the Cathedral to commemorate him. The church was packed with Praguers and tourists."

She turned to him admiringly. "You're a brilliant yarn-spinner! Can you tell me another Wenceslas legend?"

"A farmer who lived in Křížová village lost his horse. He searched for it along Blaník cliff and suddenly saw an opening in the rock. He went inside and found himself in a corridor. As soon as he was inside, the cliff closed behind him. He entered a huge hall and in the centre of the hall he saw a large stone table. Sitting round the table were Czech knights in full armour with helmets on their heads. The farmer's eyes nearly popped out! The knights were asleep with their heads on their hands. From time to time, one of the knights would raise his head, look at Wenceslas and ask: 'Is it time?' Wenceslas would shake his head and so the knights slept on. Suddenly, the farmer heard his horse neighing outside the cliff. He ran back down the corridor, jumped on his horse and rode home. When he came to his village he saw that people were looking at him in amazement. A servant girl leaving the well with a bucket of water on her head, screamed and the bucket crashed to the ground. When he went into the farm-house he found his wife dressed in mourning, sitting at the table weeping. When she saw him she fainted away. The farmer learned that instead of being away an hour he had been away a whole year! Everyone had given him up for dead. The knights will sleep on in Mount Blaník until our hour of need."

"But your country's had bad times and the knights went on snoring!"

"They'll only leave the mountain in their shining armour, riding their splendid horses when we find ourselves in the worst possible situation.

"The Blaník legend inspired ordinary people in times of terrible repression, especially in the Baroque era." Blažej smiled, "In the 1950s at a time of economic crisis, President Novotný quivered like jelly when he heard that Wenceslas' statue had come to life and had galloped off towards Blaník. He telephoned his Finance Minister who managed to intercept the knights on the outskirts of Prague. To calm them, the Minister read out optimistic details of the new Five Year Plan. When they had heard it, Wenceslas turned to his knights: 'Back to Blaník, Gentlemen! This is not the hour of our people's greatest need. They will be in much greater need of us five years hence!'"

Alice felt dazzled by the bustling activity in the square — flower-sellers, sausage-stands, puppet-stalls, shoe-shiners, an American born-again Christian preaching to a crowd of curious Czechs and crowds of young sightseers laughing and joking on the benches among the bright flower-beds.

But Blažej's face was melancholy. He sighed. "We Czechs are bewitched by our national myths. I see Wenceslas as a passive, servile young man who preferred to buy friendship from the Germans rather than inspiring his people with feelings of pride and independence. Boleslav was ruthless and ambitious but he was a patriot and a great Central European warrior-prince. He united Slav territories under the Přemyslid dynasty and he unified Bohemia. He even minted the first Czech coins in Prague..."

She turned to him in surprise. "But he was a murderer! Probably he was envious of his brother and lusted after power."

* * *

Cyril
and
Method

As they crossed Charles Bridge, Blažej pointed to the statue of Cyril and Method, "Christianity spread to our lands in the first half of the ninth century. About 66 years before Wenceslas' death, these missionaries came to Moravia to convert the Slavs. The ruler of Greater Moravia, Duke Rostislav, sent envoys to Constantinople to ask the Byzantine Emperor to send learned men speaking Old Slavonic to his lands. The Moravian envoys, travel-stained and weary, stood before the Emperor and were astonished to see a forest of beautiful girls with jewels in their hair, massed behind the imperial throne."

Alice smiled, "But the Slavs didn't get the lovely girls. They got Cyril and Method! She stared at the saints. Stern and dignified, they towered above three pagan Slavs imploring them to administer the sacrament. She giggled, "The pigeons have shampooed Cyril's hair. It's snow-white!"

"For a long time the Slavs went on worshipping their pagan gods of fire, wells and the field," said Blažej, suppressing his irritation, "They buried their dead in forests and on cross-roads and gave them gifts for their sojourn in the other world. Sometimes they buried a whole cartload of goods. Prague's Loretto Square was one of the largest Old Slavonic burial sites. Even now in some Moravian villages, the ancient customs go on. People celebrate the end of winter by watching little straw effigies of Morana float away in the streams..."

"Who's Morana?"

"She's death... winter. People still put coins on the eyes of the dead and they paint eggs in Springtime. Old Slavonic times were full of mystery and superstition," he continued. "In the evenings the old people in the cottages told tales of ghosts, nymphs and werewolves, while outside in the darkness the sacred white horse of Svantovit ran across the landscape. Old women watched the flames of the fire and foretold the future and they repeated what they had heard from voices deep in the wells. Sometimes the flames were menacing and if someone saw a black boar grunting in the mud this meant danger for the tribe and possibly war. The Slavs would start to temper their swords and prepare for war. In wet weather it was essential to placate the god of thunder, Perun, the Lord of Heaven."

She gave him a keen look, "What did Christianity give the Slavs?"

"The concept of one God. A shift from pagan worship to the goal of striving for Heaven and eternal life..."

"And the fear of Hell-fire!"

"The Slavs lived in harmony with the natural world and the rhythm of the seasons. Their life was centred in the tribe. Christianity brought the concepts of discipline, individual responsibility and work. Also, in time a wider world. The understanding of Latin opened up the civilized world to educated Slavs. The Old Slavonic language circulated mainly in legends."

"You make Christianity sound like a crushing weight, like travelling uphill with a rucksack of bricks!"

He smiled, "Perhaps it was. A handsome, virile young priest in Bohemia had a great problem. He was so passionate that his penis kept jumping up and sticking out like a poker. He dreaded seeing a pretty woman. It even jumped up in the most solemn moments of the Mass. Finally, he took the advice of a stern monk who told him that nettles were the answer..."

"Nettles?"

"Yes, he was to discipline his member by beating it with a switch of nettles. He shut himself up in the church and tortured himself for three days..."

"What happened to him?"

"He nearly died. His mortification marks the coming of Christianity to Bohemia."

Alice leaned against the stone parapet of the bridge looking at the broad, serene river and the palaces, churches, towers and ancient mills that lined its banks, "I'm trying to imagine Romanesque Prague."

"Prague is in the very centre of Bohemia and very close to the geographical centre of Europe. In Romanesque times it was already a trade centre in a land of dense forests inhabited by wolves. Some time in the late ninth century the Czech prince, Bořivoj, built a castle known as Praha on a headland overlooking the Vltava. The Praguers needed the protection of the Castle and they built their homes beneath it in the Lesser Town. In the tenth century, a new castle, Vyšehrad, was built on the opposite side of the river. There's mention of a market-place, too, probably the Old Town Square, towards the end of the eleventh century. "He paused". Yet... Prague wasn't quite a town. There was no real municipal organization until the first City Magistrate was appointed in the early thirteenth century." He pointed to the Lesser Town bridge tower, "That tower guarded the 12th century Judith Bridge. There were only two stone bridges in Europe at that time and this was one of them. Some of Prague's houses, too, were built of stone, whereas in most of Europe they were made of wood."

* * *

As they walked across the Third Castle Courtyard, Blažej suddenly put his hand on Alice's shoulder. Startled, she looked up at him.

"Please look down!" He pointed to the courtyard paving, "This courtyard looks rather stark and uninviting but it conceals mysteries. You're standing on a thousand years of history! These stones are both paving-stones and roof-stones. Under your feet are the remains of fortifications, the palace of the Czech Prince Soběslav, the foundations of churches, the graves of princes and the remains of houses and out-buildings."

She looked at the massive Romanesque remains on view at the side of the Cathedral.

"Our 14th century King Charles IV was a small man," Blažej continued, "stooping under a hunchback, but he could consume a lot of wine and he was a connoisseur! His precious wine vats were stored here in his cellars where once Prince Soběslav entertained his women, received envoys and sat in judgement. Much of Romanesque Prague lies in cellars. The

Praguers had to do battle with the Vltava which often overflowed its banks and flooded streets and houses. In the 13th century they introduced flood-control and the town's streets were raised about nine feet. Romanesque Prague is thickly coated with Gothic!"

* * *

St George's
Basilica

41

Enthroned
Madonna

She looked with pleasure at the glowing beauty of St. George's Basilica. "This church was built in Wenceslas' reign." said Blažej, as they went inside. "It's the oldest Romanesque monument in Bohemia and this is the rarest Romanesque sculpture in my country." He pointed to the relief of the enthroned Madonna being crowned by angels, "Christianity brought the cult of Mary. Perhaps she softened some of the forbidding strictness of the early missionaries."

"The quality of mercy," she replied.

* * *

"We're quite close to Prague," he said, as they walked down a country road lined with beeches and across a field of cut corn. "This is St. Martin's of Kozojedy. I call it one of my gems. The church has been given a Baroque coat but the tower is pure Romanesque."

42

She looked up at the soaring tower with its square, wooden belfry, "Who was St. Martin?"

"He comes on a white horse when the first snow-flakes appear. Seeing a beggar covered in sores, shivering at the edge of the forest, he dismounted, sliced his coat down the middle and gave half to the beggar..."

"So they both froze!"

Blažej ignored her comment, "The Romanesque churches were the seat of the all-powerful God and their towers summoned people to duty and to prayer."

"There's something very sober about this little church." she said. "Maybe these massive walls gave people a sense of security..."

He nodded. "A refuge from tribal wars, the dense frightening forests, fear of pain... sudden violent death..."

"And six days of back-breaking work!"

St Martin's
of Kozojedy

43   * * *

"I'm taking you on a short drive to Prague - Štěchovice," he said, "because I want to show you the church of St. John of Nepomuk. It's an Art Nouveau Church, possibly the only one of its kind in Europe..."

"Why show me an Art Nouveau church," she interrupted, "when we're looking at Romanesques Prague?"

Blažej reflected, "Well, Prague, my weird city, was built up in layers through the centuries — Primeval, Romanesque, Gothic, Renaissance, Baroque... and then many other layers. I think great artists contain these layers in their imagination. K. Hilbert, the architect of this church felt the spirit of Romanesque and expressed it in twentieth century concrete."

She stared in wonder at the church, "I expect Hilbert was influenced by these primeval cliffs. There's an ancient spirit in that tower!" She gazed at the tremendous solid tower,

St John
of Nepomuk

crowned with a red-tiled belfry. Art Nouveau figures of Christ and the Evangelists seemed to be growing into the structure of the high windows.

"Look at the gargoyles!" He pointed to the contorted faces high on the tower, "Pagan faces. This church expresses the spirit of the pagan Slavs. It symbolizes survival after great disasters... fire, flood, earthquakes. It's like the phoenix arising from its ashes." He went off to get the key to the church and came back accompanied by a young priest wearing an old sweater and corduroy trousers.

"This interior seems to combine tranquillity with the joy of nature," she looked at the delicate salmon-pink interior with its arches decorated with abstractions of green foliage. "It reminds me of Moorish churches I've seen in Spain. It's as though the architect's brought the wild forest into the church and imposed a kind of Byzantine order on it."

The priest pointed to the intricate carvings on the font and on the pillars.

"Miracles!" she said. "The concrete looks like lace!"

They climbed the steps to the belfry, avoiding tiny pigeons nestling on the stairs. Below them lay a forest of green and the Vltava gleaming in the gentle sunlight of late afternoon.

* * *

"Who was St. John of Nepomuk?" she asked, as they drove back to the centre of town.

"He was a fourteenth century saint. Some accounts say he was tortured and drowned in a sack in the Vltava on the orders of King Wenceslas IV because he refused to disclose the Queen's secrets confided to him at confession. Others say he infuriated the King by appointing an abbot against the royal wishes. His body didn't sink! It floated in the Vltava and glowing lights appeared around it. His bones are said to lie in a magnificent tomb made from thirty-seven hundred-weights of silver in St. Vitus' Cathedral. For many years a holy relic was on display. It looked like a bit of brittle leather but it was said to be the saint's tongue. However, scientists claimed it was a sliver of brain-tissue. When it was moistened with a sponge, it never dried. Maybe it's still damp to this day! Apart from his statue on Charles Bridge, the oldest of the statues, there are many other statues of him in the Bohemian countryside."

"Perhaps the church we've just seen has some of his spirit as well as the ghosts of the ancient Slavs?" she suggested.

"Perhaps... a monument to survival through unimaginable disasters!"

* * *

Rotunda
of the Holy Cross

"I've one more spot for you today," he said as they drove into the centre of town and down Konviktská Street.

"I like this little church," he continued, as they stood in

front of the Rotunda of the Holy Cross. "It's a lovely round gem among these boring nineteenth century tenements and it brightens up this little quarter of town. It was the parish church for the Vltava people — fishermen, raftsmen, millers, dyers and tanners."

Alice fidgeted. "Can't you tell me a story?"

"A whore plied her trade right here, where you're standing! She was known simple as "Yee". She couldn't talk and she expressed all her emotions — joy, grief, love, pain, in this one syllable. Her presence in this holy place infuriated some of the townspeople and one evening she was attacked and beaten on her bottom."

"Who attacked her?"

"A great furry monster! It was as big as two thick-set fellows when one is standing on the other's shoulders. A gigantic hairy ghost. Serves her right!" he added severely, "she had no business to be here."

Alice turned to him shocked, "Poor creature!"

* * *

At sunset they sat in the courtyard of At the Golden Melon surrounded by tall, stately houses. Alice watched the play of light on the fountain in the centre of the courtyard.

"Lovely Moravian wine! Why are you drinking mineral water? Do you feel you mustn't drink on the job?"

"It's not that, I don't like alcohol."

She looked at the statue of Eve standing by the fountain. "Eve's everywhere in Prague!"

Blažej looked surprised. "Is she? I haven't noticed."

"You need young eyes like mine."

"I'm not that old!" he protested.

"Thirty?"

"Thirty-one!"

"I'm only twenty-two! I suppose you look on me as a mere student?"

He looked at her reflectively. "Certainly not. Not a 'mere' student! On the whole, you're a really good listener."

She frowned and abruptly stretching her legs under the table, she kicked him on the ankle.

"Oh. I'm so sorry!"

* * *

"Romanesque lies hidden in the cores of these houses," he said, as they crossed the Little Square. Suddenly he seized her arm.

Alice jumped. "What's the matter?"

"Please, look down here!"

She drew away from him quickly and peered down the steep steps.

"Go down!"

"But I don't need the toilet!"

"Please be kind to your guide and descend to the bowels of the earth."

Reluctantly she went down the steps.

"You're in a Romanesque house."

She climbed up panting, and leaned against him for a moment. "I'd tell you to go to Romanesque if I didn't need you tomorrow!"

* * *

"It's been a tiring day for you," he said, as they shook hands in the hotel lobby, "I hope you're not too exhausted?"

Alice laughed. "The day's nearly killed me!" She looked at him intently, "But there's been a kind of ancient magic in it."

THE SECOND
DAY·
GOTHIC

BLAŽEJ SAT WAITING for Alice in the small lobby. Her appearance as she came stumbling down the stairs, bare-foot and in an over-long blue dressing-gown, was watched with interest by a group of spruce Germans at the reception desk.

"Sorry," she said dismally, trying to flatten her tousled hair. "I overslept."

"There's no hurry. I'll wait for you in the restaurant. Did you sleep well?"

She glared at the newcomers and raised her voice, "I dreamt of ghosts, werewolves and white horses!"

Blažej ordered coffee and rolls and looked at her in surprise as she seemed to float through the door in a strange dress which appeared to be made out of patchwork. The skirt ended in a series of long tasseled points which almost touched the ground. Round her neck were strings of amber beads.

She looked at him guardedly, "It's Gothic Day, isn't it? I thought this dress looked vaguely Gothic." She took a roll. "This bread's amazing! It tastes home-made."

"Prague's aromatic with fresh bread. Private bakeries are springing up everywhere, even in the Metro stations. It's the time of opportunity. Do you mind if I give you a short introduction to Gothic while you have your breakfast?"

"How short?" She looked at him suspiciously. "You know I don't like lectures."

"About four minutes."

She started on her second roll, dunking it in her coffee.

"The Přemysl princes, descendants of the mythical Libuše, rose to kingship in 1085 when Prince Vratislav II was crowned the first king of Bohemia. Like most warrior chieftains in Europe at that time they resorted to all kinds of stratagems to consolidate their power, even murderous ones..."

She looked up quickly. "Murderous...?"

"When their rivals the Slavníks, who had built up another powerful princedom in Bohemia, sent off most of their warriors to fight for the king of Poland, the Přemysls seized their opportunity and in September 995 they sacked the Slavníks' stronghold at Libice nad Cidlinou and killed all the members of the ruling dynasty! But their ambitions stretched far beyond Bohemia. They dreamt of glory and conquest and their goal was a great Slavonic state in Central Europe..."

She hesitated over the last roll and then took it. "Did they succeed?"

"Nearly. But they came up against the ambitions of the German Emperors, the Popes and their own nobility who were suspicious of their grand designs. One of our kings, Přemysl Otokar II, even had plans to become Holy Roman Emperor and his territories extended to the Adriatic Sea and included parts of Italy. He even swept Florence and Sienna into his domains and he ruled the most powerful state in Central Europe. He had tremendous military and economic power and was known as the 'King of Gold and Iron'. His son, Wenceslas II, united Bohemia and Poland. But the Přemysl dreams came to an end in the early fourteenth century. In 1306 Wenceslas' young son and heir was murdered at Olomouc by an unknown assassin..."

"So who became king?"

"There was no male successor to the throne. Eliška Přemysl, Wenceslas' sister, married John of Luxembourg who annexed the Czech lands to the Holy Roman Empire. His son was Charles IV..."

"The connoisseur of good wine?"

"And many other things! He was an art patron, a town planner way ahead of his time and a brilliant diplomat. He was Holy Roman Emperor as well as being King of Bohemia, but he liked our people and our language and lived here. During his reign Prague became magnificent. It entered a Golden Age of Gothic and became the cultural and political centre of Europe. It was one of Europe's largest cities, larger than Paris or London with 40.000 inhabitants."

"How many people lived in London?"

"About 35.000."

"The Přemysls left a lot of legends but did they really achieve anything?" she asked, as they left the hotel and walked towards Náměstí Republiky.

"Their dreams of Empire turned to dust but they founded the Czech nation. The Czech lands had a thriving economy, they were a kind of California in Central Europe. A flourishing mining industry had grown up and Bohemian coins were much in demand in the Middle Ages. The Czech groschen was a European hard currency. Also, by the dawn of the Gothic era a strong national consciousness was developing, a feeling of identity and a pride in being Czech. Our chronicler, Dalimil, wrote the first story of the nation in Czech rhyme. There was a proud nobility, a rich clergy and a prosperous middle-class enriched by trading in silver."

"We'll leave the car for a while," he continued, as they walked past Obecní Dům into Na Příkopě. "I'd like to take you for a walkabout through Staré Město, the Old Town. It was a bustling centre in Romanesque times and in the

Můstek Metro —
excavations

thirteenth century a royal charter gave it legal status as a town. Na Příkopě means 'on The Moat' and we're walking on the site of the moat which enclosed the first Prague town."

"I thought we were going to walk!" she grumbled, as he led the way down Můstek Metro.

"We are, but look at this!" He pointed to the excavations in the corner of the station. "Most people rush past to the escalator and never see this. You're looking at part of a small thirteenth century bridge which spanned the moat. The Old Town was surrounded by a double wall as well. It had thirteen towers and the fortifications ran roughly where Na Příkopě, Národní and Revoluční Streets are today."

As they turned into Havelská Street and walked through the massive Gothic arches, Alice took out her street map and looked at the dense network of small winding streets and alleyways, "Staré Město looks like a spider's web! It was

Havelská Street

At the Golden Lilies

shut in by its walls, its towers and the Vltava. So what happened when the population grew?"

"Overcrowding. There's a story that 278 people lived in 12 houses. Medieval street traders haggled and bartered here under these arcades," he continued, "where they had some protection from the bitter winter winds and driving snow."

She looked at the colourful market running down the middle of the street. It was packed with shoppers crowded round fruit and vegetable stalls, flower stalls, piles of wicker baskets, wooden toys, and boxes of fresh eggs and home-made jam.

"Entrepreneurs! Everyone in Prague seems to be selling something to someone!"

Blažej laughed, "It's a new sensation for us. For forty years we weren't allowed to do it."

* * *

"A medieval shop window!" he pointed to the House of the Golden Lilies in the Little Square with its huge Gothic window.

55

Above it and on each side of the arch were golden heraldic lilies and to the left a tiny Gothic portal. "Prague was a city of bustling activity in medieval times. The most important East-West trade routes led through Bohemia. Merchandise from far-away places was brought to Prague and here the craftsmen were able to imitate it and sell it on the spot. The town was full of craftsmen trying to better themselves. Trade flourished with Italy, Flanders, Poland, Hungary..."

"What about England? Did English people come here?"

"We were beginning to get to know each other in the fourteenth century. Czechs went on pilgrimages to Canterbury and they went to London, Oxford and Cambridge. And the English came here. Some came as courtiers, for Charles IV's daughter, Anne, married your Richard II. Some came to do business, some came as diplomats and some came to find refuge..."

"Refuge from what?"

"Persecution! As you know, Wycliffe's ideas were spreading in your country and his followers were in danger. New ideas were coming into this town," he continued, as they walked into U Radnice Street. "Ideas about space and time and town-planning. And Prague was a magnet for odd people, too."

Alice looked at him with interest. "Odd people?"

"Artists, magicians, soothsayers, circus people..." He stopped in front of a Gothic house and she looked at the large grinning frog with bulging eyes above the portal.

"We're standing in front of At the Green Frog! A craftsman lived here, a Gothic tailor. He fell madly in love with one of the circus people, a brilliant and beautiful tightrope walker..."

"Was he handsome?" she asked quickly.

"He was inventive. Apparently she spurned his advances and told him to get back to his yarn and scissors. Desparate to win her favours, he decided to become an acrobat. A brilliant craftsman, he sewed himself a superb green costume and became a frog. He learnt to put his legs on his shoulders

56

and move around on his hands. Strenuously, he practised every night and became so confident that he began to hop around the Old Town Square in the moonlight. Once he was spotted at dawn by a burgher's wife and rumours spread around the district of a terrible green monster or ghost. Stories were told in taverns and in the market-place and with each story the frog became larger and more menacing. Finally, after a solemn meeting, the leading burghers decided to call in the constabulary. This house was surrounded and when two of the braver constables approached to batter down the door, they found to their surprise that it was ajar... Cautiously they crept inside and in the tailor's workshop they found a great green frog standing on its head!"

"Did the tailor get his tightrope walker?"

"I don't know everything."

"But you're my guide!"

He smiled.

At the Green
Frog

* * *

"Prague's got a lot of interesting Gothic houses," he said as they walked into the Old Town Square. "I want to show you one of my favourites."

She watched fascinated as a contortionist had his wrists padlocked by two small boys who then tightened heavy chains round his body. A little straw hat lay upturned in front of him. She took out a twenty crown note.

"Far too much!" said Blažej quickly. "Please, let me give him two crowns."

Horse-drawn carriages taking foreigners around town went

Horologe

swiftly past. She saw a coca-cola trolley, stalls with fine lace, earrings, ceramics and brilliantly-coloured puppets. An old man with brawny arms and blackened face was hammering metal into bell-shapes over an open brazier. In a nearby booth a bearded man was skilfully dropping batter onto hot metal and serving crepes to a hungry group of tourists. A great throng stood looking up at the Astronomical Clock waiting for the statuettes of Christ and the Apostles to appear through the two small doors above the horologe. The clock struck eleven and Death the Reaper raised his hour-glass and tolled his passing-bell.

"The clock dates from about 1410 and was probably made by Mikuláš of Kadaň. Another brilliant clock-maker, Hanuš of Kruže perfected it in 1490 and a huge crowd gathered here when he started the mechanism. There were citizens and artisans, students, Masters of the University, priests, children and apprentices, practically the whole of Prague! The clock's fame spread throughout Europe and many foreigners came to admire it. There's a legend that Hanuš was overwhelmed with orders but he turned them down because he wanted his beloved Prague to be the only city to possess such a wonder. But the Town Councillors were afraid that he would be lured away by offers of gold and they devised a terrible plan. One day, as Hanuš sat over his drawings, three heavily disguised men burst into his room. Two of them seized him and the third plunged a dagger into the fire and put out his eyes..."

"Did he die?"

"For a long time he lay in pain and misery. His work had been his whole life. One day, knowing that his life was coming to an end, he decided to take his revenge. He summoned one of his apprentices and told the boy to lead him to the clock. Then as Death tolled his bell, Hanuš thrust his hands into the complicated mechanism and sabotaged his own work. The clock groaned to a standstill."

* * *

She took Blažej's arm as they threaded their way through the crowds. "The whole world's coming to Prague!"

He laughed. "Apparently twenty thousand visitors cross Charles Bridge every three hours at this time of year." He led her across the square. "This is the house I wanted to show you, At the Stone Bell. It was originally Romanesque and in

At the Stone Bell

the second quarter of the fourteenth century it was transformed into this wonderful Gothic tower, probably for John
of Luxembourg and his family. I think it was unparalleled
in Central European town architecture.''

She looked with pleasure at the austere, serene beauty of
the stone house.

"It's got something very special. I think it's the most
beautiful house I've ever seen. It's so grave and aloof and...
stately.''

"But you've been everywhere — Paris, Rome, Venice...''

"Yes, but this is Gothic magic!'' She looked with interest
at the lofty interior with its fragments of delicate Gothic
statues.

"Lovely concerts are held here.''

"I'd like to go! Can I invite you?'' she asked.

Blažej was taken aback. "I'm afraid I have very little
time...''

She took his arm again. "You're not used to a girl asking
you out, are you?''

"Perhaps not. But seriously, I work all the time. I do my
job, go home, study English and go to bed. This is the time
to make money. If I don't work now, I'll never...''

"Never what?''

"Maybe I'll tell you sometime.''

"Your life sounds boring, all work and no play!''

"But I like my work.''

He pointed to the house-sign on the corner of the building.
"There's a legend that Janek the Bell lived here. He looked
after Mr Brouček on his fantastic trips. Do you know about
Mr Brouček? His name means 'Beetle' in English.''

"Janáček...?''

"Right! The Excursions of Mr Brouček. It's our greatest
comic opera. Mr Brouček spent most of his life drinking away
his sorrows in the Vikárka tavern, moaning about his awful
tenants and tax-collectors and gloomy articles in the Press.
One evening he collapsed and was whisked away to the moon
with a piece of good Czech sausage in his pocket. After

61

escaping from the amorous advances of a determined Moon-woman, he comes back to Prague in a beerbasket..."

"What's that?"

"A kind of trolley used to get drunks home after a heavy night's boozing. He goes on dreaming and finds himself in Gothic! He's among the Hussite heroes defending Prague against the mighty forces of the Empire. He's a real creep and when he tries to bargain with the enemy to save his skin, his friends stuff him in a barrel and throw him on the fire. He wakes up with a number one hangover in a dirty, empty beer-barrel!"

"Serves him right for rejecting the Moon-Lady!" Alice laughed. "I've heard a lot about good Czech beer!"

"It's been the ruin of many a Beetle!"

* * *

At the Golden Unicorn

He led her through a great portal and into the passage-way of At the Golden Unicorn on the southern side of the square. "Look at the reticulated ribbed vaulting! The front part of this passage-way is absolutely original and this vaulting is the work of Matěj Reysek in 1498. People are still debating whether he was a Medieval or Renaissance artist. The pear-shaped ribs lead out from small pyramidal consoles creating a dense network pattern. This huge building has a four-wing central section at Železná Street and a pentagonal back wing

At the Golden Unicorn — vaulting

dating from 1523 that reaches as far as Kamzík Street. It's a monumental Old Town patrician house."

She tried to open a tiny door on her right set deep in an ancient portal. It had a stone scroll above it.

"That doorway probably led to a series of small rooms which were often rented out to tenants."

"Where does it lead to now?"

"To a new private photographic studio. Your films will be developed while you wait."

* * *

No 601
Celetná Street

As they walked into Celetná, Blažej pointed to number 601 with its indented Gothic gables.

"They're like white dragon teeth!" She pulled out her small camera and took a picture of the house backed by one of the great towers of the Týn Church.

At the Black Sun — courtyard

"Even in those days some houses had fire-protection gables some five hundred years before they came into general use," Blažej said. "This house still has its original steep Gothic roof-truss of spruce-wood."

He paused before the house, At the Black Sun. "This house has a medieval core from about the mid-fourteenth century. It encloses a trapezium shaped courtyard and the wings have Gothic barrel-vaulting..."

"Can we go in?"

They went through the passageway into a charming courtyard. Alice looked at the house, decorated now with wrought-iron balconies and pots of bright flowers. At the end of the cobbled yard was a picture of St. Anne over Gothic archways. To her left there was a small door under a Gothic arch and through it she glimpsed a stairway. "I'd like to go up."

He looked dubiously at her long skirt. "Would you like to see the attic? The attics of medieval houses are full of ghosts!"

She hitched her skirt above her knees and climbed nimbly up the stone steps and then a dusty wooden stairway. They entered a vast loft. The oak beams were pitted with age and the floor thick with dust. Ladders against huge beams led to another loft above.

Blažej smiled. "You're standing in the Middle Ages!"

They began to climb down and he turned to watch her. Suddenly, she seemed to trip, clutched at space and losing her footing fell heavily into his arms with a small shriek. He almost lost his balance and they swayed on the steps. Their cheeks touched. He steadied her and she drew away quickly. "Sorry about that! I nearly lost my guide!"

They stood and looked at each other for a moment and he was surprised to find that her face which he had taken for ordinary had a curious elfin look — pointed chin and large light grey eyes. He had an uneasy feeling, almost of recognition. She reminded him of someone... of something. He pushed the thought aside. "Shall we go?"

She sneezed and whipping out a roll of toilet paper, she tore off a square and blew her nose. "Dust!" she smiled at him.

* * *

They walked down a tiny medieval lane, almost submerged in a tangle of scaffolding, behind the Týn Church and he pointed to Týnská 10, a massive house with small high windows and a medieval roof like hands folded in prayer.

"It's like a castle!" she exclaimed.

"A house in Gothic times was like a badge of town nobility. The wealthy trader had risen to be one of the town elite and his house proclaimed his rank and fortune. Downstairs there was the great living-room known as the palace and the kitchen.

No. 10
Týnská Lane

This house is unusually spacious. Most medieval houses are long and narrow. Space was a luxury in the Old Town."

"What did they do for toilets? In medieval York they emptied their chamber-pots into the street."

"Here too! This lane lying in the shadow of the Týn Church was rat-infested and awash with excrement. Pigs

Týnská Lane

rooted among the cobblestones and hungry dogs prowled through passage-ways. In summer the street almost disappeared under a quivering black blanket of flies..."

"Life must have been short in Týnská," she said, as they walked towards the car. "In medieval York a woman was lucky if she lived to be twenty-five."

He nodded, "It was short here-below but the spires of the great Týn Church held out the promise of the life to come. The hungry mason in Týnská was an insignificant link in the Chain of Being which stretched through the humble minerals through the vegetable and animal worlds and on through the feudal hierarchies to the angelic ranks and the throne of God. But he was promised that Death, the Great Equalizer, would scythe away the privileges of class and money and sweep him into the community of the faithful."

"If he did what he was told!" she murmured.

* * *

Blažej parked the car in Ke Karlovu Street.

"I'd like to show you St. Catherine's. By the end of the fourteenth century, there were one hundred churches, monasteries and chapels in Prague. It was known in Europe as the "Hundred Towered City".

"How many are there now?"

"One hundred and thirteen. Altogether there are 550 towers. This church with its former convent was founded by Charles IV and built between 1355 and 1367. It has a Baroque facade but its spire is Gothic and one of the most beautiful in Prague. It's known as the 'Prague Minaret'."

She gazed at the slender, soaring spire. "What's the key to Gothic?"

"Light! The Gothic towers strain heavenwards towards celestial light and the church interiors with their towering pillars and high pointed arches try to capture the light. The cathedrals were like cloaks over sacred spaces, spaces of the imagination. They soared above the mundane world of money-grabbing, violent streets, dung, stench, sores... They spoke

69

to medieval people of the luminosity of Heaven — clarity, harmony... peace."

She looked at him curiously. "Are you religious?"

"I don't know. I was a good Marxist student and now I'm an entrepreneur. Being an entrepreneur is a great adventure!"

Prague
Minaret

"I think you're a passionate man!"

"Oh really?" He leant against the cloister wall and looked at her attentively. "And what do you think I'm passionate about?"

* * *

They sat near an ancient well in a garden oasis lined with Gothic loggia in the shadow of St. Thomas' church.

She fidgeted. "Aren't we trespassing?" She looked up at the small windows.

"Don't worry! No one will chase us away. This is a home for Senior Citizens. It's a peaceful place. I'd like to talk about the fourteenth century church here in Bohemia. It stank of corruption! Sex, simony, nepotism, pluralism and all the other 'isms'! Wheeling and dealing."

"In England, too! Phoney relics were peddled on the streets. I'm thinking of Chaucer's pardoner with his sales-talk and his tickets to heaven."

"Indulgences were sold here too, on the Prague streets. The Papacy had sunk very low. It was involved in bloody feuds and political manoeuvres. The Great Schism in the Church meant that for nearly twenty years there was one Pope in Rome and another in Avignon..."

"I thought there were three Popes?"

"Yes, inflation! There was another Pope in Pisa at the beginning of the fifteenth century." The abbots and bishops in Bohemia grew fat on property deals and squeezing tithes from the poor. Monasteries became hotels for the nobility! One priest, Protiva was the owner of a brothel. One night, drunk and naked, he was chased through the streets by the magistrates because he'd lost his clothing gambling among the whores. Convents like St Agnes were founded here with high ideals but in the fourteenth century rumours spread that there were all sorts of goings on between the monks and nuns. The monks were housed in a building which looked directly into the nuns' dormitory. I don't suppose we need believe all the tales of orgies and swindling but there's no doubt that entry to the priesthood had become a kind of meal ticket..."

"Like Communist Party membership!"

He laughed. "The church was a great monopoly over men's souls. Monopolies sometimes need a kick up the back-

St Thomas'
Church

side. John Hus summed it up when he said it would be easier to find a stag with golden antlers on the bridge on Prague than to find a worthy priest."

Alice gave him a side-long look. "Sounds as though those monks and nuns had quite a fun time."

He frowned. "Perhaps you've never been without money? It was no fun for the Prague poor. The fourteenth century was a time of economic crisis in Europe and the Prague vagrants were desparate. They slept rough on the streets or under bridges or huddled up against the fortifications. Many lived out their lives and their deaths in the streets. The symbolic figure of Přemysl the Ploughman — strength, fertility, revival and the sunny cycle of sowing and harvesting — meant nothing to them as they shivered in the night streets, crawling into piles of manure for warmth, and dying in their thousands of hunger."

* * *

A musician in St. Thomas' church unlocked the door to St. Dorothy's chapel for them and they stood before the Gothic statue of Christ on the Cross. She stared in wonder at the delicate modelling of Christ's thin, beautiful face. His mouth was slightly open.

"There's great suffering in this face," she said at last, "He looks as though he's suffered for a long time, long before his crucifixion." She looked at the gaunt body and thin arms.

"I think this statue's unique. It gives us a glimpse of the sad underside of Czech Gothic. He's not an aristocratic figure fashioned for a town nobility and he's not a writhing, contorted figure made to shock and horrify worshippers into repentance. He's a crucified Czech beggar, the lumpen-proletariat of Czech Gothic."

"Look at his small, delicate hands! I think he was a fine craftsman, thrown out of work in hard times, struggling for survival, his talents unwanted..."

73

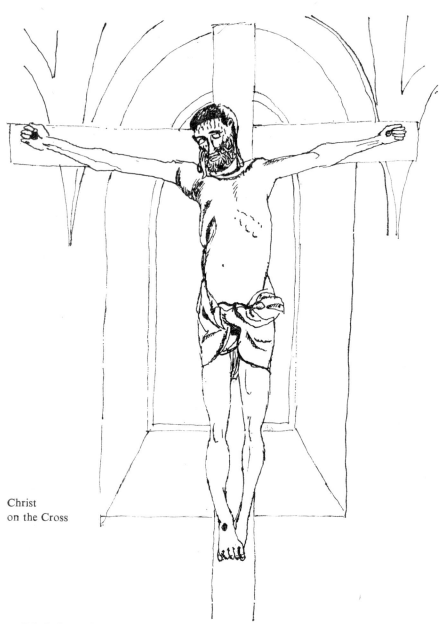

Christ
on the Cross

Blažej nodded. "He was one of the hungry dispossessed of the Prague streets."

* * *

He turned into Thunovská Street and the little car rumbled as it climbed the steep cobbled street.

"I've reserved a table here," he said, pointing to the King

of Brabant. "I wanted to find a Gothic resting-place." He pointed to the great Gothic ringed portal and window arch, "The interior's been modernized but it's pleasant enough."

Alice looked at the six tables with their dark red cloths. There was a bar at the end of the small room and modern paintings under subdued lighting on the low walls.

"My feet are killing me! I should have worn trainers." Crossly, she took off her shoes and threw them under the

King of Brabant

table. He ordered a glass of beer and his usual mineral water.

"Why don't you have a beer?"

"I've already told you. I don't drink..."

"So you'll be as sober as a judge and I'll be a tipsy client!"

"You'll hardly get drunk on one glass of beer."

She scowled. "Maybe I'll have two glasses or even three."

"The client is king!" He controlled his irritation, "You must do as you please."

The waiter brought them pasta with sheep's cheese but they ignored their plates.

She stared into his pale, frowning face with its crest of black hair. "You strike me as being a bit on the stiff side. It must be difficult for you having to be polite all the time. Don't you ever want to punch your clients on the nose?"

He leaned back and clenched and unclenched his hands, "Very rarely! Most of my clients appreciate what I do for them."

She reddened. "Are you suggesting I don't?"

"That's not what I said."

They glared at each other.

Suddenly a tall crowned figure robed in velvet and ermine stood by their table, bowed and sat down next to Alice. He was followed by an enormous dog which sat down at the end of the table, regarded her with fond eyes and lunging forward swiftly, took a gulp of her pasta. The stranger took off his crown and hung it on a hook above her head. "That's better! Heavy is the head that wears the crown. And I'm always being castigated for being the pusillanimous, whoring son of a great father."

She gaped at him. "Who's your father?"

"Charles IV, former Emperor and king of this strange land."

"Your Highness," said Blažej formally, "allow me to present Miss Alice Brown". He turned to Alice. "You have the honour of meeting His Majesty, Wenceslas IV, a frequenter of this hostelry."

The king took Alice's hand and kissed it lingeringly but **76** his eyes were on her breasts. "A beautiful girl is such an ornament! He glanced down at her legs but they were shrouded in her skirt. He looked at Blažej and sighed. "But a king never competes! And I must find Rye..."

He rose and disappeared through a small archway at the end of the room, followed reluctantly by the colossal dog.

"Who's Rye?"

"His magician. Prague's the home of Happenings!"

She looked at the wall above her head. "He's forgotten his paper crown."

"It was always his habit. Please keep it as a memento of our lovely meal together."

They looked at each other for a moment and burst out laughing.

* * *

"I'm not that interested in Royals," she said, as they started walking back towards the car. "The English Royals are incredibly boring, except for Prince Charles. I rather like him in spite of his large ears. But your Royals are all tucked away in museums, so maybe you could shake the dust off them for me?" She squeezed his arm. "If you can forgive me for being such a pain over lunch, that is."

Blažej had experienced sharp pangs of irritation at various times during the morning, rather like short, acute bouts of indigestion. He turned to look at her smiling face and was surprised to find himself quite cheerful.

"I'll willingly tell you about Charles IV. Two worlds met in him because he was both Slav and Westerner. Also he and I have something in common..."

"Can I guess it?"

"You already have! A passion for this town. Charles' vision for Prague was truly monumental. He founded Nové Město, the New Town, which was laid out in regular and broad streets, unusual for that time, and he planned a huge range of building projects. He wanted to relieve the Old Town of the incredible noise of craftsmen's workshops and provide market-space for the merchants flocking into Prague, so he founded the great cattle-market on Charles Square and the horse-market on Wenceslas Square. He took a real interest in business and made a lot of trade regulations. All foreign merchants who crossed the Bohemian frontiers had to come first to Prague to show and sell their goods."

He glanced at Alice but couldn't tell whether she was listening or not.

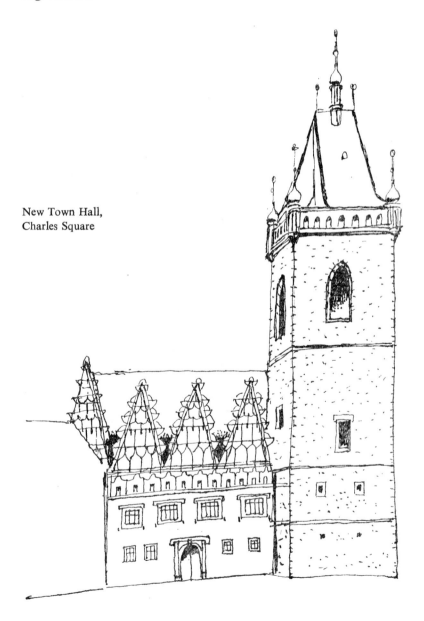

New Town Hall,
Charles Square

She was quiet for a while. "You told me yesterday he was a hunchback, or is that one of your legends?"

"As a young man he was badly wounded at the Battle of Crécy where he fought heroically beside his blind father, John of Luxembourg against Edward, your Black Prince. Some say that the sword-thrust he got at that time gave him a slight hunch. Perhaps that dreadful battle in which most of the Czech knights were slaughtered, gave him a horror of war. He did go to war occasionally and briefly but he preferred diplomacy and successful financial deals. He bought twenty towns and castles in Germany and extended the frontiers of Bohemia almost to the gates of Nuremberg. Berlin became a provincial outpost of the Czech state. And his four wives brought him allies and land . . ."

"Four!"

"He outlived them all, although his fourth wife, Elizabeth of Pomerania was a tough lady. She could bend iron bars and snap swords in two!"

Alice clutched his arm and bent down to remove a stone from her shoe. "What else did Charles do, apart from collecting wives?"

"He was a fanatical collector of holy relics! Every time he went abroad he added to his collection. He wanted Prague to have the biggest and best collection in the world."

"Did it?"

"Not quite, but in a letter to one of his Archbishops dated 1354, he claimed that he had the best collection after Rome. This passion of his was a field-day for forgers and some of them were priests!"

She laughed. "I read somewhere that in fourteenth century England there were two complete sets of St. Dunstan's bones!" She looked at him mockingly. "Leaving bones aside, do you have anything else in common with your hero, apart from your love of your town?"

"Language! Charles grew up speaking French and he wrote mainly in Latin but he learnt Czech and spoke it well. When he reformed the law-courts he decreed that Czech must be used in the courts. He had a great love of learning and 144 years before Columbus set sail, he founded our University. It was the first University North of the Alps. He said that Czechs should not have to beg for crumbs of learning abroad but should have a full table at home." He paused, "He was a

Charles IV

complex man, a soldier and a scholar, a practical town-planner and a mystic. He would stretch himself out in prayer on the cold stones of his chapel at Karlštejn for hours on end. If urgent messages arrived, they had to be put through a slit in the wall..."

"You make him sound like a saint!"

"He could be tough! He kept the nobility in their place. In 1355, after spending some months in Italy, he returned to Bohemia and found that this authority was being challenged by a robber-baron, John of Smoyno. Charles had knighted him some time before and honoured him with a golden chain. After besieging Zampach Castle he hanged John of Smoyno and it's said that the threw the rope around his neck saying that it was not only golden chains he had in his gift..."

She glanced at Blažej's intent face. "He really is your hero, isn't he?"

"I look on him as a great king," he replied, rather stiffly. "No country has that many! Who was yours?"

She hesitated. "We've had great queens!" she reflected. "I suppose what really matters is if their greatness lives on after them. Did Charles leave a great legacy?"

"He turned a medieval town into a great imperial city famed in Europe and studded with architectural gems and works of art. He was a talent-spotter and employed geniuses like the young Peter Parler to work on his projects. Peter built the Bridge Tower, probably the finest in Europe and he worked on St. Vitus'Cathedral for nearly half a century. Charles encouraged learning and gave the Czechs peace at home and prestige abroad..." He smiled, "It's a lot!"

Alice made a face. "You've given me a load of facts! Surely a great king leaves stories...?"

"He had an adventurous life and miraculous escapes. In 1331, when he was in his twenties, he was sent by his father, King John, to Italy to administer the royal lands and he narrowly escaped death there. A group of conspirators had met in a country church and were plotting to kill the Prince. They even took an oath over the sacred wafers to stick together and carry out their plan. But just as the priest had blessed the Host, the place was shrouded in darkness and a tremendous gust of wind battered the church. Terrified, the conspirators huddled together and when the next great gust came, the priest who was standing by the altar, felt the wind tear the Host from his hand. He found it lying at the feet of Marsiglia de Rossi, the chief conspirator, and the plotters fled from the church in horror."

Alice laughed, "Miracles...!"

"That miracle was followed by another. The plotters had been tamed by their dreadful experience and from that moment they became Charles' loyal allies."

She beamed. "Have you got any more Charles' stories?"

"Once he went on horseback with a trusted companion, Bušek of Velhartice, from Křivoklát to Prague. They stayed overnight in the House of the Burgrave near the Castle. It was winter and a great fire was roaring in the hall and candles had been lit for their arrival. They sat by the fire and filled and refilled their goblets with good Bohemian wine. After a jovial evening they staggered off to their chambers but in the early hours they were disturbed by footsteps as though someone was walking through the hall. Charles told Bušek to investigate but when he entered the hall he found no one there. He piled logs on the fire, lit some candles and went over to the goblets which they'd left empty on a bench. He found that they were now full to the brim with wine! He drank deeply from one of the goblets and returned to his room. Charles sat on his bed wrapped in his cloak and soon he heard the invisible someone again. The footsteps seemed to come closer and then moved away. At that moment one of the goblets fell with a clatter to the stone floor. Bušek woke up and looking into the hall, both men saw the goblet flying through the room and bouncing from wall to wall as if hurled by an invisible hand. And again they heard the mysterious footsteps..."

"What happened in the morning?"

"A change of heart! Charles had been very fond of good red wine but after that strange night he became a teetotaller."   82

"He sounds a strict sort of person," she said, looking at Blažej critically.

"He wasn't strict in his younger days. In 1347, when he was thirty-one, he took part in the Christmas celebrations in Basle. There were balls and feasts and dancing and Charles was the life and soul of the parties. His flirtatious manner with the ladies which people said he'd learnt at the French court, and his short tight clothes, all gathers and pleats, gave rise to some caustic comments which even reached the Vatican. Charles got a sharp rebuke from the Pope advising him to mend his ways."

"Did he?"

"Yes, he took the Pope's advice and as he got older, he led an austere life. But he could be amazingly tolerant about other people. He put up with a lot of haranguing from fanatics. On one occasion, Jan Milíč of Kroměříž, a particularly fiery preacher, raged at Charles and even called him Anti-Christ, but Charles took it calmly without turning a hair."

"That's incredible for the fourteenth century," she said, impressed. "People got beheaded or hanged for much less."

"Charles' reign was a Golden Age," he said, as they reached the car," but trouble was brewing when he died in 1378. He was aware of corruption in the Church and he even protected popular preachers who denounced wordly priests and self-indulgent Praguers. One of them, Conrad Waldhauser, actually persuaded the Prague ladies to throw away their jewels and costly dresses! But corruption still went on and there were other troubles, too. The lesser nobility had their eye on church property, craftsmen envied foreign merchants, peasants were crushed by heavy rents. Preachers began to prophesy the end of the world. Christ would arrive and all sin would end! Kings, Princes and Prelates would disappear. The poor would be freed from their chains and the law of God would prevail. Twenty-four years after Charles' death, John Hus was preaching in the Bethlehem Chapel. Revolution was in the air!"

83   * * *

"You remember I told you yesterday about 'Yee', the mute whore?" said Blažej, as they walked along Konviktská towards Bethlehem Square, "This area was notorious for its brothels. One of the radical reformers Milič of Kroměříž, the preacher who gave Charles a piece of his mind, set up a home here for prostitutes, called 'Jerusalem'."

"Milic would have been busy if he was around today! I've been told that prostitution is rocketing in Prague. There are thousands of them. You can see the young pretty ones in smart clothes and heavy make-up swarming around the posh hotels in Wenceslas Square, but there are countless others of all ages, in poorer districts, too."

"I'm an entrepreneur but I've never said that everything in the free market comes from heaven," he said bitterly.

Alice looked at him in surprise, "I'm only commenting," she said gently.

Bethlehem
Chapel

84

He relaxed, "I suppose I'm a bit touchy about my town." He put his hand on her shoulder, "We're looking at the Bethlehem Chapel. It was founded in the late thirteenth century by Prague patricians, against the Bishop's wishes, so that sermons could be given in Czech."

She stared at the cool, austere building with its twin-gabled roof. "It doesn't fit in with Gothic! I'm trying to think why..."

"It's plain. Concentration on the word of God. The founders rejected all the intricate sculptural ornamentation common at the time. They didn't want anything to distract the faithful. It's message is severity, gravity... simplicity. It's had a turbulent history. It was bought by the Jesuits in Baroque times and then torn down in 1786. However, parts of the original walls remained and dwellings were built into them. Reconstruction began in the early 1950s..."

"Reconstruction?" she interrupted, rather irritably. "I keep hearing that word. How is it done?"

Blažej sighed, "It's complicated..."

"I mean, how was it done here?"

He brightened, "A pork butcher lived here between the two World Wars. He smoked famous Prague sausages! Kubíček, an architect, got friendly with him and started digging in his smoking-house. He came on a Gothic portal, foundations, a well and fragments of Hussite inscriptions. Later, in the early fifties, thousands of old documents were examined — property deeds, pictures, plans... Samples of mortar were analyzed and texts by Hus were discovered on the original walls and the size and spacing of the letters were analyzed. By comparing them with the full text preserved in manuscript, it was possible to define the position of the windows by interruptions in the continuity of the texts." He paused, "It was a mammoth task! Jaroslav Fragner was the architect in charge of the work and when he had finished an amazing thing happened. A young archivist found a plan of the chapel dated 1786, inside an old book. It showed that Fragner's reconstruction was brilliant. The curb-stone on the well differed from the original by only a few centimetres in height."

"You said the early 1950s... Why did the communists take such an interest in this place? I didn't think they had much time for chapels!"

"This place was special. We were forever being told in school about the noble Hussites sho fought for the common man. Also, in the sixteenth century, Thomas Münzer, the Anabaptist peasant leader preached here of revolution, equality and socialism..."

"Is that what Hus preached?"

"Hus preached over a hundred years before Münzer. He attacked the corruption in the church and called for reform. Although he came from a humble background in Moravia, he was a very important man when he began preaching here. He was a professor of the Philosophy Faculty at Charles' University and Confessor to the Queen. He was known as a scholar, for his skill in debate and his eloquence. He had studied Wycliffe's writings and although he didn't agree with all Wycliffe's views, he came away from his studies with something which was dynamite..."

She looked at him eagerly, "Dynamite?"

"The idea that people should go directly to the Bible for the word of God."

Her face fell, "I don't see why that's so explosive."

"It was new to the European mind. The Bible had always been filtered to the congregation by the priests. For Hus, the Bible was the source of divine inspiration and the conscience of the individual paramount."

Alice nodded, "I suppose it would pull the carpet from under the feet of the whole lot of them — Cardinals, Bishops, and Abbots... They'd all be out of a job."

"If taken to its logical conclusion... But Hus concentrated on the clergy's wheeling and dealing. He wanted a better, purer church and one which remembered its duties to the poor. Tailors, cobblers, seamstresses, journeymen, clerks and fish-wives came here to listen to him. The words and music of the hymns were written up on the walls for them. People

86

were moved and excited by his sermons and when the Pope's indulgence-sellers entered the Old Town Square in 1412 preceded by drummers, Prague was in an uproar. Expecting trouble, the magistrates passed a law forbidding any discussion of indulgences on penalty of death."

She laughed, "How ridiculous! I can't imagine anyone stopping a Czech from discussing anything!"

"Our history hasn't given us a lot of space to discuss things freely. Three young men tried to remove the indulgence-sellers. They were seized and publicly executed. Then bands of students singing hymns brought the corpses here for burial. Hus was excommunicated and orders were given to raze this building to the ground. But the Hussites defended it successfully."

"Who was King while all this was going on?"

"Wenceslas IV. You met him over lunch!"

* * *

"I'd like to show you a painting of John Hus," said Blažej, as they went into St. Agnes Convent. "It's a nineteenth century painting and very dramatic! It gives a glimpse of Czech consciousness."

Hus stood before his accusers but he had been painted as judge rather than defendant. His prosecutors seemed to shrink into insignificance before the tall, gaunt, dynamic figure. Black-robed, one arm raised to heaven, he seemed an explosive force in the great ornate church.

"I wonder what he was really like?"

He smiled, "Some say that he was as round as a cask! He was robust, energetic and liked jokes."

"What happened to him? You said Prague was in an uproar when the indulgence-sellers moved in."

"He left Prague and went to the countryside where he preached in the open fields. Thousands flocked to hear him. Meanwhile, Wenceslas IV's brother, the Emperor Sigismund, got the Pope's reluctant consent to summon a General Council of the Church to hear Hus'case. Sigismund gave Hus

87

a safe-conduct for his journey but it was a mere scrap of paper! Hus started on his long, fatal journey in October 1414 and on arriving in Constance he was immediately imprisoned and in June 1415 he faced his judges in Constance Cathedral. His hearing which lasted four days was a farce! He was constantly interrupted, was never allowed to develop his case and faced absurd accusations..."

"What kind of accusations?"

"He was accused of saying that instead of the Trinity — God in Three — there were four holy manifestations, one of which was himself! Steadfastly maintaining that the Bible rather than the Pope was the true source of God's word, he

John Hus

refused to recant and was condemned as a heretic to the terrible death by burning. On 6th July 1415, the city magistrates took him to a field half a mile from the city walls and he was tied to the stake. It was a turbulent day with a high wind and racing clouds. A silent crowd, wrapped in cloaks watched while the magistrates, like so many black crows, ordered the kindling of the fire. Soon Hus was enveloped in flames but his voice could still be heard in prayer. Then a great gust of wind blew dense grey smoke into his face and suffocated him, bringing his terrible agony to an end. The Executioner was ordered to throw his ashes into the Rhine so that no trace of his martyrdom should remain."

Alice shuddered, "You said this morning that the key to Gothic was light! What about the darkness... the cruelty?!

"The Gothic coin has two faces. There was passionate belief... no shades of grey." He reflected, "There was also great... fortitude. One of Hus' friends, Jerome of Prague who had supported him brilliantly during the stormy debates at Prague University and who had travelled to Constance to visit him in prison, was arrested near that city a year later and also sentenced to burning. He had travelled the world and had been welcome at royal courts. He's been described as a charming man of great learning and with attractive manners. We have an account of his death because it was witnessed by the Italian, Poggio Bracciolini. Although Bracciolini was a Papal Legate and one of the establishment, he was also a humanist and a man of feeling. He was greatly moved by Jerome's death and wrote eloquently about it in one of his letters. He described Jerome's clear, beautiful voice, the nobility of his gestures and the way he quoted calmly from the Classics and the Bible while the flames crept towards him."

Alice sighed, "I've got a lot of thoughts in my head but I'd like to sit down and have a coffee!" She turned away from the painting, "Who knows, I might meet a Hussite!"

* * *

89

"Let's talk of cabbages and kings," she said, as Blažej tried to catch the waiter's eye.

He looked mystified.

She laughed, "It's an English quote! I'm thinking about Wenceslas' remarks over lunch. I thought he was really sexist, by the way."

"Would you like Becherovka with your coffee? It's our famous liqueur."

"No thanks! I feel odd if I'm drinking and you're not."

"There's no need..."

She cut across him. "It must have been hard for Wenceslas having a brilliant father. My father's very successful and thinks he knows everything. He once told me I'd never make it as a barrister like him because I'm not tall enough! Not that I want to be one." She smiled suddenly. "Thanks for your offer of Becherovka. I'd like to try it."

"You said yesterday that you want to be an artist..."

"I'm already one! I've done your portrait." She rummaged in her bag and brought out a rather scrumpled piece of paper.

He looked at himself with a sense of shock. High cheek-bones, widely-spaced eyes, crest of black hair, prominent nose, small scar on right cheek, furrowed brow. The likeness was remarkable.

"You make me look very... severe!"

She looked at him gravely and put the sketch in her bag, "I'd like to hear about the mysterious Mr Rye'."

"All sorts of stories circulated in Prague — in the taverns and market-places and by the firesides — about the strange Mr Rye. It was rumoured that he was in collusion with the spirit world. He appeared unannounced before the king at Hradec where the wine was flowing freely and Wenceslas was making merry with his nobles. The guards didn't want to admit such an odd-looking shabbily dressed character and drew their swords. Rye merely winked at them and they became as stiff as posts. He had frozen them to the spot! When he entered the banqueting-hall he was dressed in shimmering, many-coloured silks and wearing pointed shoes, and when he left he was dressed as a pilgrim."

She sipped her Becherovka, "It's good!"

The king's jester was jealous of Rye's wizardry and his friendship with the king. One day, when he made a caustic remark while reaching out for some fish, Rye gave him a piercing look. The jester shrieked for his fingers had begun to stiffen. Then his wrists grew hair and his hands widened and hardened until they had become horses' hoofs! The king and his nobles were amazed and burst out laughing, although there was probably a trace of fear in their merriment. Wenceslas ordered Rye to conjure the jester's hoofs away. He did so but changed them into ox's hoofs!"

Alice had her elbows on the table and was supporting her chin on her hands. She stared at Blažej intently.

"Rye's most fantastic performance was in the Old Town Square. A great tournament had been organized with all sorts of games and festivities. Preparations had been going on for weeks and Prague was wild with excitement. Waggons came from Germany with clowns, jugglers, strong-men, strange animals and magicians. One of these magicians was world-famous. A great platform covered with cloth of gold had been put up in front of the Týn Church. The Royal Herald appeared and the trumpets sounded and the King, Queen and courtiers took their places..."

"Was the German magician as good as Rye?"

"He swallowed swords and great flames and contorted his body into extraordinary shapes as though he was made of rubber. The Germans applauded him loudly and the crowd was amazed."

Blažej paused and gulped some coffee, "Suddenly, a kind of tremor went through the crowd and all heads turned towards the Town Hall. Then a great roar went up from the crowd. Out of The Town Hall came a two-wheeled chariot drawn by a four-in-hand of cocks. The first pair were real cocks, the second pair were bigger, the third still bigger and the fourth as big as horses. They strutted gravely and with dignity and even the first pair seemed to know they were carrying something extraordinary. On the chariot-seat sat a strange figure, mighty and strong, of superhuman size with a gigantic head. Behind it, there was another figure, very tall with thin legs. The cocks crowed and flapped their wings as they circled the square. 'Rye! Rye! This must be Rye!' people shouted. Then Rye began to perform strange tricks assisted by his thin companion. They were excellent, wonderful tricks but there were still surprises in store. The German juggler, small, slight and dry, stood before the king and with a bored face copied all Rye's wizardry quite effortlessly. The Czechs were dumbfounded and the Germans began to cheer. Wenceslas sat frowning at his sorcerer's defeat and the gigantic Rye stood aside with bent head. Then when his rival had finished his performance and had bowed to the royal dais, Rye stepped forward and clapped his hands. His assistant grabbed the German from behind and handed him to Rye who pinned his rival's hands to his sides, twisted him and then opened his enormous mouth and began to devour him! The Czechs in the Square yelled and cheered as Rye gulped down the juggler who was waggling his legs, until he had swallowed him. He only spat out his boots. Renewed cheering broke out when Rye's assistant began to shout in a penetrating voice that his master had indigestion after swallowing such a morsel and that a big tub full of water should be brought immediately. Rye lent over the tub and disgorged his odd snack which was clearly giving him some discomfort. The juggler splashed into the tub and crawled out drenched to the loud laughter of the whole Town Square. Rye bowed low and then went off in his cock-drawn chariot."

* * *

Blažej parked the car in Kunratice and they walked in mellow afternoon sunshine into woods, climbed up a steep ridge and looked down onto sunken ruins, half-hidden by trees.

"This is Nový Hradec, Wenceslas'castle-retreat! We're in   92 a Prague suburb but in Gothic times it must have been half a day's ride from town."

Alice sat down on the dry ground, "There's a tree in the middle of the banqueting-hall!"

He sat down beside her with his back against a tree and lit a cigarette.

"That's your sixth today!"

"You're counting! He got up and walking to the edge of the crumbling rampart, he stared down at the ancient stones, "I think Bohemia's been unfair to Wenceslas. He was always popular with the common people because he lightened their tax-load and brought down the prices of bread and meat, and perhaps because his weaknesses made him seem human... But he was hated by the great noblemen and court officials because he promoted people of lower rank like knights and citizens. His enemies spread all sorts of slanders about him until he became the centre of a black legend."

She began to sketch the ruins, "What slanders?"

"People said that at his christening he urinated in the Holy Water and did so again at his coronation at the age of two! It was even rumoured that he blinded Hanuš, the famous clock-maker and that on one occasion he had his chef roasted on a spit because he had spoilt his lunch! He could certainly be cruel as the terrible death of John of Nepomuk proves, but I think his character deteriorated under the constant pressure of trying to find solutions to insoluble problems! When he became king at the age of seventeen, the Church was cracking apart in the Great Schism. He had to cope with warring factions in the Church and the intrigues of the great noblemen, including his treacherous brother, Sigismund..."

"And the Hussites!"

"He sincerely wanted peace and it was said that in the early years of his reign a man could travel undisturbed through Bohemia carrying a bag of gold. And he tried to protect Hus for as long as he could. When the Archbishop of Prague decreed that all Wycliffe's writings should be burnt and that

Hus' preaching should cease, Wenceslas supported Hus and even ordered the Archbishop to compensate the owners of the manuscripts!" He put out his cigarette and sat down next to Alice, "Wenceslas bounced like a rubber ball between the factions and got lost! His nocturnal ramblings through Prague with rowdy companions became more and more frequent and so did his visits to the King of Brabant — visits followed by hang-overs and outbursts of rage."

"Wine, women and song?!"

"Yes, women... He probably owed his life to a woman, a bath-house attendant."

She was intent on her sketch, "I'm listening, although you always suspect I don't."

"Wenceslas was seized by the League of the Lords, a confederation of Bohemian nobles which even included some of his relatives. Determined to get control over all state offices, they made him their prisoner... However, he was allowed to attend the royal bathhouse on the Vltava and the story goes that he got friendly with Zuzana, a glamorous young bath-attendant. She appeared before him in a transparent knee-length shift and as she washed the royal chest he gazed at her beautiful body and stroked her slender back. Amidst the steam, they came to a whispered understanding. Throwing on her cloak, she ran to the river and hired a boat. She tied a towel round his middle and taking him by the hand, she led him out of the bathhouse and rowed him upstream to some bushes. Then they ran here to Nový Hradec. I don't know if Wenceslas managed to hang on to his towel."

She looked up from her drawing and frowned, "She took a huge risk! I hope he rewarded her."

"Apart from the royal favours which she probably received here at Hradec, she became very rich. He gave her 12 hundred groschen and a yearly annuity. Bath-attendants and barbers had always been despised but Wenceslas made them into an honorable guild with a green parakeet as their emblem."

"Was that his emblem?"

"No, his was a kingfisher. If you look at his emblem on   94

the Bridge Tower, you'll see that the kingfisher is in a ring bound with a thin veil fastened at the bottom with a knot. Wenceslas designed it himself and some say that the veil's a bath-towel!"

She put away her sketch-book, "A kingfisher... the symbol of intuitive knowledge..."

"Wenceslas died in this small castle in 1419," he said, as they walked down through the wood. He was buried in Zbraslav Abbey but the Hussite Wars gave him no rest. Within a year, the Hussites took his body out of its casket and soaked it in beer saying,

"You liked drinking with us when you were alive!"

* * *

"I can see he's important," she said, gazing up at the statue of Žižka, "he's got Prague at his feet!" The town lay below them, its gleaming spires bathed in the gentle sunshine of a late summer afternoon.

"He's 9 metres high, 5 metres wide and he weighs over 16 tons! He was a country squire with a genius for war, rather like your Oliver Cromwell three hundred years later. It was here on Žižkov Hill that he commanded the Hussite troops — lesser noblemen, tradesmen, small farmers and farm labourers — against the might of the Emperor Sigismund's crusade. In July 1420, Sigismund held Hradčany and Vyše-hrad, and in order to capture Prague he needed to hem the

95

city in from the East. This hill, formerly known as the Vítkov, was a key point for Žižka, too. It was essential to hold it in order to secure communications with the rest of the country and keep up Hussite morale."

"Who were the crusaders?"

"Everyone! They came from all over Europe — Germans, Frenchmen, Italians, Hungarians, Austrians and Englishmen. Some came to fight heresy, others were mercenaries out for plunder. Žižka knew that he had to prepare for attacks by heavily armed horsemen. He had trained a disciplined lightly-equipped infantry. They used flails, those terrible spiked balls attached to chains, and daggers. His tactic was to chain the iron-clad peasant waggons together with picked marksmen sitting beside the drivers. The waggons became forts against which the charging enemy cavalry were smashed to pieces. The battle here was a truly heroic moment in our history and in the Hussite movement. The Praguers were greatly out-numbered but they had desparate courage and belief in their cause. There were women here, too. They came in their hundreds to build the fortifications. They even used the oak stalls from the Church of St. Michael! During the battle when the enemy seemed to be gaining ground, one woman refused to retreat saying that a Christian should never give way to Anti-Christ. She was immediately cut down..."

Blažej lit a cigarette. He glanced at Alice but she appeared not to notice. "Žižka's tactics and the amazing persistence of his supporters, many from the new Hussite community of Tábor, saved Prague and was looked on as a holy miracle by the Hussites. But other crusades followed. In 1430 Joan of Arc threatened to join the invaders and would probably have done so if she hadn't been occupied with your people! The last crusade was routed in 1431 and by that time the nobility of Europe had lost all appetite for fighting the Czechs."

"So... the Hussites won?"

"Yes... and no! Once the crusades were over, the Hussite movement broke apart. On one side were the radicals from Tábor and on the other the moderates who were prepared to

96

compromise. The Táborites went much further than Hus had gone. They abolished class distinctions saying that everyone was equal before God, banned vestments and held all their services in Czech. The nobility and patricians looked on them as dangerous revolutionaries. At the battle of Lipany where Czech fought Czech, the radicals were defeated. It was a massacre rather than a battle for according to some accounts 13,000 Táborites were killed. After Lipany it was only a

Žižka

question of time before the moderate Hussites negotiated with the Catholics. Bohemia had suffered terribly during the wars and people were desparate for peace. In 1457 George of Poděbrady was elected king by the Czech people and he brought order and stability to the country. He came from a noble Hussite family and at the age of fourteen he had fought at Lipany and seen the horrors of civil war."

Alice was thoughtful, "What did the Hussite movement do for your country?"

Blažej sighed, "Your questions are... so difficult!"

She laughed, "But you're my guide!"

"The Czech groschen really did have two sides. Maybe Hus' sacrifice shakes our system of comfortable values, we're forever compromising and over — ready to adapt. The Hussite movement contributed to the European spirit because it emphasized individual conscience and this inspired our people in times of darkness. Jan Palach who set fire to himself as the Russian tanks thundered into Prague in 1968, was a great admirer of Hus. The movement had importance for Czechs in another way, too. The Hussites' devotion to the Bible and hymn-singing enriched our language. In the 15th century, Aeneas Sylvius who became Pope Pius 11 said that although Czech women were wicked, they knew the Bible better than Italian bishops and had a great love of learning."

"What about the other side of the coin?."

"Bohemia paid a very high price for the Hussite revolution. The destruction was tremendous — death, torture, the burning of libraries and sacking of churches. By the 1430s many of the Hussites were little better than brigands. The peasants suffered most of all, their crops destroyed and no certainty of sowing and reaping. By the end of the wars they were more under the thumb of their local lords who had benefited from seizing church property, than when the wars began."

Alice sighed, "The little man always loses out! Wat Tyler and his followers were crushed in England. You almost seem to be saying that... Hus died for nothing."

"Not for nothing... In 1485 when your Richard III was

fighting Henry Tudor on Bosworth Field, the Bohemian Estates met at Kutná Hora and a religious truce was agreed between the Catholics and the Utraquist Church..."

"Utraquist?"

"'Sub utraqua specie'. It means 'in both kinds'. The Hussites wanted to receive both the bread and the wine at Holy Communion whereas the Catholics had insisted that the wine was for priests alone. The Hussites or Utraquists made the chalice their symbol. The Kutná Hora truce meant co-existence and tolerating each other's services."

"How long did the truce last?"

"It lasted, with some hiccups, until the Battle of White Mountain in 1620 when we were conquered by the Catholic Hapsburgs and religious toleration was thrown to the winds."

* * *

"Jan Jenštejn was an interesting character," Blažej began, as they drove towards Hradčany.

"Was he real?"

"Real?"

"I never quite know when you're making things up!"

"Do we ever know what's real...?" He checked himself, "Jenštejn was real, all right, larger than life! Seducer and saint. Fornificator and monk..."

"Who was he?"

"Archbishop of Prague. A haughty, ambitious cleric who made arrogant claims for the church and filled his treasure-chests at the same time. He infuriated Wenceslas in all sorts of ways. On one occasion he got into a petty quarrel with one of Wenceslas' favourites, Jan Čuch, the Court Marshal. It was about a weir that Čuch had built near Jenšteyn's lands. The Archbishop sent his servants to remove it and there was a fracas. It's said to be the first occasion when fire-arms were used in Bohemia! Wenceslas imprisoned Jenšteyn in Karlšteyn for a time. More seriously, Jenšteyn upheld the authority of the church at the expanse of royal power and became the patron of John Nepomuk. Wenceslas' rage knew no bounds and Jenštejn would have paid for his defiance with his life had he not managed to escape and find refuge in Rome. Apart from political manoeuvering, Jenšteyn's great interest was women! He enjoyed setting snares for them, seducing them and casting them aside. One night he returned home late after a riotous party in Prague and saw a woman standing in the deep snow before his palace. Slim, dark-haired, enduring the bitter cold, she stood there motionless. He walked up to her and saw that she was a pretty, young peasant-girl he had taken to his bed and then abandoned. She fell on her knees before him. 'Sire, Sire, Help me, I implore you!' He turned away and went up to his room where his servants removed his costly clothes and brought him mulled wine. Before retiring for the night, he went to the window in his night-cap to admire the beauty of the winter night. A great white moon shone down on the gleaming landscape. An owl hooted. He opened the casement and the terrible cold seemed to graze his face. Then he saw the woman, a tiny dark figure in a dazzling ocean of snow. She was looking up at his window. He stared at her for a moment and then threw himself into the furs on his couch and fell asleep at once."

"What happened to her?"

"It was a bitter Bohemian night. She froze to death."

Alice scowled, "I don't know why you're telling me about this playboy! Or why you think he's interesting!"

"There's more to come. The story's got a Gothic ending. Some time later, Jenštejn heard about the sudden death of his old friend, the Archbishop of Magdeburg. The Archbishop was dancing at a ball when suddenly there was a great cry, 'Fire! Fire!' It was only a malicious joke but everyone took to their heels, the Archbishop leading the way. He'd drunk a lot of wine and was wearing tight clothes to show off his figure, and slippers with high curled toes. He slipped on the steep stairway leading to the garden and broke his neck. Jenšteyn took this as a dreadful warning. In 1493, he gave up his archbishopric, retired into his castle and lived like a monk for the rest of his life. He spent his time in prayer and meditation, read mystical works and wrote melancholy tracts about Consolation and Death the Benefactor."

She gave Blažej a sardonic look, "The death of a woman he'd wronged didn't shake him but the death of another Archbishop did!"

"We can't be sure... We'll never know how many ghosts came to him in the night hours."

* * *

Alice dug her heels in like a mule as they approached the Gothic Gallery next to St. George's Basilica, "Oh no, not a museum! My feet are tired."

Blažej took her arm, "Please! I only want to show you one picture. The gallery's about to close."

He led her across the gallery to a long, narrow room at the back, "The five paintings on this wall are by Theodoricus, Charles IV's court-painter and one of our greatest artists. Have a look at this painting of St. Augustine! I'd like to know if you find it extraordinary."

She looked at the painting carefully for some time and then walked up and down with rising excitement, looking at the others, "It's the eyes! I dont't know if they're looking outward or inward but they're seeing something extraordinary."

"Theodoricus rejects illusion! He was one of the first artists to depict the human face in a realistic way. These massive, motionless figures are real people to me because there's something fascinating in their faces, perhaps a curious longing for the transcendental. Gothic art expresses a kind of inner light and it expresses solitude, the great solitude of the Central European person... Solitude is Theodoricus' melody."

"I'm amazed by their noses! Each one's different and they're large, even bulbous. They're quite sensual, too, and not idealized in any way. Look at his!" She pointed to St. Vitus in his beautiful flowered gown, "He's got a huge nose

101

and a thick strong neck like an ox." She examined the picture, "The composition's very precise and geometrical. The outlines of his head and shoulders and forearms form a circle. But his face lives. It's very young and gentle and sensitive. He's looking at something beyond this world..." She returned to St. Augustine who was clasping his breviary, "Look at his veined hands! His knuckles are red, perhaps with rheumatism. And look!" she added delightedly, "his right thumb-nail's dirty!"

Blažej's spirits soared. He had a sudden almost overwhelm-

St Vitus
by Theodoricus

ing impulse to hug her, to dance away with her, to climb impossible heights. There had been many clients over the past few years, a long grey procession of them and their faces had dimmed with time, but not a single one of them had given more than a glance to his beloved Theodoricus. Accustomed to monitoring and controlling his emotions from a hard childhood through years of professional experience, he subdued the impulse, though with difficulty. When she turned towards him he was looking towards the exit with his usual frown, "I think we'll have to go or they'll throw us out!"

* * *

He drove slowly down Na Příkopě and pointed to the house At the Black Rose, "Peter Payne, one of your compatriots lived there!"

"Who was he?"

"He was an Oxford scholar inspired by Wycliffe and he became Lollardism's theoretician. He took refuge here in 1414 because he was being persecuted for his opinions at Oxford and he became an ardent Hussite supporter. He was learned and eloquent and discussions went on late into the night in that house. In 1429 he set off with a nobleman, Menhard of Jindřichův Hradec, a few companions and an escort of 200 horsemen to Presburg where they tried unsuccessfully to come to an understanding with Emperor Sigismund. Later, in 1433 he was one of the 15 envoys who were sent to Basle to negotiate with the Catholic Cardinal Cesarini and Duke William of Bavaria who was representing Sigismund. Their aim was to present the Hussite case and heal the rift between the Catholics and Utraquists. There was tremendous excitement in Basle as they rode into the city with their escort of 300 horsemen. Men, women and children crowded on the roof-tops and at windows to see the strange Hussites who had defeated great armies and destroyed cities. Apparently they were well-received and banqueted by the city authorities but Payne's speech to the Council of Basle caused an uproar! He praised Wycliffe and his doctrines, described how he had been persecuted at Oxford and denounced the worldly priests. There were furious interruptions by some of the English clergy who were present and an unholy stormy scene followed." He laughed, "Payne was known as Mister Englis in Prague and there was even a ballad about him,

'The devil sent us Englis,
He walks stealthily through Prague,
Spreading doctrines from England,
That are not wholesome for Bohemia'."

Alice stirred restlessly in the small car, "An English trouble-maker abroad! I wonder if I'll make a mark on Prague?"

"You already have!"

She looked at him but he was concentrating on the road. The absurd car bumped over the cobblestones as he negotiated the small streets behind Náměstí Republiky.

"Will you be seeing your girl-friend tonight?"

"No... she's busy. She's a teacher."

"Do you love her?"

He glanced at he quickly but she was looking calmly ahead.

"Love...?"

"I mean, does your heart beat faster when you see her?"

A car stopped without warning in front of them and he swerved sharply.

"I'm at the age for settling down and starting a family, or so my mother tells me at least twice a month! I've known my girl—friend for... six months, now. Of course, I like seeing her! I'm always glad to see her."

Alice smiled.

* * *

With a screech of brakes, he pulled up at the modest hotel.

She extricated herself slowly and stretched. Then she closed the door and put her head through the window and he turned to see her beaming face.

"Blažej! You're a great one for Gothic!"

THE THIRD DAY·
RENAISSANCE

BLAŽEJ STOOD in his tiny bathroom, a mere partition between living-room and kitchen, half-listening to the radio. He stared into his cracked shaving-mirror. It was going to be a day of immense sultry heat with evening thunder. He did not want to see Alice for he forecast emotional storms. "Trials and tribulation!" he said aloud, fingering his stubble. At the same time, he wanted to see her very much. "Bedevilled by ambivalence!" he said loudly with a fleeting sense of pride in his fluent English. He realized that until three days ago his life had held few surprises. Clients were merely clients, parents were predictable and... He shut off the thought and considered his income. The week with Alice would carry him through to the end of the month. He would be able to repay a few small debts and buy a water-pump for Šemík; the car was over-heating badly.

He parked in Na Poříčí Street and walked towards the hotel. It was already very hot and his light shirt felt damp. Alice came skipping towards him and he looked at her in surprise. She seemed different each day. She was wearing a short white dress of some very flimsy, gauzy material with a narrow gold belt, and she had twisted a yellow scarf round her head in a circlet. All she needs is wings! he thought. The plain, cross girl at the airport in her pleated skirt had disappeared and so had the patchwork girl who had contrived to fall heavily into his arms in a medieval loft. But had it been contrivance? He was uncertain.

"Hello Blažej", she waved a paper-back, "if you're not a Lion and a Fox, you're not a true Renaissance man. I've been reading Machiavelli to get into the mood".

They shook hands, "You're very well-read!" he said.

She punched him lightly in the ribs, "Don't be patronizing! I've read a lot because for ages my mother refused to have TV. My father had to sneak off to the pub to watch it!" She sighed, "Maybe I'm not totally modern... now I'll have to discover whether you're a Lion or a Fox or some other animal. Yesterday you were a bit on the stiff and menacing side like a polar bear".

107

He smiled, "It's going to be a tropical day, I might be a bit of a boar..."

She clapped her hands over her ears, "Ouch, no puns! Can we walk today? The midget Šemík will be like an oven".

They walked into Náměstí Republiky and she looked at the stalls piled high with curious clothes, wooden spoons and tiny caged birds. "What's the key to Renaissance?"

It was Blažej's turn to sigh, "I was afraid you might ask me that question..."

"But you have to answer my questions, it's what you're paid for."

He looked at her, shocked.

Suddenly she put her arm round his waist and gave him a quick hug. "Oh murder! I'm hugging a strange man in the street. Don't worry, look on me like a younger sister."

He glanced at her but she seemed serious. For the first time he noticed a mole on her right cheek, "You've got a beauty-spot!" he said involuntarily.

She made a face, "You're probably looking at my nose, I was given an undersized one. You're trying to avoid my question, I need the Renaissance key." She tapped him on the arm, "Did you know that Lucretia Borgia was hauled before the Inquisition because of her golden hair? Pure gold, like a radiant sun on her head. As she walked through the streets of Rome men were dazzled by her beauty."

"Fair hair like yours?" he asked, teasingly.

She ruffled the short hair at her neck. "I don't dazzle! Why are we looking at the Powder Tower, it's Gothic isn't it?"

"It's a fake. It was restored in 1883 by Joseph Mocker. The original was built at the end of the fifteenth century and was part of the Old Town fortifications but when our king Vladislav Jagellon went to live in Prague Castle, work on the tower stopped and it became a gunpowder store. But look at the window, it's original! It was designed by the brilliant architect and wood-carver, Matěj Rejsek."

Powder Tower
window

She stared up at the rectangular window with its decorative gable, "It looks Gothic to me..."

"It is and it isn't! It's transitional. We're glimpsing Renaissance, its spirit came late to Bohemia, over a hundred years after the awakening in Florence."

"Why?"

"Prague was rooted in the Middle Ages. The whole period between the Battle of Lipany and the Battle of White Mountain in 1620 was filled with religious controversies. Theology was the great topic and for most Czechs reading the Bible in their own language was more important than reading Erasmus or your Francis Bacon. The spirit of the new times, the pleasure-seeking Renaissance spirit, was rebuffed by this medieval town."

"A butterfly on cold Gothic?"

"Some people amused themselves, of course. Noblemen and wealthy merchants tried to outdo each other with their gorgeous clothes and they rode in sledges with heated stoves. In Prague confectioners became important people. But deep in the Czech psyche there was medieval asceticism — the fiery torch of John Hus."

She gazed at the forbidding bulk of the Powder Tower, "Perhaps the Hussite revolution was your Renaissance? It was a revival, wasn't it? A revival of early Christian ideals and getting back to the Bible. The Italians revived the classical world."

He looked at her in surprise. "You may be right. It was difficult for secular ideas to edge in here. Lutheran ideas were coming from Germany and fanatical Calvinism from Geneva. The religious pot went on boiling! It didn't have a chance to die down. And the Catholic Church put its house in order and went on the offensive armed with the Jesuits. Europe was split into two great ideological camps..."

"Cold War!" She looked at the colourful holiday crowds milling round the glittering splendour of Obecní Dům, "Something's happening here... I can sense excitement...

110

You told me on the way from the airport that there's hope in the air. Maybe it's Renaissance time."

"Maybe ...we went to sleep for forty years!"

* * *

They climbed up the stairs of the Old Town Hall and stood in the gallery. He looked at her radiant face as she admired the view.

"Prague's quite something, isn't it?" she said, enthusiastically.

"I wanted to show you the towers of Týn Church from here. They were completed in 1511 and I think a miracle happened linking Gothic with Renaissance. Look at the little turrets on the corners with a circular balustrade between them. Their octagonal roofs are Gothic but the small decorated bay-windows proclaim Renaissance."

She stared at the windows, unconvinced. "These labels, Gothic... Renaissance... it's all so vague."

"I'd like to explain it simply..."

She turned to him angrily, "I'm not stupid... why simply?"

He was startled, as always, by her abrupt changes of mood, "Gothic was concerned with people and life here and now. Challenge, questions, exploration. Copernicus, Columbus, Gallileo, Raleigh. Delight in the human body, Michelangelo's David. Music, dance, making merry, embraces... Man as the measure of all things."

"I daresay it had another side... stop name-dropping, it's hot!"

He felt the scorching sun on the back of his neck and looked up at the sky. It seemed white with heat, "Shall we go down?"

* * *

As they passed the Old Town Hall, he pointed to the carvings of flowers and figures on the main entrance portal, "Matěj Rejsek again. And look at the window, a lovely Renaissance web! This house on the corner, the House at the Minute, was originally Gothic and was rebuilt in the six-

Old Town Hall
portal

Old Town Hall window

teenth century. The amazing sgraffito decorations are from the seventeenth century."

"This house has a completely new look," she stared at the extraordinary decorations depicting biblical and mythical scenes, "I wonder what they mean? The bound king with a crown on his head, pierced by three arrows... The slings and arrows of... Oh, never mind! Why's it called the House at the Minute?"

"No one knows. The stone lion is a survival from the time when it was a pharmacy. At the White Lion."

113   She chanted loudly,

At the Minute

"'In a minute
There's time
For decisions
Which a minute will reverse...'"

Several tourists stared at them curiously and he felt embarassed and registered his irritation.

She turned to him mockingly, "You'd like to have an invisible cloak, wouldn't you?"

He sighed, "Sometimes I'd like to make myself invisible like a Renaissance magus..."

114

"Magus?"

"Maybe I'll tell you later."

* * *

As they walked down Havelská street, Alice suddenly disappeared into a crowd around one of the market-stalls. After what seemed an interminable wait she reappeared holding a large puppet.

"Lucifer!"

He looked at the wicked face with its tiny red eyes, protruding teeth and pointed ears. "Allow me..." he tucked it under his arm.

"Thanks!"

He pointed to number 3 with its faded painting of the Archangel Michael, "Renaissance!"

At Brunwiks

She stared at the empty statue-niche high on the facade, "The saint's flown away!"

"Look at the house next door, At Brunwiks, it's one of the best-preserved Renaissance houses in Prague."

She looked up at the three great windows decorated with stone foliage, "It's strange to see a Renaissance house above Gothic arches."

He opened the door and they went up a steep flight of steps and looked down into the narrow courtyard.

"The Renaissance needed light, space, symmetry... airiness" he said, "it was hard to find this in a stone medieval town. Gothic resisted! So the builders put arcaded galleries into miniature courtyards and created Renaissance portals in narrow streets."

"Like icing on a plain cake," she said happily.

* * *

Swallow —
tail roofs

116

As they wandered down Husová Street, Blažej caught her arm, "Look up! Don't miss the Prague roofs! Those are swallow-tails and they've flown in from sixteenth century Venice! These little streets have hardly changed in four hundred years," he continued, as they went into Melantrichova Street. He pointed to number 10, "Jiří Melantrich, the famous Prague printer, lived there. He brought out five editions of the Bible in Czech and the work of humanists like Erasmus."

She looked at the mediocre nineteenth century house, "Poor Melantrich! where's his home?"

"Demolished. It was a fine Renaissance building with a beautiful portal and courtyard loggia but it was pulled down in 1895."

"Philistines! But it's much worse in London, so much of our past has gone, even in country towns. Boring office-blocks, department stores, estate-agents... Every high street looks much the same. I wonder if you'll be able to preserve Prague?"

He led her across the street, "The two houses on this side of the street are unusual for the Old Town... they're stately."

She looked at the five crowns on the facade and at the fine carved doorway.

"It's Renaissance, about 1616," he said.

"It's colossal! One of the biggest doors I've ever seen," she examined its carvings of falling draperies like stage-curtains, "Prague's a city of fantastic doors. Huge imposing ones, tiny mysterious ones leading to odd courtyards, broken ones, collapsing ones... I can imagine them groaning on their hinges in the night wind as it howls down these little streets."

"This grand house is Tayflův Dům," he said, leading her to number 15. They went down a cobbled passageway into a great flaking Renaissance courtyard and she stared up at the high crumbling house with its intricate wrought-iron balconies, "This is where I'd like to live, somewhere romantic."

117

He smiled, "Perhaps not so romantic in winter. But there was romance in this house. Some say that Frederick of the Palatinate, the Winter King, used to visit this house before the Battle of White Mountain and that he was fascinated by Jan Tayfl's charming widow, Esther."

At the Five Crowns

She lent against the cool courtyard wall, "Esther?"

"Esther Halbenstreit was a merchant's daughter and she'd learnt about business from childhood. She married a prosperous burgher, Jan Tayfl and with his savings and her dowry they bought this house. He was a solid man but

Courtyard
of Tayfl's
house

without much talent for business. After his death she went into business in a big way. She was a true entrepreneur... She understood all the nuances and complexities of business and she liked the adventure of really large transactions." He paused and smiled, "And she understood the market. She managed the firm herself and developed a business network across Europe reaching the dazzling heights of the Renaissance merchant princes..." He paused and lit a cigarette.

"Not bad!" She looked at her watch, "Your first today?"

"Absolutely," he lied, "Esther made this house magnificent. The furniture was made of rare wood. There were inlaid chests, exquisite tapestries and paintings by great masters. She gave great banquets and imported rare, spiced dishes which were served on delicate porcelain. The guests sat at a great table laid with silverware and crystal under Venetian candelabras and surrounded by ornate mirrors. She was visited by royalty and received guests from the Castle. But those were turbulent times and her wealth excited envy. She decide to hire a carpenter to construct a false ceiling for her and under it she secreted her huge money-bags and jewels and gold. However, nothing is safe in this world. The carpenter betrayed her and led the Emperor's soldiers to the house. Within minutes they cleared out the rewards of a lifetime, her whole treasure!"

She put her hand on his arm and smiled into his eyes, "I think you're rather Gothic, you've got a moral up your sleeve, haven't you?"

He drew away and stubbed out his cigarette, "Maybe we should never cling to anything."

* * *

"At the Two Golden Bears!" he said, pointing to the house-sign.

Handing him her shoulder bag and camera, Alice took out her sketch-book and began to draw the solid bears faced by armoured knights and the tiny goblin face with huge ears above the portal. A hop-bine chiselled in stone twined round the great door.

"The portal dates from around 1570." He watched her sketching for a while, "May I take a picture of you? I like to keep a record of my clients," he added hastily.

She nodded, absorbed in her sketch.

"I'd like to take you inside," he led her into the huge, gloomy vaulted hall with its massive stone pillars. She stared in wonder at the tall, blackened oak doors with their flower-like bosses of iron and great handles. She opened one of them with difficulty and surveyed a blank wall.

At the Two
Golden Bears

"Ghosts?" he inquired.

She smiled. "Did you know there's a bell in Vienna which calls ghosts to itself? I'll expect you to show me a Prague ghost-bell."

They went through a passageway into a little courtyard with Renaissance loggia and Tuscan pillars, "The famous journalist, Egon Erwin Kisch was born here in the late nineteenth century." Blažej explained. "His father had a draper's shop on the ground floor. In his articles Kisch described the Old Town's maze of narrow, winding streets, cobbled courtyards, passages and odd corners full of petty thieves, whores, tricksters, scroungers and eccentrics..."

"Things don't change! An Englishwoman at my hotel told me that when she looked at her change from a thousand crown note she found she'd been given 500 Polish zlotys and she hadn't planned to go to Warsaw!"

* * *

They walked down Dlouhá Street and he thumped on the door of At the Golden Tree, "One more Old Town courtyard!"

An old man with a bristling white moustache led them into a beautiful, flagged courtyard with elegant loggia decorated with leaves and flowers. Blažej smiled, "A touch of Florence."

She looked at some of the tiny doorways under the graceful arches, "What's in there?"

"Peoples flats." He began an animated conversation with the old man who seemed to be in a towering rage. He stomped up and down waving his arms and shouting.

Alice observed him with interest, "What's got into him?"

"The Renaissance sun shone here. But this stately place will soon be a hotel. It's been bought by foreigners and he's furious about it."

She looked at the crumbling arches and sighed, "I suppose you need foreign capital?"

At the Golden Tree

"We do but there's a terrible housing-shortage in this town. This old gentleman lives here!"

* * *

She groaned as they walked into Karlova Street, "I'm melting! My feet hurt and I'm thirsty!" She prodded Blažej as they went into the lobby of At the Golden Snake, "Another Eve!"

"Deodatus Damajan, the owner of the first Prague coffee house, At the Three Ostriches, near Charles Bridge, lived here. He came to Prague penniless, sold his coffee from a street barrow and made a fortune."

123

She laughed shortly, "I wonder if the barrow-boys in Wenceslas Square will make a fortune? It's not so easy to be a millionaire."

"Some of them already are!" He led her to a small table with a view of Liliova Square, "This is my table and it's probably where your author, Francis Crawford, sat writing his strange novel, The Prague Witch when he came here from India. His witch, Unorna, lived in that great house opposite, At the Golden Well. It stands out in Prague because of its shape. This little square is the Renaissance heart of the Old Town and that house is extraordinary. It's built like an irregular triangle. The blunt apex of one angle is facing us and it's got one side on Karlova Street and the other on that narrow alleyway. Overhanging passages are built out over that dim lane. Look at the great oriel window! There's another window above it and under the pointed gable that dark, unglazed porthole. The house is like a great floating ship."

She stared at the bizarre stucco reliefs of saints which stood out in strangely contorted attitudes by the window on the first and second floors.

"They're the patron saints of Bohemia and they were done in Baroque times by Jan Oldřich Mayer, probably to ward off the plague." Blažej took a shabby book out of his briefcase and handed it to her, "The Prague Witch!"

She leafed though the closely printed pages, "Three hundred and fifty-one pages and no pictures!"

He opened the book, began to read:

"'Prague is constructed on the same principle as the human brain, full of winding ways, dark lanes, and gloomy arches, all of which may lead somewhere, or may not. Its topography continually misleads its inhabitants as the convolutions of the brain mislead the thoughts that dwell there, sometimes bringing them out at last, after a patient search for daylight, upon a fine broad street where the newest fashions in thought are exposed for sale in brightly illuminated shop windows and showcases: conducting them sometimes to the dark, unsavoury court where the miserable self drags out its unhealthy existence in the single room of its hired lodging.'"

He closed the book and looked at Alice. She was listening intently.

"Crawford's characters wander in the bitter cold through the labyrinth of the Old Town lanes, the endless turnings, nooks and passageways leading to no one knows where. The novel is set in deepest winter. The wind screams down Karlova. Prague is a bitter city under lowering skies... Workmen by the frozen Vltava are cutting the ice into blocks for burghers' cellars..."

She leaned forward eagerly, "I'd like to come here in winter!"

125 At the Golden Well

"You should come. You can see things better in winter, Prague doesn't have many tourists in January."

"I don't know what you've got against tourists," she interrupted crossly, "you make a living out of us!"

"You're very sharp..."

"But it's true!"

"He sighed, 'Yes...'"

She put her hand on his arm, "I know what you mean, the Praguers get their town back in winter."

He nodded, "Glittering, frosty days and then grey misty days... Prague is steeped in its melancholy dream..."

A waiter approached and Blažej ordered mineral water, coffee and salads, "All Czechs are melancholy! You English look out over the ocean but we're locked in the heart of Europe, we look within. Shakespeare was the only one to give us a sea-coast! We like doses of solitude." He sipped his coffee, "I can't bear anyone watching me shaving," he said suddenly, "It drives me mad."

"I like privacy, too." She ignored her salad, "I suppose you see me as a lonely girl hunting for a man? That's what most men think when they see a girl travelling on her own."

He smiled, "I think they're right!"

She frowned, "That's silly! Some girls like to see the world. What does your girl-friend feel about you escorting a moderately pretty girl around Prague?"

"Very pretty, I'd say. But I'm not your escort, I'm your guide." He stirred his coffee with unnecessary zeal, "An attractive young girl like you has a boy-friend, surely?"

She sighed, "He's called William and he's not exactly my boyfriend... We go around together. He's an oil-company executive and says he's going places. I'm unkind to him really. You see, he talks about money all the time and when he asks me to marry him I can't help laughing." She gulped her mineral water, "He's rather fat!"

"But you'll have to think about marriage some time, won't you?"

"Not until I'm at least thiry-one..."

126

"Won't you be rather old?"

She scowled, "How ridiculous! You're thirty-one and you're thinking about it." She leaned forward and stared into his eyes. Her face was grave, even grim, "Blažej, I'll come to Prague in ten years time and live next door to you, I want to see Prague in the snow. I'll be thirty-two and you'll be forty-one so we'll be very mature. She took his hand, "Will you give me your promise that you'll welcome me?"

He burst out laughing, "Alice, we've only known each other three days..."

"It's enough!" She got up.

"Alice, please don't be cross! I'm your faithful guide and I've got my living to make. Besides, I haven't told you about the Prague Witch."

She hesitated and then sat down with a thud.

"A handsome man, The Wanderer, comes to Prague. He's searching for Beatrice, the woman he loves and he's looked for her in many cities across Europe. He thinks he sees her in the gloom of the Týn Church and he follows her back to that house, At the Golden Well. He rings the bell and a servant conducts him to a great room with a glazed roof. There, on a high carved chair sits Unorna, a strikingly beautiful red-head with strange eyes, one grey and one brown. After talking to her for a while, he almost falls under her hypnotic spell and only leaves the house with a great effort of will. Returning to the Týn Church, he meets the extraordinary gnome-like Keyork Arabian. Keyork, a man of immense learning, has one over-riding passion — to prolong his own life. In a locked room in that house lies an ancient man, he's one hundred and seven years old. Unorna keeps him in an hypnotic trance and every day Keyork comes from his sinister study in the house At The Black Mother of God, filled with skulls, skeletons and embalmed bodies, to study the old man. He believes he can prolong the man's life indefinitely and discover the secret of prolonging his own. But he must have Unorna's help... Meanwhile, Unorna falls in love with The Wanderer."

Alice leaned forward eagerly, "What happened to the old man? Did the Wanderer find Beatrice?"

He smiled.

As they crossed the lobby, he paused under the golden serpent in the lobby, "I'll make you a promise, I always keep my promises!"

She looked at him cautiously.

"I promise you that if you come back to Prague in ten years time, I'll book our table. We'll drink hot soup and I'll ask your opinion on The Prague Witch."

She smiled, "I'll think about it!"

* * *

They crossed Malostranské Square and walked into Sněmovní Street and Blažej pointed to number 6. "At the Golden Swan, my favourite Renaissance house!"

She looked up at the great yellow-grey house. A cloud of starlings whirled past agains an intense blue sky, "Extraordinary gables, they're like upturned chess-pieces."

"It's a unique building because it's two houses joined by an in-between house. It's a man and a woman, each different but still a unity. And between them the child..."

The man looks like a fortress and the woman's slender and graceful... I think the child's outstripped its parents!"

"It was a wealthy burgher's house built in the sixteenth century by Ulrico Aostalli. The windows are open," he continued pensively, "the striped feather quilts have been aired, the chamber-pots emptied, the iron bed-linen's been put away in the oak chest ...the fragrance of tranquillity."

She made a face, "Domesticity!" She walked up the tiny shadowy lane by the side of the house, "I see it differently, a place of secrets! The servant-girl creeps out at night to meet her lover. There's danger lurking here, too, perhaps the knife in the dark."

At the Golden Swan

* * *

"It's too hot for galleries," she moaned as they went into the Third Castle Courtyard.

"I want to show you St. George. He's Gothic but his horse is Renaissance."

She looked at the slender figure of the saint with his narrow waist and delicate body. Booted and spurred, he held his

129

lance aloft. The dragon's snout lay across his left spur and its tail was wrapped round the horse's left leg.

"Peter Parler designed this statue in 1373 and it was sculpted by Masters George and Martin of Cluj. Sections of it were recast in the sixteenth century. It's the oldest medieval free-standing bronze statue in Central Europe."

"What's Renaissance about the horse?" she stared at its

St George
and the Dragon

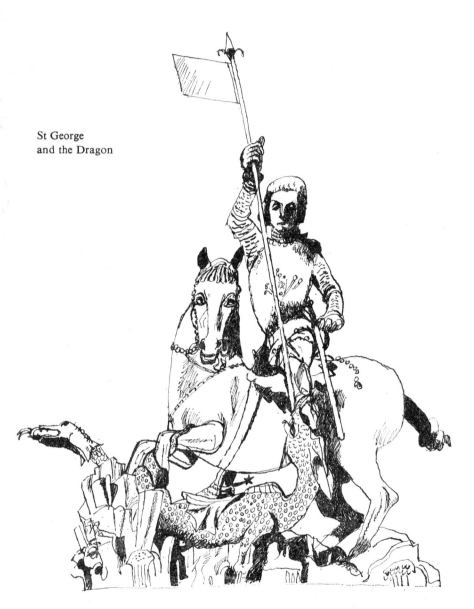

braided tail, "It looks like one of those great bulging Uccello horses to me, a bolster with legs!"

Blažej was aware that he resented being contradicted. His clients had contradicted him about hotel accomodation but never about works of art. But, then, he reflected, many of them had never really listened to him, "Can't you see? St. George is idealized. He's frail, spiritual, etherial, the personification of purity and valour. But the horse is real. There's something stirring in Czech Gothic, a new sense of movement, a fresh perception of the animal world."

She shook her head, "If it was a real horse it wouldn't be looking down at the dragon with pointed ears. It's ears would be laid back and it would be rearing up with spouts of steam coming from its nostrils." She moved behind the statue, "Look, its right hoof is lying limply on the rocks doing nothing at all, the only thing moving here is the dragon."

Silly emotional female, he thought, she just wants to argue.

"The horse moves!" he said obstinately.

She took a square of toilet paper from her bag and wiped her face. Then she turned away from the statue crossly, "Blažej, you've got no horse-sense!"

"The Czechs have a dove-like nature," he muttered as they left the statue.

* * *

They crossed the Third Courtyard and he pointed to the windows of the Vladislav Hall. "Those rectangular window linings were probably the first Renaissance features outside Italy. They were made just a year after Columbus' first voyage."

"Who was king at the time?"

"Vladislav II. He was elected in 1471 and ruled until 1516 and he left his mark here. For over a hundred years the Castle had been abandoned by royalty..."

"Why?" she interrupted.

"After Charles IV's death in 1378, Wenceslas IV preferred

to live at the Royal Court in the Old Town where Obecní Dům stands now."

"Near his girl-friends?"

"Then there were the Hussite wars", Blažej continued, "the Hussites seized the Castle in 1421 and held it for thirteen years. The destruction was tremendous, the building began to decay and the fortifications crumbled. King George of Poděbrady brought order to Bohemia but he too, chose to live in comfort in the Old Town rather than in a mouldering monument. When Vladislav became king, he lived at the Royal Court for thirteen years. However, he moved here in 1484, mainly because he was afraid of rioting mobs in the Old Town. He built new fortifications here and his brilliant court architect, Benedict Ried, began the reconstruction of the Royal Palace. What strikes you first about this place?" he asked quickly as they entered the Hall.

"Size! It's gigantic! It's amazing to find such a huge hangar in a Gothic castle where the rooms were usually quite small."

"Ried sacrificed the entire second floor of the main palace, including one chapel. It was exceptional for that time."

She looked awestruck at the great ceiling patterned with interlaced stone ribs. "Ried's work is known as Vladislav Gothic but I feel the Renaissance in it," Blažej continued. "He designed the ceiling just a few years before your Henry VIII came to the throne. Humanists like Erasmus and Thomas More were at the centre of a ferment of ideas. Thomas Wolsey, that Renaissance Prince, would soon be Chancellor and owner of Hampton Court Palace. The ceiling's a multitude of strands... threads of thought... a complex network..."

"Turmoil in stone?" she suggested.

"Tumultuous in a way, it's full of swirling movement. The thoughts twist and turn in coils and arcs and then stream into space. But it's not a melancholy turmoil, there's a belief in man's potential..."

She sat down on one of the stone window-ledges and stared up at it, "A map of ideas? Voyages into unknown seas?"

132

Vladislav Hall

He sat down next to her, "I think it's a huge web of concepts and it tries to speak to people and influence them. Gothic wanted to take people away to God." He hesitated, "I think it mirrors the Renaissance psyche. Look at the stone ribbons flying about and tying up in many different directions... it's a maze of dialectics!"

"Yes, excitement... a celebration of new times." She punched him lightly on the chest, "but I wouldn't have thought of that on my own."

"Your Thomas More said that God created the machine of the world in admiration of man, making him the only one capable of understanding complex things. And therefore God loves the curious and careful observer and admirer of his work rather than the one who passes it without noticing it, in stupid rigidity and without the slightest emotion like an animal lacking reason."

"Utopia?"

"Yes, can I go on quoting?"

"Wait, I've got a quote, too! Leonardo! 'There is nothing to say about some people except that they are a passage-way for food, the producers of night-soil and the fillers of toilets.'"

Blažej stood up and began striding up and down. His black hair stood up in tufts, "Dualism! Pietro Pompanazzi!: 'Man is not simple but diverse, by no means firmly fixed but dual by nature and his place must be in the middle of the mortal and immortal essence...'"

She clapped.

"Giordano Bruno, who wrote his Dialogues in Prague, says: 'Every permanence is a beginning without an end and an end without a beginning. Every permanence is therefore an endless movement embodying the beginning and the end...'"

She got up and began to walk up and down on the opposite side of the hall, "The things you see in a ceiling! But it's full of daring... the impossible in stone."

He strode towards her, "Thomaso Campanella: 'The magus does not regard the face of Heaven suspiciously but   134 like a physicist and undertakes remarkable feats by combining active forces with the passive...' Bold investigation, inventiveness! This ceiling foretells the mathematical discoveries of Geronimo Cardano, research into epidemics by Girolamo Fracastovo, advances in anatomy by Versalius, Michel Servet's and Andreas Cesaljoino's research on the circulation of the blood, Gilbert's discoveries of magnetism, Helmont's work on plant nourishment..."

"What about the astronomers?" she interrupted, "Copernicus, Kepler, Gallileo... and what about ecology? Leonardo had something to say..."

As they left the hall, she turned back for a last look at the ceiling, "Those ribbons remind me of the old telegraph messages, those long strips of paper, when the wind blows into them."

"I blew here like the wind one night! I was desparate to earn some money and I flew up and down on roller-skates carrying stacks of plates at a reception for President Bush."

"Did you drop any?"

"No, I'm an inventive man... I'm only partly Gothic."

* * *

"The Czech Kings were often absentees from the Castle and from Bohemia," he said, as they walked towards the Castle Gallery. "Vladislav II belonged to the Polish Jagellon family and he was also King of Hungary where he spent many years of his reign. Both he and his son, Louis, who succeeded him in 1518 and who was also King of Hungary, had their hands full fighting the advancing Turks. The great Ottoman Empire under Sultan Suleiman the Magnificent was then at the peak of its power and in 1526 the Turks defeated King Louis, then aged twenty, at the Battle of Mohacs in Hungary. It was one of the most significant battles of the sixteenth century..."

"Was Louis killed?"

"He was drowned after the battle while he was trying to ford a river. His army had been annihilated. After his death,

Ferdinand of Hapsburg who had married Vladislav's daughter Ann, was elected King of Bohemia..."

"That seems weird, why a Hapsburg? I didn't think the Czechs had much time for the Catholic Hapsburgs. Most of Bohemia was Protestant, wasn't it?"

He nodded, "Perhaps it was a fatal choice in view of what came later. But at that time the Hapsburgs ruled most of the known world. Ferdinand's brother was the Emperor Charles V, ruler of Germany, the Netherlands, much of Italy and Spain with its vast overseas Empire. Europe was terrified by the Turkish drive into Europe from Constantinople and feared the triumph of Islam. After the Battle of Mohacs, the Turks swept over the Hungarian plains, seizing most of the country and Bohemia trembled. Many people thought that only the Hapsburg dynasty had the power and resources to end Suleiman's conquests."

"Were they right?"

"Probably. But maybe there were other reasons for Ferdinand's election..."

"What reasons?"

"Spanish gold! The Bohemian royal debt amounted to something like 300,000 gold ducats and if a Bohemian nobleman had been elected he wouldn't have been able to find that kind of money. Ferdinand offered to pay half the debt immediately. Some hefty bribes were made, too! Lev of Rožmital, the most influential nobleman in Bohemia, was offered 50,000 gold ducats if he supported Ferdinand. Once elected, Ferdinand was usually away from Bohemia in Germany or Hungary. By 1529 the colossal Turkish army of Janissaries was outside the gates of Vienna with its tents and war-trumpets and later Ferdinand's successor, Maximilian, was constantly doing battle with the Turks in Hungary. When his son Rudolf succeeded him in 1576 the Turkish menace had faded and Rudolf was more often in Prague than Vienna. He liked this town with its educated people and its architectural treasures. In 1583, although he was Holy Roman Emperor as well as King of Bohemia, he decided to live here permanently and for the first time since Charles IV, Prague became the capital of the Hapsburg Empire and a leading European city. Rudolf inherited a rich land. Bohemia had recovered from the Hussite wars and was doing so well in business and agriculture that its taxes paid for more than half the running-costs of the whole Hapsburg Empire."

Alice lingered at the gallery entrance, "You're lecturing and it's terribly hot!"

"Let's just wander through, it may be cooler inside..." he pleaded.

"I doubt it," she said crossly, "I just can't get worked up about those Turks at the moment. Anyway, serves the Christians right! They seemed to spend most of their time killing each other."

She followed him into the gallery reluctantly, "Who was the most remarkable character in the Czech Renaissance," she asked.

"Rudolf, he was an amazing character! He extended the Castle and turned the royal rooms into a great private museum. He sent his agents all over Europe to collect the works of great artists — Michelangelo, Leonardo, Raphael, Rubens, Breughel. We're told that four stout men carried one of Dürer's masterpieces over the Alps for him. He was a skilled painter and goldsmith himself and had an eye for quality. And he encouraged Czech painters and sculptors, too. He collected all sorts of things — clocks, scientific apparatus and curiosities. When an inventory of his collection was made after his death it listed 3000 paintings and two and a half thousand sculptures, priced at 17 million guilders..." He chuckled.

"What's funny?"

"Rudolf's favourite painting was Leda and the Swan. The bureaucrat in charge of the inventory listed it as, A Naked Woman Clobbered by a Goose!"

She smiled faintly, "Maybe he hit the nail on the head. You said Rudolf collected curiosities?"

137   "Relics. Nails from Noah's Ark and a phial of the dust

from which God created Adam! But his love for art was genuine and he could lose himself in contemplation of a painting or a beautiful vase for hours at a time. He gave up attending court ceremonies like balls and tournaments unless they were absolutely essential for reasons of state. He liked to withdraw to his private rooms and beloved paintings, or busy himself among his astrolabes and celestial diagrams. Perhaps his passion for privacy had something to do with his up-bringing at the Spanish court with its emphasis on etiquette and the ruler's superiority and inapproachability. He couldn't stand it if a diplomat breathed into his face! He liked the Castle because it's got a kind of splendid isolation from the bustling town and he found a further isolation when he crossed the little wooden bridge spanning a deep overgrown moat to the north of the Castle. On the other side he entered his private garden with its lofty Summer Palace, greenhouses and exotic plants. This was his little paradise, a refuge from daily cares. Unobserved, he watched the sports in the Ball Game House or went to inspect his menagerie. He loved animals, expecially lions and horses. He even gave the deer in the

Horse
by Adrien de Vries   138

Brandys Game Reserve names! He watched over his lions very carefully for the fortune-tellers had predicted that if one of them died, its death would foretell his own. Here's one of his horses by Adrian de Vries. Rudolf spent hours in his luxurious riding-school where the horses had marble troughs."

She looked at the thoroughbred's pure lines, "At last! a Renaissance horse."

Blažej nodded, "The Renaissance proclaimed individuality and the artist was no longer a nameless mason or artisan submerged in his guild but a person in his own right. This is a portrait of a very individual horse."

They walked slowly through the gallery and he pointed to a wall of paintings on their right, "Nudes! Rudolf loved women's bodies and his taste was copied by many of the aristocracy who commissioned nude portraits. This shocked Protestant Prague to the core."

"I'm not surprised." She looked at the paintings with distaste. A smirking Venus faced the gallery ogled from behind by a lascivious Cupid.

"The Renaissance reclaimed the human body. In contrast to the strictness of Gothic, painters were enchanted by its light and shade and three-dimensional qualities..."

"You're only saying that because you're my guide!" she interrupted irritably, "I find all this repulsive! It's not a love for the human body, it's lust for female breasts and backsides. I can just imagine crowds of old men drooling over all this female flesh..."

"Rudolf was only twenty-four when he came to the throne..."

"To hell with Rudolf! You're trying to tell me this is art. It's no more art than those rags on sale in Museum Metro with gloating men milling round them. Fully-dressed males just love contemplating naked women as objects. These paintings are no different from those car advertisements with naked women draped across the bonnets. They make me want to throw up!"

139   He was taken aback by her little fury, "But what about

Donatello? Michelangelo? They sculpted naked male bodies..."

"That was different. How would you feel if this gallery was full of simpering naked men? A woman had a show in London recently — photos of naked males — and there was almost a riot. People are so two-faced."

Blažej knew there was danger in argument but he couldn't stop himself, "But why was Michelangelo's David different?"

"He's proud and noble and unselfconscious and he looks outward to the world but these simpering sillies are all coy and ridiculous." She scowled, "They're women forever gearing themselves up to be stared at by men, they're not looking outside themselves at all."

He was astonished, "I've never thought of it that way..."

She brought her face close to his so that their noses almost touched, "Do these boring bottoms turn you on? Are you feeling sexy?"

He shrugged, "No, I think a woman looks far more seductive in a clinging dress." He glanced at her short, low-necked dress and looked away quickly.

She marched towards the exit, "I'm fed up with bare buttocks!"

He walked quickly after her, "Alice, we seem to have changed places. You called me Gothic and I thought of you as a Renaissance type..."

* * *

They stopped at an ice-cream stand near the Castle gates and Blažej bought two large green ices, Alice seemed calmer, "Delicious! English ices always taste synthetic."

They left the Castle and walked slowly towards the Summer Palace, "Did Rudolf have a wife?" she asked.

"He never married and this brought him into deadly conflict with the Queen Mother, the Empress Maria. She couldn't stand Rudolf's negative attitude to marriage. After all, it was the duty of a ruler to produce a son and heir."

"I think it was really clever of him to avoid marriage!   140

Elizabeth I, the Virgin Queen was ruling at the same time, wasn't she? She kept all her suitors dangling..."

"Rudolf had a mistress, Katerina Stradová, the daughter of an artisan and they had a daughter, Donna Carolina. They lived in the Castle but it seems he avoided them as much as possible. His love-life was... a bit eccentric."

"In what way?"

He coughed, "Well, it's a bit... vulgar."

She looked at him indignantly, "I'm twenty-two, for heaven's sake!"

"He arranged for pimps to bring women to his stables at night and when they were tied up to the mangers without... their underwear, among the rank smell of horses' bedding and dung, he... crept up behind them. Then he left quickly and went back to his private rooms."

He took out his handkerchief and wiped his face, "We've arrived at the Belvedere," he said with relief, as they went

Belvedere

into the charming formal garden laid out with low-cut box-hedges. "This was the royal Summer Palace built by Ferdinand I for his wife, Anne. Some say it's the purest Renaissance structure outside Italy and it's probably the most beautiful. It was designed by Paolo della Stella between 1535 to 1537 and built by Italian masons. Work started in 1538 and went on for twenty-five years. The architect Boniface Wollmuth, completed the upper floor."

She looked up at the strange roof-truss, "It's like an upturned ship!"

"This building must have seemed strangely out of place in what was still a Gothic Hussite town," he said. "It could be seen from all parts of Prague like a Renaissance light-house. The elegance and airiness of the building come from the Venetian arcades." He turned to her, "What does it say to you?"

"Life here and now! Dancing, night revelry, lovers' meetings..."

"Rudolf came here frequently and preferred it to the Castle. He kept his menagerie here and once he looked out of that window," he pointed upwards, "and saw one of his stable-girls ride past on his pet lion. He built an observatory here for his astronomer, Tycho de Brahe, and sat out at night with astronomers like Kepler discussing the cosmos..." He looked at her and saw she was very pale. The heat was overpowering and as he looked across the garden he saw the heat-waves shimmering over the scorched lawns, "Shall we go and stand near the fountain?"

He took her arm and led her down one of the narrow box-edged paths, "This is the Renaissance Singing Fountain, designed by Francesco Terzio. As the water falls into the bronze bowls it sets up vibrations and if you listen carefully you'll hear its voice..."

She turned to him furiously, "You're droning on and on! Can't you stop being a guide even for a few minutes? I'm hot! I'm so hot I'm going to die! I'd like to strip off my clothes and jump in."

142

His anger rose, "Then why don't you?"

She sprang away from him and seizing the bronze basin, she leaped into it and pressed herself against one of the great lion-gartered satyrs shouldering his deer. She stood with bent head and outstretched arms and the sparkling water

143

Singing Fountain

cascaded over her, flattening her hair. Her flimsy dress clung to her body outlining her breasts and slender legs. Pale and distant she seemed to merge into the fountain and become part of its decoration.

He stood motionless. For the first time all the details of the fountain fixed themselven in his brain. It was a marvellous, delicate thing. On the higher bowl the pissing cherubs played amidst their riotous foliage and above them stood the solitary, joyous piper. Strange figures crouched under the fountain with huge breasts and horns; they've got an Asiatic look, he thought.

A group of tourists with a guide had arrived and were staring at Alice.

She jumped out and danced towards him. "I feel better" she flicked her wet sleeve in his face and he felt it sting his cheek.

"I'll take you back to the hotel…"

"No way! I'll find another guide!" she tripped away and disappeared into a copse.

Like a gaggle of geese, the tourists eyed him curiously. One of them raised his camera and took a picture. Blažej turned abruptly and went down a winding path into the trees. He found her sitting on a sagging bench mounted on a grassy parapet, wringing out her skirt.

"Have you got a handkerchief? I'll take you home."

"Where's home? Don't be stuffy!" she gathered up a handful of wet skirt and leaning towards, rammed it in his face.

Something swelled up in him. Rage! The pent-up fury of years burst out in elemental rage. Years of fussy clients, fruitless searches for car-parts, petty possessive girl-friends, scraping for a living, censorious teachers, self-censorship, electricity black-outs, water-cuts, gas-cuts, a cramped flat with walls like paper, dreary queues at the supermarket for a wretched wire basket…

"Whore!"

He threw himself at her and seizing her by the throat he forced her head back against the bench.

"Ahhhhh".

Her desperate cry mingled with another sound, also desperate. A great groaning, rending and finally a snapping sound. The seat of the bench tore apart and with a shattering noise the whole back cracked apart. They fell heavily backwards down the parapet and into some bushes.

He lay on his back and looked blankly up at the trees. Then he heard a moaning sound. His training as a guide re-asserted itself. She was injured... hysterical? Snapshots flew through his mind. Anxious parents at the airport, a vicious boy-friend, stretchers, doctors, hospital bills... his reputation. He scrambled to his feet and went over to her.

She was lying on her back, her skirt twisted above her knees, laughing up at the sky.

"Blažej, you look like a satyr! You've got twigs in your hair."

He gave her his hand, "And you look like one of the witches of Endor," he said sourly. Her left cheek was smudged, and dirt and twigs clung to her dress.

He pulled her up the parapet and they stared in silence at what remained of the bench. The back had gone and the seat had split horizontally and stood up in two shards among a crumble of legs.

She gave him a side-long look, "It must have been a Russian model!"

He doubled up in a kind of convulsion and staggered away holding his stomach. Alarmed, she rushed after him and pulled him round to face her. Great gusts of laughter swept through him and finally he threw back his head and guffawed.

"Blažej! It's the first time I've heard you laugh loudly!"

As they walked through the box-hedges to the garden exit, she stopped and patted the stone lion on his rump, "I've never seen a lion with one tooth before."

He was still gasping, "Lucky lion! He'll only have one ache."

* * *

145

"I'll get a taxi," he said.

"What for? I'll soon be dried out. Why should I miss Renaissance just because you tried to kill me?"

He looked at her face but it was calm, "Are you bruised?"

"No, I'm indestructible," she shook out the skirt of her dress, "Blažej, do go on being my guide!" She took his arm and looked up at the sky, it was like a purplish-grey lid. "It was the heat, you know!"

That was it, he thought, the heat... The hottest day of the year and possibly the hottest for a century. But he had difficulty in remembering their itinerary. "My shirt's soaked," he muttered.

"Renaissance!" she said encouragingly, patting his arm.

"Yes, here we are, the Schwarzenberg Palace!" He took out his handkerchief and wiped his neck. He stared at the great Renaissance structure but couldn't think of anything to say about it.

She took out her Pocket Guide, "'... commands the top of Neruda Street... Architect was Augustin Vlach... the sgraffiti date from 1567 and have been restored several times... after the Belvedere the most imposing Renaissance structure in Prague... built on a T-plan with cour d'honneur...' Heavens, how boring!"

He recovered, "Perhaps you can imagine it in Florence? A meeting place for the Platonic Academy chaired by Marsiglio Ficino..."

"I like the diamond sgraffiti and the foliage under the eves. And the upturned chess-piece gables. But it's magnificent rather than beautiful."

He nodded, "Grandeur. A great fire broke out in 1541 and swept through Hradčany. Afterwards, some great noblemen took the opportunity to develop the square with magnificent palaces which would proclaim their power and status. The Renaissance saw the dominance of the nobility, a sad fact in our history. The towns which had a proud tradition of independence had their rights eroded in Vladislav's reign. His code of 1500 listed the privileges of the nobles and knights and ignored the towns. Only knights and nobles were regarded as free men. Then there was the beer-battle..."

"Beer?" she looked at him anxiously.

"The towns had always had a near-monopoly of the brewing trade, a highly profitable business. Many of the great nobles established breweries and forbade the sale of rival brands on their estates. That hit the towns badly. Ferdinand also struck out at the towns by appointing royal judges to control them. The town councils were not allowed to meet or call citizens' assemblies without royal permission".

"My Welsh Tudors were cleverer! They kept the nobles in their place and backed the entrepreneurs," she commented.

"The onslaughts on the towns left fourteen hundred noblemen as the greatest force in the land. Many of them ruled their estates like haughty princes and trampled on their serfs.

Lobkovic —
Schwarzenberg Palace

The once free Slavs became miserable tenants overwhelmed with feudal dues and rents."

They sat down on the grass in the tiny park in the middle of the square.

"This palace was built by the Lobkovic family and only passed to the Schwarzenbergs in 1719," he continued. "Towards the end of the sixteenth century Jiří of Lobkovic fell out of favour with Rudolf. He was a proud nobleman ambitious for the throne and he made many enemies at court and got caught up in a web of intrigue. In 1593 he was Chairman of the Lands Diet and he drew up a document reminding Rudolf of his obligations and various unfulfilled promises. Rudolf began a systematic investigation into the Diet and Lobkovic's role as Chairman and Lobkovic's enemies awaited his downfall. His brother Ladislav fled the country but Jiří remained and kept all his offices. For some time Rudolf took no action but after a massive slander campaign by Lobkovic's enemies, he expelled him from Prague. He was in imminent danger of execution but Rudolf let himself be persuaded by pleas from the Lobkovic family and their friends to consider the lesser sentence of life imprisonment. Lobkovic was thrown into Ličkov Castle where he died. He had been a fervent Catholic and perhaps he was a fall-guy. . . ."

"How?"

"By striking at Lobkovic, Rudolf was probably hoping to tame the Jesuits who were forever accusing him of Protestant sympathies. Lobkovic's nineteen year old daughter, Eva, devoted herself to helping her father. She loved him so much that she had chosen to stay with him rather than getting married to a prominent man with a brilliant social position. She got up petitions and wrote many letters to Rudolf on her father's behalf and her goal was to obtain an audience with the king for she hoped her charm and eloquence would move him. However, she got nowhere. . . all her attempts to see Rudolf were blocked. . . ."

Alice lay on her stomach plaiting daisies into a small chain, "Why?"

148

"The Emperor's Chamberlain, Filip Lang, took a huge bribe from her family but did nothing to help her. Lang was something out of the ordinary! He started from nothing, rose to great heights and died destitute on prison straw. He was a Jew who came to Prague from the Tyrol with his few possessions on a farm-cart. He was brilliantly clever and rose into the aristocracy and finally into court circles. Since a Jew was not permitted to hold public office he became a Catholic convert. His influence over Rudolf which lasted for eight years, was extraordinary and he became the real power at court. Although Rudolf was cultured and intelligent, he had a gullible side. Lang was unusually good-looking with a charming smile, a velvet baritone voice and pleasant manners. Possibly Rudolf who was a retiring man liked his flamboyance and self-confidence. During his eight years of power Lang ruthlessly feathered his own nest and his corruption almost reached the level of the Renaissance Popes! He sold positions at court for vast sums, sold off some of Rudolf's precious thoroughbreds and even started wheeling and dealing with the king's art collection. Only those whom Lang admitted could get an audience with the king and he even kept Rudolf's sister waiting three months. Eva Lobkovic found it impossible to get past Lang so she wrote an Apologia intended for the public in which she exposed the King's injustice. This hit the court like a bombshell and she was in terrible danger. Her Apologia was treasonable, of course, and treason was punished with the dreadful agony of hanging, drawing and quartering..."

"What happened to her?" Alice interrupted.

"Rudolf decided to send her to a nunnery."

"And Lang...?"

"In June 1609 he was arrested. His thefts of Rudolf's art treasures were the last straw. He was investigated for a year, stripped of his offices and wealth and his Catholic baptism was revoked. He was condemned to life imprisonment in the White Tower and its said that he died in a dark cell in a pool of his own excrement."

She sat up and stared at the great palace, "Poor Eva! Your story has a real Renaissance flavour!"

"Yes, the Renaissance abhorred mediocrity!"

* * *

"Prosperous burghers, masons and artisans lived here. Rudolf's court attracted foreign artists and craftsmen to Prague: Italians, Germans and Dutchmen; painters, sculptors, engravers, metalworkers and jewellers. But this was an Italian colony. Vlašská Street means Italian Street."

Vlašská
street

They were walking down Vlašská Street as it wound steeply towards Malostranská Square. She studied the tall, plain houses. Some had great gashes and holes in the walls. Some were empty with blank windows. Ancient doors hung askew, some tied up with wire. There were traces of foliage around the austere, rectangular windows.

"I expected more decoration from Renaissance!"

"There was plenty of decoration on windows and portals but in many ways the Renaissance was a reaction against late Gothic," he replied. "Renaissance emphasized symmetry, order, harmony... a stripping away of gargoyles, turrets, excessive foliage — anything that cluttered a building. It was trying to get back to pure, Classical form."

"Look up!" she pointed to Joseph holding the child Jesus. It's unusual to see a man with the baby. He's guarding the police station!" She turned to look at Blažej and saw that his head was bent and his back seemed hunched.

"Alice..." he cleared his throat, "I..."

She put her hands over her ears, "Say nothing!" She smiled, "Please don't apologize for trying to strangle me! It's a scorching day and I've been very silly. I'll be more mature in ten years time, I promise you." She lent against him gently, "Can't we forget what happened and go to a pub?"

His anxieties fell away from him. He imagined them as tangled skeins of grey knitting. He looked down at the cobblestones and kicked them, "By all means! Let's go to Rudolf's!"

* * *

They sat on high stools in the Rudolf II in Maislova Street overlooking a small, rectangular kitchen area. The chef was cutting mushrooms into wafer-thin slices.

"Are you hungry?"

She shook her head, "I'm going to disappear for a minute." Blažej ordered open sandwiches, mineral water and a glass of dark beer. He stared out at the darkening street. Heavy thunder clouds hung above the town and he recognized the uncanny silence which preceds a great storm. Should he cut short their itinerary? he wondered. He felt tired and yet felt a strange reluctance to do so. She reappeared and he saw that her hair was wet and her dress was once again moulded to her body.

"I washed it. Don't worry, no one will notice in this dim light." She sat down and stared wide-eyed at a group of workmen with tiny hammers who were restoring an intricate pattern in the small cobblestones on the opposite pavement.

Delayed shock? he wondered, perhaps she's a bit crazy...?

She swivelled round on her stool and gave him a searching look.

"Was Rudolf just a bit crazy like you, or was he really mad? I read somewhere that he was a fisherman of fools."

"He's a very controversial figure in our history. Some see him as a shambling figure who busied himself feeding his pet lions while thick layers of dust accumulated on the dispatches in his study. A neurotic, superstitious Emperor whoring with stable-girls, surrounded by crooks and tricksters and

At Rudolf's

burrowing like an ostrich to avoid the problems of his reign..."

"What do you think?"

He hesitated, "He was a mass of contradictions!"

"Good, I like weird people!"

"He was King of Bohemia and Holy Roman Emperor for 36 years and the first 18 years of his reign were peaceful ones. That's a long time in politics and it's more than most modern presidents achieve! I think that for much of his long reign he was fairly sane and a true Renaissance man."

She stared vaguely round the little pub. There were only four tables, "Renaissance man...?"

"He was a very well-educated and sophisticated person. As a child he'd studied hard at the Spanish court and he'd had a humanist education along the lines of Castiglione's 'Courtier'. Castiglione's book, a best-seller at the time, described the ideal Prince — a universal person, an all-rounder with many skills and talents. Rudolf studied philosophy, mathematics, astronomy, music and he learnt to draw, dance and fence. He spoke Italian, Spanish, French and Latin as well as German."

"What about politics?"

"His father, Maximilian, hadn't trained him in government. Rudolf disliked being a ruler and saw politics as a passing show, and he had no interest in the religious in-fighting raging through Bohemia. He was fascinated by science and astrology and surrounded himself with brilliant people — the Austrian, Johannes Kepler, the Englishmen, John Dee and Edward Kelley and the Danish astrologer, Tycho de Brahe, the man with the Iron Nose. There were scoundrels at his court, too, but he usually had the good sense to throw them out."

"Why did Tycho Brahe have an artificial nose?"

"He lost part of his nose in a duel and had a silver one made. He had an unfortunate death but perhaps I won't mention it while you're eating!"

153   She pushed away her sandwich, "What happened?"

"He was drinking great quantities of beer at one of Rudolf's banquets. Court etiquette insisted that no one should leave the table until the king rose. The story goes that Tycho, unable to relieve the call of nature, collapsed with a burst bladder. He'd been a brilliant astronomer and he'd invited Kepler to Bohemia to work with him. Rudolf attracted very gifted people to the Castle."

She stirred impatiently, "So he wasn't mad at all, he's just had a bad write-up!"

"Some clever people gave him a good write-up. The painter Heintz thought he was a kind and gentle person and the Venetian Ambassador Contarini and the Prague physician Jesenius thought him wise. Some say that his so-called madness was due to the 'French disease' which was as common then as Aids is now, but maybe his moods — constantly swinging between depression and euphoria and terrible bouts of irritation — came about because he was forced to be something which he wasn't. He wanted to be a leisured, private person, a connoisseur of art and a scientist searching for truth. He wanted to sit in the moonlight on the Belvedere terrace exploring the secrets of the cosmos with his dreamy astronomers. But he was thrust onto the bloody sixteenth century stage. He had to deal with the manoeuvres of his brother Matthias who was constantly trying to dethrone him, a mass of intrigue at court, bitter religious conflicts, the Turks in Hungary... He couldn't cope with it all and retired into his private world. The most interesting thing about his portraits are his eyes. They're observant, very intelligent and they seem to speak of a second, inner life... They're certainly not the eyes of an obsessed or half-mad person. It's possible that he feigned madness and hid his intelligence to avoid pressures, particularly the conflicting opinions of his advisers. During the later years of his reign he suffered more and more from melancholy, a Renaissance trait."

"Why was melancholy a...?"

He cut across her, "There had always been a Catholic   154

clique at court and in the later years of his reign Rudolf seemed to sink into a kind of apathy and he came more and more under the influence of fanatical advisers. In 1602 he issued a threatening decree which endangered the Protestants. It was useless as well as wrong-headed because he had no way of enforcing it. But it encouraged the Catholic nobility to try and re-establish Catholicism on their estates. One of them, Jaroslav Borinto, Lord of Martinic, set hunting-dogs on his peasants to drive them into the churches where the Jesuits were preaching and he ordered that the Holy Wafer should be forced down their throats! Rudolf even tried to enforce Catholicism on Hungary with disastrous results. The Hungarian Protestants allied with the Turks. In 1604 Hungarian troops devastated parts of Moravia and four years later Matthias was marching on Prague. Although in 1608 the Protestant nobles still supported Rudolf, mainly because he'd made big religious concessions to buy their loyalty, he infuriated them by revoking all his concessions a year later. The Protestant Lords began to arm their retainers and the Prague streets were full of noblemen and knights and their retinues. The New Town Hall was packed with Protestant Lords who first knelt in prayer and then listed their grievances. Prague was in an uproar and Bohemia on the verge of civil war. Bowing to the pressure, Rudolf brought out his famous Letter of Majesty granting religious toleration but he'd left it too late. Desperate for support, he made the fatal mistake of inviting his cousin, the Archduke Leopold, into Bohemia with an army. Leopold's troops marched into South Bohemia in 1611, seized Budějovice, Tábor, Krumlov and various other towns and then arrived outside Prague and besieged Malá Strana. It was the last straw. Rudolf was forced to abdicate by the Protestant lords and in 1611 his brother Matthias became king. It's said that Rudolf appeared at a window in the royal apartments and shouted.

'Prague, ungrateful Prague! I made you famous but now you are expelling me, your benefactor. God's vengeance will come down on you...'"

Alice was silent.

"Sorry! Am I lecturing?"

She shook her head, "Bohemia was close to the Counter-Reformation wasn't it?"

He nodded, "When Rudolf died in 1612 Bohemia was only eight years away from the Battle of White Mountain and conquest by the Catholic Hapsburgs, our three hundred years of darkness. Rudolf was a very intiutive man and perhaps he sensed the coming catastrophe..."

"He'd contributed to it, hadn't he?"

"In some ways, but Bohemia was a difficult country! Sixteenth century Europe believed in the slogan, 'One ruler, one faith'. It's true that Henri IV had permitted two faiths in France but he had no option after three decades of religious war. In Germany, the Princes decided the religion of their subjects and this was the practice across Europe. Rudolf ruled a country with a huge Protestant majority and a minority of militant Catholics. He didn't care much for any of them! He preferred to talk to Kepler or summon the mysterious Rabbi Löw to the Castle."

* * *

"This part of the Old Town is called Jewish town, "he explained, as they walked up Maislova Street towards the Jewish Cemetery. "As early as the beginning of the 10th century there were Jewish settlements in Malá Strana and below Vyšehrad and during the 12th century they settled in the Old Town. They lived in narrow winding alleys like this street, between the Old Town Square and the bend in the Vltava river. From 1179 when the Church decreed that there must be a wall separating Jews and Christians, this area became a ghetto, and from the sixteenth century any would-be Jewish settlers arriving in Prague were compulsorily settled here. By Rudolf's reign about 7000 Jews were packed into a network of small squalid verminous lanes and the overcrowding was terrible. Most Jews had to struggle for survival for they were only permitted to go into business 156 and lend money. Few people like money-lenders! Every time the Jews raised their interest rates there were outcries against the wicked money-grubbers forever claiming their pound of flesh. There were some terrible pogroms here and constant demands that the Jews should be expelled from Bohemia. However, our kings and the debt-ridden nobles needed Jewish loans, especially in wartime. Some Jews became immensely rich like Mordechai Maisel who spent a great deal of his fortune on renovating the ghetto, but the Jews here never rose to the heights of the Jewish merchant princes in Venice, Augsburg or Amsterdam."

"It looks as though it's been shaken by a giant's hand!" she looked in astonishment at the cemetery with its confusion of granite and sandstone slabs, strangely illuminated by a lurid light from the storm-filled sky. Some stones were erect, others slanting at every angle or flat on the ground. "It's as though a great army fell here and the soldiers had turned to stone as they fell..."

"From about 1439 the Jews had to bury their dead as their religion forbade them digging up human bones and as there was no other burial-ground in the ghetto, corpses were buried in successive layers," Blažej explained, "There are said to be between 10,000 and 12.000 gravestones here and perhaps 80.000 graves. No one knows for sure... The tombstones are worth studying. Look at this pointed marble one from 1613 with a goose sitting on the Star of David! It's the tomb of David Gans, a Renaissance historian and astronomer who corresponded with Kepler and visited Tycho de Brahe three times in Benátky nad Jizerou Castle where Rudolf had built Tycho thirteen rooms to house his scientific apparatus. The stones are carved with all kinds of animal forms and the tombs with reliefs of human figures are unique, you won't find them in any other Jewish cemeteries. This massive tomb covered with Hebrew inscriptions is Rabbi Yehuda Löw's and his wife Perl's, though it's not the original. In Rudolf's reign the ghetto became a magnet for philosophers, alchemists, and astronomers due to the Rabbi's extraordinary character. He astounded people with his learning and was believed to have supernatural powers."

She looked in amazement at the countless tiny pieces of paper weighed down with stones or small coins which covered every ledge on the tomb and were wedged into its crevices on all sides.

Blažej smiled, "Prayers and wishes! People still believe in the Rabbi; he was a philosopher, writer, alchemist and educator. Tycho de Brahe came here from the Castle to visit him and he became so famous that he was granted an audience with Rudolf in February 1592…

"What did they talk about?"

"No one knows! David Gans tells us that Rudolf received the Rabbi very jovially and that they talked privately face to face like friends. But he says that their discussion was top-secret. Löw's studies of the Cabala and other mystical texts fascinated Rudolf and attracted many scholarly Jews to Prague from different parts of Europe."

Rabbi Löw's tomb

158

"What was the Cabala?" she asked curiously, as they went into the Museum next to the cemetery gates.

"Mystical writings which were thought to be God's revelation to Moses and which were written down by various scholars from the 9th to the 13th century. They were rediscovered in the Renaissance..."

"Why?" she asked.

Blažej felt irritated and at a loss. He had a slight headache.

"Exploration?" she offered, "People were bold enough to explore the mysteries of the universe?"

He nodded, relieved, "The Renaissance was a time favourable for magic. Through complex permutations of the sacred Hebrew alphabet which was thought symbolically to contain the names of God and the whole universe, the magician could contemplate celestial mysteries."

They walked across the Museum to the far wall and he pointed to some drawings, "There's the Rabbi with his creation, an artificial man — the Golem."

She looked at Jiří Trnka's picture of the towering white-bearded Rabbi in his curious woollen cap like a balaclava and his fur — collared cape. Mikoláš Aleš's illustration showed Löw in his laboratory looking up in awe and horror at his creation. The Golem's mindless face floated in a cloud of vapour above him.

"Did he create the Golem in a laboratory?" she asked half-jokingly.

"It's said that Jossile Golem was brought to life in some brickworks where Smíchov stands today. The formula for bringing the Golem to life was given in a 13th century cabalistic text. There were seven days of intensive preparation before the ritual — baths, fasting, meditation. The ritual took place at four in the morning, went on until midnight and three people took part in it representing the elements of Fire, Water and Air. When the first man walked round the prostrate clay figure of the Golem, it began to get warm. When the second man walked round, it began to get mist and hair began to grow on his head in clouds of steam. Then the Rabbi placed a cabalistic formula, the Shem, written on parchment, on the creature's forehead. The Golem stirred, got onto its knees and staggered to its feet. It towered head and shoulders above the Rabbi who was a very tall man himself. Then they all faced the four corners of the earth in turn, starting with the east, and recited from the Book of Genesis."

"How long did the Golem live?"

"We don't know... It lived quietly between life and death and only arose to obey the Rabbi's commands. Every Sabbath the Rabbi removed the Shem from its forehead so that it could rest. But one Saturday the Rabbi, preoccupied we're told with his daughter's illness, forgot to remove the Shem. The Golem awoke from its lethargy and was seized with a mad fit. Some say that it had fallen in love with a beautiful Jewess, possibly the Rabbi's daughter, whom it had glimpsed through a window embracing her lover. In a mad rage, it smashed furniture, benches, walls... It lurched through the streets in an orgy of destruction. Panic spread through the ghetto and the Rabbi was called from the synagogue where he was lighting the Sabbath candles and he rushed to the Golem just in time to stop it uprooting a linden-tree. The Golem succumbed to the power of the Rabbi's gaze and he went up to it and removed the Shem from its forehead. The Golem fell to the ground and was shattered. Its remains were carried to the grounds of the Old New Synagogue and the next day they were buried in the synagogue loft, wrapped in prayer-shawls and covered with books. The Rabbi gave strict orders that no one should enter the loft and the staircase was removed."

Alice had been listening intently, "Did anyone ever try to get into the loft?"

"There were many attempts. In 1580 after a great fire at the Vienna Theatre, the Prague magistrates brought out new fire-regulations and an iron ladder was put in the synagogue leading to the loft. But no one dared go up it for some time. Then two men decided to go up..."

"Who were they?"

"Abraham Chaim, the Temple Verger, and his son-in-law-, Balbier. Chaim had taken part in the ritual of bringing the Golem to life and had been in charge of its remains. He didn't succeed in reviving the Golem, all he did was to bring on the plague! A day later, Balbier's two children died and he took this to be God's punishment. The Golem's remains were put on a Prague death — waggon and taken secretly to a burial — ground in Žižkov which at that time was wild land beyond the town. It's said that the Golem was buried there in March 1592."

"So that was the end of the Golem?"

"Perhaps... in the eighteenth century the Prague Rabbi, Ezechiel Landau, tried to discover the truth about the Golem legend. He underwent a strict cleansing ritual and fasted. He only spent a few minutes in the synagogue loft and when he came down he was terribly pale and his whole body was trembling. He renewed the strict ban on anyone entering the loft. A century later, Egon Erwin Kisch, the famous reporter, went up to the loft. He didn't believe in the Golem but he thought something might be hidden under the floorboards. He found nothing."

She looked at him sharply, "I'm rather surprised that you didn't try to get into the loft yourself!"

"I did! I didn't really want to go, but my friend Zdeněk talked me into it. It was March 1984. We climbed up to the loft with crampons. The loft measures 15 by 8 metres and it looks like an empty granary. It has rather a strange atmosphere as the lofts of ancient buildings often do. The Old New Synagogue is 700 years old! We went over the dusty floor with a radar antenna but we didn't find any Golem clues. Some passers-by had spotted us on the roof, so we left quickly. Stories about the Golem have haunted Prague through the centuries. People have claimed that they've glimpsed him in small lanes and passage-ways, an extraordinary figure, hairless, with a yellow face, mongol features and wearing loose clothes. He's said to walk with a strange lurching step as though he might fall at any moment...

Then he'd turn into an alleyway or doorway and vanish without trace."

She turned back to the drawings and stared at them for a long time.

Blažej stood next to her looking at them sombrerly, "Rabbi Löw misused his spiritual powers..."

She looked at him in astonishment, "But the Golem wasn't real, he's only a legend."

He frowned, "The Renaissance alchemists explored many mysteries and made important discoveries but the Rabbi over-reached himself, he tried to be God."

She was still looking at the drawings, "The Golem reminds me of something... someone. She looked puzzled, "Yes, Caliban! That bearlike, witless creature, the witch's son. He was forever collecting wood and lusting after Miranda. A kind of Golem on that magic island, existing only as Prospero's slave."

He looked at her attentively, "But all Prospero's creatures came out of his own head."

"Shakespeare's you mean?" she said, smiling.

"No, Prospero's. Shakespeare's characters have a life of their own! There were different Prosperos, high ones... base ones... he was a wizard as well as a Renaissance Prince."

* * *

As they walked across Karlovo square, daggers of lightening split the sky. Blažej seized her hand, "Hurry, let's get away from the trees!"

He pushed open the portal of the Faust House and as they went into the Renaissance courtyard they felt the first heavy drops of rain.

"This way!" she rushed across the courtyard to an open doorway and they climbed some steep stairs leading to a network of small empty rooms. She went into a room overlooking the courtyard and threw open the window. The rain was like a sheet of metal. She sat down on the dusty floor with her back to the wall. Part of the floor had been taken up

162

revealing sixteenth century beams, black and pitted with woodworm.

"We're trepassing!"

"Who cares, at least we're dry!" she said, impatiently.

He squatted against the opposite wall, "But you like water, it's your element."

She looked at him angrily, "Don't mention water, I hate being teased." She got up, "I feel trapped in here, let's go!"

He walked to the window. Cascades of rain were falling into the courtyard and small lakes were forming on the cobblestones. He could hear the clatter of the rain on the roof tiles.

"We can't go out in that," he fumbled for his cigarettes.

"Please don't smoke! I can't stand smoke in a small room."

He put the packet back in his pocket, "This place was

Faust House

inhabited in pagan times and it was probably a place of sacrifice…"

"It's stuffy in here and I've got a headache," she went to the door.

Blažej got there before her and stood in front of it, "Alice it's raining cats and dogs! Please wait a bit…"

She looked at him sullenly. Then she sighed and returned to her spot on the floor, "I'm tired," she closed her eyes.

He sat down beside her, "There were magical practices in this house…"

She raised her head, "Can you hear footsteps?" she asked anxiously.

He listened, but the great house was very still. Somewhere in the courtyard he could hear the whine of a door swinging on its hinges.

"You said there were magical practices here…?"

"This house dates from the founding of the New Town and in the fourteenth century, Prince Václav of Opava lived here. He studied the natural sciences and the occult and the house began to get a reputation for witchcraft. On August 20th 1507, Faust's name crops up in a letter by Johann Tritheim, Abbot of Sponheim, to a royal astrologer, Johann Wirdung. Later, in 1587 Faust's life-story first appeared in a German book and three years later an English version appeared in London. According to the anonymous author, Faust visited this town during his wanderings across Europe. We're told that he was born around 1480 in Germany. He studied theology in Germany and magic in Poland. Some of his contemporaries had some damning things to say about him. Cornelius Agrippa called him a drunken vagabond and Philip Melanchthon, Luther's friend, called the famous globetrotter a wicked animal and the Devil's sewer…"

She smiled, "They didn't mince their word in those days!" Did Faust really call up the Devil?

"According to the book of 1587, he called up the Devil three times in a dark forest near Wittenberg. Devil-invocation needed a lot of preparation. Seven days of purification and then on the third day of the new moon the magus had to slit the throat of a white rooster, throw the head into a river and then jump in after it fully-dressed. Afterwards he had to put on clean clothes and only then could he begin the complex invocation ritual. Faust saw a flash of lightening and then Mephistopholes appeared before him in the forest-clearing and they signed their hellish pact in blood. When Faust stabbed his arm, the words, HOMO FUGE! MAN ESCAPE! stood out on his forearm. However, he turned to Mephistopholes who agreed to serve Faust for twenty-four years and when the time was up he'd take his soul, body, flesh and blood for eternity. Faust lived a life of luxury and debauchery. He visited great kingdoms and cities and was the honoured guest of princes and noblemen. From a high peak of the Caucasus he glimpsed Eden, the earthly paradise. He went on excursions into the clouds and to the Devil's empire and the secrets of this world and other worlds were revealed to him. He loved boasting and showing off his magical powers! Once he changed a horse into a bundle of straw and on another occasion he swallowed a whole wagon full of hay together with the horses, in front of some gaping farmers. He rode on a barrel of wine as if it was a horse and summoned geese and turkeys to his table already roasted."

He lit a cigarette but she made no comment.

"And then Hell's gong struck midnight," she murmured, "and cut was the branch..."

"Faust lived in terror but he'd always been a showman and he decided to leave this world extravagantly, boozing and feasting with his whores and drinking companions at a riotous party. Some legends say that his great farewell banquet took place in a pub but others tell us it was held here in this house. The evening wore on and eventually Faust staggered to his room and closed the door. Between midnight and one o'clock the house was shaken to its foundations by a roaring wind. There was a terrifying hissing sound as though the house was full of snakes. His companions didn't dare enter his room until dawn. It was empty. The walls were stained with blood and a strange substance — Faust's brain. His torn and mutilated body lay in the courtyard in a pile of manure. Some people said there was a gaping hole in the roof of this house and that the Devil seized Faust and carried him away through the ceiling. For a long time there was a great gap in the roof and it was impossible to find masons willing to repair the damage..."

She looked up at the ceiling and shivered, "I'm surprised anyone ever wanted to live here."

"Some people, especially alchemists, were attracted to this place with its reputation for wizardry, and Prague, at the heart of Europe, was the meeting place of Eastern and Western thought. The Emperor Rudolf was like a spider in a magical web which stretched across Europe, across the seas and into your country. Edward Kelley bought this house in Rudolf's reign and the magician John Dee and the poet Philip Sidney were also drawn here to Prague."

They went down the stairs and into the courtyard. The rain had swept away the clamminess of the day and the sky had cleared. She sat down on a marble seat near the passageway leading to the garden and looked up at the first stars.

"The weird English still come here! I wonder why we're drawn to this town?"

He smiled, "Germans, Americans, Italians, Australians and many others... We had millions of visitors in this country over the last two years. I suppose there are many reasons why people come", he reflected. "This place has something unique... a certain strength. The passions and emotions over the centuries have somehow got caught here. Sensitive people feel it very quickly when they arrive here. Prague's a kind of drug!"

She looked at him sceptically.

"Believe me, it's really true! I've got a client who comes here every month, sometimes only for an hour. We stand on Charles Bridge looking at the foaming water of the weir and then he takes the plane and flies off. He told me that the West's getting tired and that communism to the East has disintegrated but Central Europe has become a crossroads of business, science, the arts... ideas. Millions of people feel it."

He sat down beside her and pointed up at the windows on the other side of the courtyard, "When Edward Kelley lived here, blue, violet and yellow flames flew out of those windows."

"Was Kelley a con-man?"

"I don't know. He was a many-sided man. He'd lost his ears in an English pillory as a punishment for forgery but I don't think he was just an impostor with shorn ears who was forced to take refuge in Prague. He was intuitive... mystical. I think he touched on certain secrets. He was a wonderful physician and people said he could cure the incurable. He'd been trained as a chemist and maybe he combined his training with an intuitive power for healing. At the same time, he was probably a rogue as well! In his lifetime he was accused of having a mandrake root and being in league with the Devil. In England he went under a false name for a time, calling himself Edward Talbot, but this didn't bother the magician John Dee when Kelley turned up at Dee's great house at Montlake in 1582. Kelley claimed to see visions in Dee's shewestone or crystal and became his medium for seven years. When Kelley arrived in Prague in 1584, Rudolf was delighted with him. According to the French physician Bernaud who was present, Kelley demonstrated his alchemy before the king and by adding a drop of blood-red oil to a pound of boiling mercury transmuted it into pure gold. Kelley was knighted, married a widow, bought property here in Bohemia and became a very rich man."

Alice smiled, "Since he's a Renaissance man, I feel he's going to tumble from the heights!"

"He fell out of favour with Rudolf. He didn't produce gold, killed one of the king's gentlemen-in-waiting who'd been slandering him, in a duel and was accused of plotting Rudolf's death by Paver Nocturnus..."

"Whatever's that?"

167   "A night horror! An unseen vampire causing nightmares,

sickness and madness. Kelley was arrested and imprisoned and Queen Elizabeth's intervention was useless. He tried to escape from prison but the rope gave way as he was lowering himself down into the Castle moat and he broke his leg, suffered internal injuries and died in prison in 1595."

"Why did blue and violet flames come out of those windows when Kelley was here?"

"A decade before his death, from 1584 to 1589 he'd been experimenting in alchemy and angel-magic with Dr. Dee. John Dee was a man of immense learning, a friend of Queen Elisabeth and her ministers William Cecil and Francis Walsingham, and almost certainly a secret agent and a member of Walsingham's intelligence service. He was also a cartographer who advised the Elisabethan seamen, a friend of writers and poets, and a scientist, mathematician and magus. He held many seances with Kelley in which they tried to communicate with angels and the records of their sessions in England and in Prague cover hundreds of pages."

"How did they get away with it, didn't the Church object to all these goings on?"

"By 1586 they were in real danger. All sorts of rumours were spreading in Prague about the diabolical Englishmen who were practising witchcraft. People said there was an evil spirit here, they'd seen a four-legged black hen with a lizard's tail running round the courtyard. Pope Sixtus V sent a letter to the Castle commanding Rudolf to arrest them. Rudolf didn't have much time for the Pope but he had to make a gesture. He expelled them from Bohemia but they were protected by a Bohemian nobleman, Count Rožmberk, and they lived in his castle at Třeboň for two years. However, before leaving Prague they were summoned to a solemn audience with the Papal Nuncio for interrogation. Dee was a subtle diplomat and hedged his words but the volatile Kelley delivered a passionate diatribe,

'May the Doctors, Prelates and Shepherds mend their ways; may they teach and live Christ by their word as well as by their conduct. For thus, in my opinion, a great... reformation of the Christian religion would be brought about most speedily.'

"This speech infuriated the Nuncio, Blažej continued, "and after the two men had left the audience chamber, he said that he would do everything in his power to destroy them and it was only for the sake of appearances that he'd not had Kelley thrown out of the window!"

As they left the courtyard, Alice paused by the great portal for a last look at the house. She imagined Kelley returning from a journey. Waving his groom aside, he pulled his horse through the doorway, through the stone-flagged vestibule with its vaulted ceiling and out into the courtyard. The horse, thin and bedraggled, wandered off on its own through the covered passage-way into the gardens beyond. Kelley was much smaller than she'd imagined but then she remembered that five foot two inches tall would be about average for the sixteenth century. His clothes were dusty and there were black smudges on his hollow-cheeked and intelligent face He looked up at a window, waved, and then moved swiftly towards a small door on his right. Under his arm was a roll covered with sacking. Manuscripts, she thought. She felt a wave of sympathy for the small, dishevelled figure. This was the man who had dared to speak his mind before the Papal Nuncio. She imagined the gloomy, solemn room, the black-robed figures, the bookcases with their forbidding titles, the stifling authority of ecclesistical power which could destroy a man like lightening...

She turned to Blažej, "I like the way he said, 'In my opinion...'" Suddenly she jumped and gave a small shriek.

A black hen with four legs and a lizard's tail had appeared in a doorway and was scuttling towards her...

* * *

"What a crude trick! A hen by remote control..." she said, as they crossed Palacký bridge and began to walk along the river. She punched him lightly on the back but couldn't help laughing.

"Travel agencies have to have a few tricks to liven up the day," he said seriously.

"What? Haven't I livened it up?"

He looked embarrassed, "I didn't mean..."

"Of course you did! Never mind, I'm philosophical about you now."

"Philosophical?" he stopped, suprised.

"I understand you better but you don't understand me in the least. You see me as a pain-in-the neck client and a woman... but I'm a person."

He took her arm, "I don't understand... woman... person... You're emotional, aren't you?"

"Aren't you?"

He reviewed the events of the day and sighed.

"I've just remembered something," she said, "I saw Václav Havel's play, Temptation, in London's Westminster Theatre, a great barn of a place. I liked the idea... Dr Foustka rebels against a sinister Institute, run by corrupt communists, where he works and he starts practising alchemy and magic. Fistula, a seedy secret policeman with smelly feet, poses as his friend and sets a trap for him. Foustka's eventually destroyed by the Institute." She paused, "Or maybe he destroys himself. He's very arrogant and thinks that if he's deceitful enough he'll be able to take on the Institute single-handed. There were a lot of gimmicks in the play — flashing lights, ear-splitting noises, puffs of smoke. I don't want to run down your President but he's not Christopher Marlowe!"

"I've only read the play. I enjoyed it because like Foustka, I was doing something forbidden under communism, reading books on mysticism and alchemy. Because I was working as a guide and had contacts with foreigners I was watched by the secret police and some of them even rang me up pretending to be alchemists."

The moon had risen and she looked at its light on the Vltava River. She could smell river-water freshened by the storm.   170

Two barges were moving towards Charles Bridge. Poised high above them on their left was the soaring black silhouette of St Vitus Cathedral.

Blažej took her arm, "My silly black hen's reminded me of a story. In the eighteenth century one of the owners of the Faust House, Josef Mladota, dabbled in chemistry and magic. He loved mechanical devices. He had a device which automatically opened doors, dolls which sprayed visitors, a drummer boy beating his drum, two oarsmen rowing a little boat, singing statues and all sorts of objects which appeared and disappeared. People said he could summon up spirits of the dead in coloured smoke. One day a woman approached dressed entirely in black and asked to be invited to one of his evening soirees which were the talk of Prague. He felt unaccountably nervous in the presence of this woman and all his self-confidence disappeared. The following evening when the hour of the performance approached, he was trembling. The woman watched the performance with a smile. 'I can do better than that!' She summoned up Mladota's twin, opened up the ceiling and let in some stars and turned the audience into clapping skeletons. Then she disappeared! All that remained was an empty chair. For a time Mladota lay in a coma between life and death. When he recovered he destroyed all his gadgets — the mechanical dolls, the drummer-boy, the two boatmen and then he left the house."

They had arrived at a tiny park by the river below Charles Bridge. The Vltava River was streaked with silver.

Alice pointed, "Magic!"

A black swan floated in the middle of the river with its head raised to the moon. "I call this spot the Swan-Port and I've brought you here because this view of Prague on a summer night seems truly Renaissance," he said with a smile.

She looked up at the arches of Charles Bridge on the right. They reminded her of an arcaded gallery in a Renaissance courtyard. The moonlight was brilliant and across the broad river dark domes stood out against the sky. They sat down on a bench and a group of swans came shambling towards them.

171

Blažej waved to an elderly man with a beret, "He's the French professor! He comes here every evening with a plastic bag of crumbs."

"Blažej, give me a kiss!"

"No, I'm your guide!"

She nudged him, "This is such a romantic spot and I want to be able to tell my friends that I've been kissed by a handsome man in Prague!"

"What flattery!" he kissed her lightly on the lips, "that's all you'll get!"

She smiled, "What conceit! It's quite enough."

She got out her sketch-book and began to draw the swans, "Listening to rivers always makes me melancholy. They see more than me! I want to follow them to the end of their journey. Why did you say in the pub that Renaissance people were melancholy?"

Swan Port

"The old certainties were going. The Gothic world had order. The earth was in the centre of the Universe and God was in Heaven among his singing angels. Each person had a place in God's order and the Church interpreted God's message. The Renaissance brought challenge and adventure but terrible anxiety. The round world was no longer in the centre of the Universe, the Church had splintered and people had to interpret the Bible in their own way. Machiavelli revealed the technology of power and some Renaissance artists like Marlowe began to wonder if God existed at all. Gothic spoke of the sinfulness of the flesh yet Renaissance artists wanted to rejoice in the beauty of the human body. Thinkers, artists, inventors, had agonizing doubts for they had one foot in Gothic and the other in Renaissance. Explorers like Columbus voyaging into unknown seas suffered from terrible depression. The world was suddenly much bigger and the new vistas were terrifying."

She nodded, "I'm thinking of Martin Luther challenging one thousand years of Catholicism. No wonder he had nagging doubts, they gave him indigestion!"

Blažej said thoughtfully, "We Czechs are facing something of the kind. Forty years of communism gave us a kind of grey security and we were told what to think. It's a strange time for us now, East's meeting West again and it's frightening in some ways..." He watched her sketching, "You said this morning you felt excitement in the air...?"

"Yes, I'm sensing some kind of rebirth... revival. You've got beautiful buildings in a unique town. The past belongs to you and it's used by you. Maybe there'll be a great revival here like Renaissance Florence. The Italians lived among classical buildings and then rediscovered them and a lot else... The discovery of the past triggered off an explosion — creativity."

He looked at her thoughtfully, "I hope you're right! We stand at the crossroads between communism and something different."

She shivered and he gave her his hand, "It's getting chilly!"

They walked across Charles Bridge and Knights of the Cross Square and into crooked Karlova Street. The lane was shadowed from the moon by tall houses and the old street-lamps with their wrought-iron decorations gave off a gentle golden light.

"Have you got the key to Renaissance?" he asked.

She hesitated, "Magic... alchemy?"

"Perhaps. Magic in the sixteenth century wasn't witch-craft, it was part of experimental science and meant studying the hidden powers of nature. The alchemists weren't just trying to turn base metal into gold. They were inquiring into the nature of Man himself and trying to voyage into a higher state of consciousness. The alchemists saw Man as a active agent..." He glanced at her, "I'm including women, of course. Women like Mary Sidney with her interest in chemistry and astronomy and the Countess Elizabeth, wife of the Winter King Frederick, who loved philosophy and science so much that she wanted to reject all suitors! The alchemists believed that instead of being a passive creature in awe of God's Universe, Man could actively use its powers and even the angels for his own purposes. The alchemists searched for self-knowledge through science and magic and the great magicians felt that if they altered the courses of the stars and controlled the heavens the new harmony above would be reflected in the world below. The Bohemian alchemists stood at the dawn of the scientific age and were going on voyages of discovery perhaps as important as those of Columbus but their journeys were different from most Western ones. Erasmus travelled Europe and made fun of its conventions, Francis Bacon had a vision of a world run by experimental scientists, the Elizabethan seamen sailed the oceans. They were travelling out into the world but here in Bohemia alchemists were travelling inwards."

He stopped suddenly and threw open the door of number 183 in Karlova Street with a grandiloquent gesture, "Kepler was here!"

She followed him into the vaulted passageway leading to   174

the great tower-house with its arcaded courtyard and looked
at the bronze and plaster reliefs of Kepler with flowing
beard and strange little cap.

"Humble plaques for a great man!", she commented.
"Johannes Kepler was enticed here from Germany by the

Kepler's House

Emperor Rudolf's magic bell," Blažej explained, "In 1600, when he was twenty-eight years old he came to this town and began work with Tycho de Brahe, a great astronomer who made important discoveries before the invention of the telescope. After de Brahe's death in 1600 Kepler became Rudolf's chief mathematician and although he was a Protestant at a Catholic court, he was safe under Rudolf's patronage. Kepler knew all about human intolerance and nastiness for he'd had to fight to save his mother from a witch's death. She was accused of feeding devilish herbs to cows which then ran up walls!"

Alice studied the plaques, "I've read that in Germany witches were thrown alive into ovens and one woman was burnt at the stake because she put dog-fat into her stable-boy's beer to make him lustful. And there were terrible witch-hunts in Scotland, especially after King James brought out his book on witchcraft."

"Thousands suffered in Renaissance Europe, men as well as women. Kepler found a tolerant haven here and he stayed two years in this house. He sat evening after evening with a squeaking quill pen and with a rape-seed oil-lamp lighting up the darkness of his room, battling with an endless series of figures... He worked on his monumental five-volume book, The Harmony of the World, for twenty-five years and it's said that he worked on two of his famous Laws in this house..."

"What were his Laws?"

He groaned and clapped his hand to his forehead, "You torture me with your questions. I'm going to have nightmares for years! On the basis of his mathematical calculations, Kepler concluded, among other things that the movements of the planets was elliptical and his work influenced Newton. Some Praguers said he was inspired by the extraordinary Vlachchian Chapel just down the road with its elliptical ground-plan. Kepler was delighted by the natural world," Blažej continued, as they went back down the passa-

176

geway, "and he was fascinated by the geometry in matter, particularly in snow-flakes — crystal paradoxes, each one unique yet forming a perfect hexagon. His work inspired one of the great scientific breakthroughs. Without his laws, we wouldn't be able to understand cosmic space. Look up at the stars!" he said loudly as they returned to the street. He gripped her arm, and hissed in her ear, "Space travel was born here in Prague!"

She smiled, "Blažej, I think I'm beginning to like you!"

"You're not so bad either, in spite of..."

"Being a female client?"

"You're not a female," he protested laughing, "You're a mad nymph!"

"Would you like to travel the world with me?"

"Certainly not; you'd be much too tiring!"

"But not dull?"

"No, never dull."

"And do you think I'd like to travel with you?"

"Why not? I'm a good guide!"

They crossed the deserted Old Town Square, "Not everyone was bothered with science and space-travel," Blažej said cheerfully, "There were all sorts of Renaissance happenings here. A mock volcanic eruption like an exploding Mount Etna showered the Square with sparks and a mighty dragon rushed between the crowds belching fire."

They paused in front of her hotel.

"Blažej, I've been thinking about your horse, I mean St Jiří's Gothic horse which you saw 'moving'. I think you were right in a way. It's a transitional horse, rather like your wheelbarrow-car... but I bet it It had more horse-power!"

* * *

He walked past Obecní Dům and down Národní towards the river. He was surprised to find that he wasn't tired, quite the contrary. It had been a strange day but the night was serene and he looked up at the Milky Way. When he reached the Vltava River, he lit a cigarette and began to whistle between puffs,

'East is East,
West is West,
We meet...'

The river looked almost white in the moonlight. The streets were empty but he saw two lovers embracing on Palacký Bridge. He crossed the square and began to walk past the Faust House. Then he paused and stood staring up at the blank windows.

The moon shone down on the forbidding Baroque facade.

Suddenly he froze. Deep within the massive house he heard the deep chime of an ancient clock or gong.

One... two... three... four... five... six...

It was midnight.

THE FOURTH
DAY·
BAROQUE

BLAŽEJ SAT IN THE SMALL LOBBY and waited for Alice. He looked at his watch and sighed.

She rushed in from the street, "Sorry to be late! I've been exploring. I've been round the Havelská Market again. It's great! There was a woman making strange animals out of vegetables. And I bought these earrings, what do you think?"

"There as big as the Klementinum! You're seeing the new Prague — markets, bustle, excitement, new shops, travel agents, discos... and hamburgers, of course!"

She laughed, "My American friend, Liz, won't have to travel here from Texas with frozen ones any more. It's Baroque day, isn't it? I'm looking forward to it... can I make one suggestion?"

"Go ahead," he said, smiling.

"I think you smoke too much, so every time you try to light a cigarette I'm going to ask you a difficult question. Do you agree?"

"Agreed! As long as you don't expect me to know everything," He looked at her curiously as they walked towards the Metro, "You're in a good mood! I thought you might be tired after yesterday."

"You forget I'm younger than you!"

"Please don't rub it in. Won't you be hot in that dress?"

She was wearing a high-necked, black silk shift. She began to hitch it up, "Shall I take it off?" She took his arm, "Sorry! I'm going to be the perfect client today. Just don't tease me that's all..."

"But you like having a go at me...!"

"I'm in mourning for your country... three hundred years of darkness!"

He burst out laughing, "What will you wear when we get to communism?"

"I've got a hammer and sickle boiler-suit!"

"I've been trying to find an English key to Baroque for you. I went to the library and borrowed Robinson Crusoe. Daniel Defoe's England forms such a contrast to what was going on here in Bohemia. English seafarers crossed the oceans, the East India Company controlled the fairy-tale riches of India while on the other side of the world the English had settled Virginia, New England and West Indian Islands. Trading companies made their way into Russia, the Baltic, Turkey and the Levant. Fortunes were made out of trade because English merchants knew that gold mustn't be left lying around in chests. Investment was the thing! Robinson's struggle on his island symbolizes individualism to me. Adventure, change, exploration, movement. Czech society at that time became static, oppressive, filled with bigotry and injustice. Here in Bohemia people studied dead languages, Latin and Greek. Defoe studied geography, history, political science, navigation..."

"It wasn't that brilliant in England! Defoe was sent to prison, wasn't he? And one of his books was burnt. I remember reading that ordinary people liked him, though. When he stood in the pillory people covered it with flowers and drank his health. I must say Robinson Crusoe bored me to tears and Man Friday seemed totally unreal."

"But it's great book. My mother gave it to me when I had tonsillitis as an example of bravery and will-power. For me, Defoe created pictures of free people, the kind that came from the Ancient World and which the Renaissance rediscovered."

"I much prefer Gulliver's Travels. It was written at much the same time, wasn't it? I like political satire. Swift had a go at the court and rubbishy politicians and hypocritical clergymen. His book's full of fantastic stories and wit."

"Neither of those novels could have been written here in Baroque times. We do have a great Baroque writer, Jan Amos Komenský, Comenius was his latinized name. His book, The Labyrinth of the World, is full of fantasy, too, but it's not funny or witty. It describes a pilgrim in an alienated city like a Baroque human ant-heap. The humans seem like insects in a Kafkaesque way. It's a powerful book but heavy... solemn."

As they went up the escalator at Malostranské Metro, he pointed to a copy of the beautiful statue by Matyáš Braun,   182

"Hope is missing! This is a copy. Still, darkness is never total, there's always a sliver of light."

"She's warm and full of life. What happened to the original?"

He reflected, "I'd like to answer all your questions but even I fail occasionally."

"Never mind, you probably answer ninety-eight percent of

Hope

them. But of course, you may not always be right!" she slipped her arm through his.

He disengaged his arm gently, "I'm only right ninety-eight percent of the time!"

* * *

They sat at a small table outside the Little Quarter café in the shadow of St Nicholas Church.

"We're surrounded by Baroque", he said. "The great dome and belfry tower symbolize the triumph of Catholicism. Look at the gigantic statues of Church Fathers on the pillars of the dome! Dominance... massivity... power..."

"I'm hungry! I didn't have time for breakfast."

He ordered coffee and rolls.

"I've got a blister on my little toe," she took off her sandal.

"I'll tell you a story and it'll go away. Listen, please!"

Little
Quarter
cafe

"I always listen to you. Is it a true story?"

"All my stories are true! Over there in U Montague, the former Smiřický Palace, the leaders of the Protestant nobility, led by Count Thurn, decided on a dramatic move in 1618 to challenge the Hapsburgs and the Catholic Church..."

St Nicholas'
Church

"Hang on a minute," she interrupted, as he reached for his cigarettes, "My history's coming back to me. 1618 was the beginning of the Thirty Years War wasn't it? Europe was divided into two camps... But what did the two sides really want?"

He laughed and put down his lighter, "You're right about the two camps, two armed camps. The Protestant Union faced the Catholic League. Your question's so difficult that I'll give up two cigarettes! Individuals wanted many different things, of course. The Protestants wanted freedom to worship and freedom to trade. They admired the English and Dutch entrepreneurs. The Catholics supported the long tradition of Empire and Church and they wanted to hang on to their feudal privileges as well." He sighed, "But it wasn't as simple as that. In Europe a reaction had set in against the materialism of the Renaissance. In a time of change and uncertainty people turned to their churches. They were caught up in theological arguments, listened to sermons, read moral tracts and spoke of miracles. In the Catholic Church the cult of saints reached amazing proportions. It wasn't just a matter of Protestants against Catholics either. The Protestant camp was divided between Lutherans and Calvinists and they feared and distrusted each other. Across Germany where all three faiths existed, the situation was explosive. The Lutherans set on Catholics in the streets of Berlin; in some states Catholic priests went about armed in self-defence and in Dresden a furious mob stopped a Catholic funeral and tore the corpse to pieces. In Styria the Jesuits hid in churches and heckled the preachers. By 1618, hundreds of German states, large and small, were arming themselves for war and your traveller from Cornwall, Mr. Taylor, was thrown out of a ducal palace and said indignantly that German palaces were becoming fortresses. Religious passions were mixed up with other motives, too. National feeling, greed for property, dynastic ambitions. Europe was seething, and intelligent people across Europe expected war."

She was watching the trams as they rattled in and out of the 186 square, "Why did the war start in Bohemia and what was the dramatic move?"

"Although Bohemia was a small country it was an important piece on the European chess-board. Emperor Matthias who succeeded Rudolf in 1611, confirmed the Letter of Majesty granting religious toleration but his heart wasn't in it. The Jesuits and their agents and the Catholic nobility did everything they could to undermine it and the fanaticism of the Calvinists added fuel to the flames. There was a climate of fear and persecution and since Matthias was old and childless, the Protestants feared the accession of Ferdinand of Hapsburg who had been persecuting Protestants in his Austrian lands.

Tension increased rapidly when the Archbishop of Hrob ordered the destruction of a Protestant church and the Abbot of Břevnov closed a church on his estates," Blažej continued, "Once again the Protestant nobles and their retainers crowded into Prague and on May 18th 1618, they issued an appeal to the Bohemian people to protect the Protestant faith. When Matthias sent an uncompromising letter from Vienna forbidding future meetings, the Protestants led by Count Thurn decided on a violent show-down and they hatched their plot over there in that house."

"The Defenestration! Throwing people out of windows seems to be a Czech habit!"

Blažej dipped his roll absentmindedly in his coffee, "But this time the scene wasn't the Old Town Hall but a backroom in the Castle. On the morning of May 23rd 1618, the Protestant nobles in full armour made their way to the Castle followed by a huge crowd. They surged through the Castle gates with the Hapsburg eagle, and went up the staircase into the Chancellery where the Governors were sitting. Jaroslav von Martinic, Burgrave of Karlštejn and Vilém Slavata, the Chief Justice, were detested as uncompromising Catholics who had refused to sign the Letter of Majesty. The door burst open and they were confronted by armed men. Count Thurn seized Slavata and William of Lobkovic grabbed Martinic. There was a great roar from the crowd packed round the door as they were dragged across the room and forced out of two adjoining windows. Martinic went first.

'Jesu Maria, help!' he screamed as he crashed over the sill. Slavata struggled desparately and clawed at the window-sill. Finally, his hands went limp under a rain of blows. Fabricus, the Secretary of the Royal Council, a tiny man, had the courage to remonstrate with the mob and was hurled after them. One of the Protestants lent over the window-ledge.

'We'll see if your Mary can help you,' he jeered.

'My God, his Mary has helped,' he shouted in amazement. The Governors had been thrown into the Castle moat, normally a drop of about forty feet but lessened by a huge pile of excrement and rubbish. A ladder appeared from a neighbouring window and Martinic and the Secretary made for it. A hail of shots came from the window above them and Martinic was slightly grazed. The other shots missed. Slavata's servants carried him off unconcious but alive."

"How incredible! what happened to them?"

"They escaped abroad. The Catholics saw their escape as a holy miracle."

"A good story!" she replaced her sandal.

"But it's true!" he protested, laughing, "It's one of the great dramatic moments in Czech History, the spark which set off the Thirty Years War. As the years went by the story was woven into legend. Slavata entertained people twelve years later by telling them how he had bounced in the moat and there was a story going round the Spanish Court that Fabricus sprang to his feet on the rubbish and bowing low, apologized to his masters for inconsiderately falling on top of them!"

* * *

"I'm glad we're going by tram," she said as they crossed Malostranská Square to the tram-stop, "Šemík's built for contortionists!"

"And to think I wanted to be a racing-driver for years."

"What do you want to be now?"

188

"A good guide. Once I met an Englishman in the courtyard of the National Gallery reading Camus' essay about Prague and I offered to show him round the city free of charge. He accepted, and I think I got more pleasure from showing him around than he did."

"Why?"

"I'm always discovering something... Prague's inexaustable. Actually I'm not from Prague, I'm from Moravia and on Sunday mornings when my friends in the students' hostel were still asleep I used to creep out and wander round Prague. That's how I learnt my profession."

"You've achieved your ambition! Have you got any others?"

"I have some plans...", he said with a smile.

"Why did you say Bohemia was an important piece on the chess-board?"

"It was a political piece. The Emperor Matthias died in 1619 and although all the nobles except two had tamely agreed in 1617 that Ferdinand should succeed him, they did a turnabout after the Defenestration and formally deposed him in August 1619. They elected a German Prince, Frederick of the Palatinate, to be their king."

"Why a German?"

"He was a Protestant and the Bohemian nobles hoped he would bring them money and allies, especially as he was married to Elizabeth, the only daughter of your James I. The election of Frederick was a much bigger challenge to the Hapsburgs than the Defenestration because it could completely undermine their power. The Kings of Bohemia had the traditional right as Electors to vote for the Holy Roman Emperors. In 1619 there were three Protestant Electors in Germany and three Catholic ones, so Frederick's vote would have tipped the balance against the Hapsburgs and struck a death-blow to their ambitions. Ferdinand of Hapsburg knew by 1619 that he would have to fight his way to the Bohemian throne and that only war would subdue the rebellious Czechs."

189

"What about King Frederick? Did the Czechs like him?"

"He and his wife had a great reception when they first arrived in Bohemia and people turned out to greet them as they travelled through the towns and villages on their way to Prague but their free and easy life-style soon offended the solid burghers of this town."

"How?"

"Frederick who was twenty-three at the time, liked playing tennis and lying in bed and swimming. He horrified Prague by swimming naked in the Vltava River in front of the Queen and her ladies. His wife Elizabeth was a brave, witty character but her low-necked gowns were thought positively indecent! No respectable Czech man allowed his wife to dress like that. She called her husband pet names, wrote love-letters to him in French and read frivolous books..."

"I rather like her! how old was she?"

"Sixteen! Your historian C. V. Wedgwood describes how Frederick rode round Prague in a red coat and with a yellow feather in his cap and how he attended balls and banquets in noblemen's houses and went to sleighing parties in winter while the spectre of war crept closer. Visitors flocked to the castle to gape at the state rooms and the royal baby. Your Mr Taylor who was in Prague at the time saw one of the visitors taking the baby's woollen shoes as a souvenir! The royal couple shocked Prague in other ways, too. After his coronation, Frederick ordered the altars and images in St Vitus' Cathedral to be removed and the story goes that his Chaplain sent two maidservants to carry the relics away for firewood. This pleased the Calvinists but the Catholics and Lutherans were horrified. Frederick had no iron in him and he wasn't built for such turbulent times. He relied on his Chancellor, the Prince of Anhalt, and turned to him in public before answering questions. At one Protestant assembly, Frederick answered an ambassador by repeating by heart the answer to a totally different question!"

"He sounds like a young version of President Reagan!"

The tram shook and rattled as it climbed small streets lined   190

with shops towards open country. They descended, crossed
some grassland and went through a stone portal and down
a tree-lined avenue. The great heat of the previous day had
mellowed into pleasant summer. Young mothers strolled by
with prams and a small, breathless man in shorts jogged by.

"I'd like an ice-cream," she said.

"I'm afraid you won't be lucky. Tourists aren't catered for
here, we've only just shed communism!"

"What a weird building!"

"It's the Hvezda or Star, a Renaissance hunting-lodge
surrounded by a deer-park, and it was built by the Emperor

Hvězda

Ferdinand between 1555 and 1556. It was designed by four architects including B. Wohlmut who worked on the Belvedere. It's got a stellate ground-plan."

"A star-shaped Renaissance dream! I like the copper roof."

They walked into woods and climbed to the brow of a broad hill overlooking a ravine.

"The greatest turning-point in Czech history happened here," Blažej explained. "On Sunday, November 8th 1620, the Battle of White Mountain was fought on this chalky hill. In a few dramatic hours my country's existence as an independent state was wiped out."

Alice sat down on the dry ground and looked at him expectantly, "What happened?"

"On the day before the battle, the Prince of Anhalt moved the Bohemian forces up here under cover of darkness and his battle lines stretched about a mile across the brow of this hill. The infantry and cannon were in the centre and the cannon on the wings. King Frederick's great yellow velvet banner with its green cross would probably have been roughly where you're sitting. The Emperor Ferdinand's forces were in pursuit, about a quarter of a mile from here..."

"How big were the armies?"

"It's hard to know because both sides lied about it! Anhalt said later that the reason for Bohemia's defeat was overwhelming enemy numbers but there probably wasn't much in it. The Bohemians numbered perhaps 15,000 and the Hapsburg forces 20,000. Count Tilly, the imperial general charged the Bohemians over there near the Hvězda to test their resistance. When they stood firm, the imperialists held a war-council to decide whether to attack or not and there was a long delay. Anhalt thought the enemy had decided not to attack but as the mist cleared, Tilly's men, backed by artillery, charged up the hill. Disaster struck because the Bohemian infantry were badly equipped and ready to mutiny and their officers tried to drive them back to their posts with drawn swords. The Hungarian troops on the Bohemian side fled from the battle-field and one account says that they

192

tried to ford the Vltava just above Prague near Smíchov and more than a thousand drowned. Utter panic spread through the Bohemian army and the soldiers rushed towards Prague pursued by their officers. Frederick's banner and all the guns were captured. Within a few hours our defeat was total..."

She stared down into the ravine and shivered, "This place has a strange, chilly atmosphere even on a summer's day..."

"This battlefield and the surrounding countryside were desolate places for years after the war. There were deserted villages, burnt-out farms and the skeletons of starved farm animals. Mercenary troops, even those on our own side, plundered our countryside."

"I don't understand... The Hussites had held out against most of Europe but this was a walk-over..."

"Bohemia had changed since Hussite times. The free peasants who had fought in Žižka's army had become down-trodden serfs and the once-proud towns had been cowed. In spite of all their claims to be good Protestants, the Czech nobles refused to pay for the war and some say lack of money was a bigger danger than the enemy. After the war, huge sums were found in their palaces, enough to equip three armies! The battle was fought mainly between mercenaries and the Hapsburg forces were better-paid and better disciplined. The Hapsburgs had Spanish gold and powerful allies."

"I thought James I helped Bohemia?"

"Very reluctantly! He finally allowed 2 000 volunteers to embark from Gravesend but he didn't have any sympathy for the Czech Protestants and an expensive war was the last thing he wanted."

"But what about religion? The Czech nobles stood to lose everything, their religion... property... their lives, if they lost the battle."

"Europe was full of religious passions but most rulers and feudal lords put their own interests first and they didn't want to dip into their pockets. In this battle religious feeling was probably stronger on the Hapsburg side. The Jesuits preached

193

to Tilly's troops as they marched and the twelve largest cannon were given the names of the Apostles!"

As they walked back towards the Hvĕzda, he pointed to the south-east wall of the park, "Moravian troops held out here heroically against great odds until almost all of them were killed. René Descartes witnessed this last stand. He was a cornet in the Bavarian cavalry at the time and described the great pile of mutilated corpses, ten or twelve deep, beside that wall. It was the grave of Bohemian independence."

* * *

As they went into the Hvĕzda she admired the exquisite stucco reliefs on the ceiling of flowers, foliage and animals, "It's like a wedding-cake! Can we talk about something cheerful?"

"I'll tell you about František Vĕk. This place is a museum devoted to Alois Jirásek and his friend, the painter Mikoláš Aleš. Jirásek was the Czech Walter Scott and he wrote a famous novel about Baroque times called František Vĕk. Vĕk, the hero, came to Prague to study for the priesthood but he fell in love with the beautiful Pauline, a mute girl. He gave up his studies and decided to be a famous actor. He even sang before Mozart who didn't think much of him! His father summoned him home in a fury and since Vĕk had discovered by this time that his talents weren't up to the Prague competition, he returned home. These are the illustrations for the novel by Adolph Kašpar."

"This is a lovely illustration!" She looked at a tiny drawing of Vĕk walking up an autumnal lane lined with strangely contorted poplars.

"You wanted something cheerful but I think there's sadness in this picture. Autumn's turning to winter and Vĕk's trudging home, his youth gone, his illusions shattered.."

"What happened to him?"

"He took over his father's shop, made a decent living, and married a village girl. Possibly he read the Czech translation 194 of Robinson Crusoe in the evenings when he'd closed the shop and perhaps he lived happily ever after."

"Poor mute Pauline!"

* * *

"What happened to Frederick and Elizabeth after the battle?" she asked, as they walked down to the tram-stop.

"They were staying in a house called At the Wolf's Throat in the Little Square, it's now number 11, the Richter House. Frederick tried to negotiate with the victors through the two English envoys in Prague, Conway and Weston. He got no reply and on November 9th the Queen's travelling carriage was prepared, Frederick mounted his horse and they left Bohemia. The day before their flight they were visited by one of your countrymen, Captain Ralph Hopton, who had ridden through the driving rain with an urgent message. Apparently 1,600 volunteers with eight cannons from your country were at Karlštejn waiting for Frederick's orders. They had just missed the Battle of White Mountain and were still twelve miles from Prague when the Bohemian army was defeated. The Prince of Anhalt put his hand on Hopton's shoulder and told him he'd come too late. Hopton staggered from the royal apartments in a daze. Maybe he was thinking of all those volunteers from your country who had travelled across half of Europe with a passionate belief in the Bohemian cause. The story goes that at dawn Count Thurn left the royal apartments and found a small, leather-bound book on the floor which Hopton had dropped as he left the house. It had been given to Hopton by John Taylor, your Cornish navigator, traveller and poet, and on the title-page was an engraving of English soldiers with an inscription:

'An Englishman's love to Bohemia: with a friendly farewell to all the noble soldiers that go from Great Britain to that honorable expedition'."

They boarded the tram and it groaned and swayed back towards Prague. As it jerked to a stop Blažej leaned across her and pointed to some buildings on their left, "The mark of the conqueror, pure Baroque! The Benedictine Monastery of Břevnov and St Margaret's Church built by Dientzenhofer. Great pillars, massive gables and steeple. Huge, solemn... weighty. They stand over the countryside like sentinels."

She looked wonderingly at the huge structures before the tram lurched forward again, "Two different worlds, the Hvězda and Břevnov... and only two tram-stops apart!"

* * *

They climbed up long flights of stone steps to the upper terraces of the Vrtba Gardens and she admired the lines of wild cherubs and goddesses with flying draperies on the shady terraces.

"Italian architects planned magical gardens on the slopes linking the palaces of the Lesser Town with Hradčany up above." he said. "This garden was designed about 1720 and the wonderful sculptures come from M. Braun's workshop..."

"I've run out of steam!" she sat down on the stone parapet.

He sat down beside her, "I've chosen this spot because I think it's the most Baroque view of Prague. At the start of the Hussite Revolution when King Wenceslas was dying, Prague was one of the grandest and most beautiful cities in the world. It deserved the title of The Rome of the North. It's undulating terrain, its two castles perched on hills, its one hundred spires, houses submerged in vegetation and between them the silver stream of the Vltava River, must have made a fascinating picture even then. The Renaissance added to this scene; glowing portals in narrow lanes, a horizontal line with buildings emphasizing life here and now, supplemented the vertical Gothic structures straining to Heaven and channelled the desire for transcendence with the mundane. Then came Baroque... huge... massive..."

"I like your lecture!" she put her hand over his gently, "but I'm still thinking about the battle. Tell me what happened after it..."

He withdrew his hand and fumbled for his lighter, "Twenty- 196

seven of the nobles, the Protestant rebels, were executed in the Old Town Square while seven hundred German cavalrymen patrolled the town. Mostly they died silently though we're told that one shouted,

'Tell your Emperor I stand now before his unjust judgement and warn him of the judgement of God,'

197

Then the soldiers' drums drowned his words." Blažej sighed, "My people love to celebrate this date but I've never understood it. The rebels were miserly!"

She looked at him in surprise, "But they weren't all miserly, surely? We don't know if the victims in the Old Town Square were misers," she added quietly.

"When the executioner had cut off the head of one of the rebels, he placed a loaf of bread where the head had been. The corpse rose from the block and took a few steps before collapsing to the mad laughter of the crowd."

"Hideous!" she shuddered dramatically and lent heavily against him.

He could smell her hair, it was like sun-baked hay. It occurred to him suddenly that his work with her would be over in a couple of days and he felt rather blank. He made an effort to collect his thoughts, "There's a story linked to these executions, it's about a mysterious stranger who lived in the forest not far from Panenský Týnec. He'd come from Prague in the late 1620s and had begged permission from the local mayor to build a modest cottage where he kept himself to himself and was rarely seen by anyone. However, one day a forester cut open his hand while he was felling trees and the stranger offered to bind up the wound. Then he got out a bottle of wine and they got into conversation and discovered that they were both members of the Czech Protestant Brethren. They talked about Prague, the war, the bad times... and so on, and became friends. Some time later, the gloomy stranger told the forester who he was. He was none other than the infamous executioner Jan Mydlář who had executed the twenty-seven Protestant rebels. He told the forester that he had terrifying recurring dreams in which he was haunted by the faces of his victims and that he'd withdrawn to the forest to live alone with his nightmares. Then he showed the forester two great swords hanging on the cottage wall. 'Those swords used to hang in my house beside the Vltava', he said, 'and I was visited there some years ago by the famous professor, Dr Jessenius who was rector of

Charles University before the Battle of White Mountain. He knew who I was, of course, and he'd come to see me because he was writing a medical book and wanted to know certain anatomical details... An extraordinary thing happened as he crossed my threshold. One of those great swords suddenly moved and it moved so strongly that it brushed against the other one. I was shocked because if someone causes one of those swords to move, then sooner or later he will be its victim'.

The Forester had been listening intently. He nodded and rose to go."

Alice looked at Blažej sceptically, "What happened to Jessenius?"

"He was one of those executed by Mydlář on the Old Town Square. He was nailed to the scaffold and his tongue was cut out. Then Mydlář cut off his head."

They sat in silence for a while and looked at the panorama below them.

"The victors plundered and murdered and a foreign nobility largely replaced the Bohemian one. The intelligentsia went into exile or conformed. Bohemia was violently re-Catholicized and the cruelty of the conqueror was felt in every town and every village. German became the official language, the language of the civil service, universities, schools... It was the village 'intellectuals' who helped preserve the Czech language..."

"How?"

"Because Protestant books were confiscated and burnt, people hid them under floorboards, in lofts and in cellars and although they were terrified of sudden Jesuit raids, they copied them secretly. In the mid — eighteenth century, Jiroušek, a villager from Polička, decided to copy the New Testament and the Psalms. He borrowed a bible from a fellow-Protestant and found a brilliant hideout in a hollow tree. 'The Singing Linden' as it came to be called, may still be there for all I know, though the last record of it was in 1932. Jiroušek climbed into the linden in the evenings when everything was quiet and he wrote until late into the night. Inside the tree he had a tiny table and he copied by candle-light. It's said that he used up 1, 204 candles! As he worked, he sang but as he was stone deaf he didn't realize he could be heard. The villagers heard the singing but no one seemed to be able to decide where it came from. Eventually, Jiroušek got scared and gave up going to the linden. Many years later, in 1781 when Jiroušek was an old man, the Emperor Joseph 11 brought out the Act of Tolerance and then Jiroušek began to boast about his activities in the tree and he became a folk hero." Blažej paused and searched again for his lighter, "A nation without its language isn't a nation at all. It's language which binds a nation. Without it, how can people find their identity?"

"Perhaps a country can find other ways of expressing itself?"

He turned to her appreciatively, "Stone! In Baroque times the Czechs found ways of expressing themselves through sculpture..."

"There's something I don't understand..." she laughed, "there's lots I don't understand! I've been looking at Baroque statues and they don't give me a feeling of gloom and oppression. There's joy and optimism in them... vitality. They don't look like statues carved by miserable, conquered people."

"The Renaissance wasn't snuffed out at the Battle of White Mountain," he replied. "Although most of the architects were foreigners, the Czech masons and craftsmen had the Renaissance spirit. Their work's full of originality and passion. There's something dynamic... a kind of whirling rhythm."

She nodded, "They look as though they're actually moving inside... I don't know quite how to put it."

"Yes, the statues do seem to move. It's as if hot blood is pulsing under the stone surface and the facial expressions are as complex as those of human beings." He found his lighter, "I think the Czechs only paid lip-service to the Church officials. In reality, the artists are singing their praise of life. 200

On the Prague hills Baroque palaces appeared amidst their greenery. House-signs like expressive metaphors appeared on buildings and ecclesiastical buildings became a kind of game with lofty materials. The Czechs took Baroque and made it their own. I think two opposing forces met and shook hands; the explosive, unbridled joy of life and an awareness of its fleeting nature — its end."

She leaned over and blew out the flame of his lighter.

He laughed and touched her cheek, "Prague is over-flowing with Baroque! It fills the streets, the portals, the attics, the gardens, the squares and the tiny courtyards."

* * *

She lent back in her seat in the Wallenstein pub and stretched out her legs under the oak table.

"We're sitting in the house, At the Tree Storks. It's a nineteenth century building but it's been an ale-house since the fourteenth century. The monks from St Thomas' monastery brewed their beer here."

"I wouldn't mind half a pint!"

The waiter approached and Blažej studied the menu, "They make wonderful potato pancakes here."

She nodded, "Don't be offended but you're paying for everything... I think it's my turn."

He shook his head, "You're my guest!"

"You'll be getting £ 100 from me this week, how much is that in crowns?"

"About 5 000"

"How many clients do you have a month?"

"About two. I would have more but it's tiring talking in a foreign language and reacting when someone speaks quickly... I can just about manage but I have to pay a lot for petrol, payments on Šemík and taxes. Things here are cheap for tourists but it's tough for Czechs. We're having to pay more for everything... food, rent... heating..." He looked at her curiously, "What about you? Will you make money with your paintings? Maybe you'll find a rich husband?"

She looked at him furiously, "That's the last thing I'm looking for!"

He put his hand over hers, "Please don't be cross today..."

She relaxed, "Making money's not so easy for an artist, but I've got lots of ideas. Do you live with your parents?"

"That's none of your business." He checked himself quickly, "Sorry, no, I've got my own flat, it's very small."

"Can I see it? Does it look interesting?"

"Interesting?" he smiled, "It looks like a tiny second-hand bookshop. I've got about two square metres to move around."

"So there won't be much room for your girl-friend?"

He frowned.

"Will you be seeing her tonight?"

"No, I'm going to a meeting of my political party."

"What's your party?"

"The Friends of Beer."

She looked at him in astonishment, "But you don't drink!"

"No, but I like the name, it's got an optimistic sound. We're aiming to get people into Parliament."

She laughed, "Blažej, you're quite human. I thought you were a bit of a stiff a couple of days ago."

"A stiff?"

"Someone who's tie's too tight... no sense of humour. Your English is so brilliant that I forget you're Czech!"

He smiled, "Thank you, I've been studying English for ages and I've had years of practice as a guide but there are still lots of expressions I don't know. Is your friend... William a stiff?"

"None of your business!"

They both laughed.

"What was your first thought when you met me at the airport?"

"Trouble!"

"Does your girl-friend rabbit on, like me?"

"Rabbit on...?"

"Talk a lot."

"She smiles a lot... no, she doesn't have much to say."   202

"Isn't that boring?"

"I find it quite restful."

"Restful?" she looked at him indignantly, "Whatever do you want to rest for? You're not that old."

He sighed, "Maybe you're right... sometimes I'd like her to come up with an idea." He looked out of the window, "I'd like to tell you about a troublesome character. To me, he's the most fascinating character of Czech Baroque," he pointed to the east side of the square, "that's his house!"

She got up and went to the open pub door, "What a wopper, it's a royal palace!"

"Twenty-five houses and three gardens were destroyed to make room for it. Its owner, Albrecht von Wallenstein, had ambitions to be King of Bohemia and he wanted his home to rival the royal palace at Hradčany. It was Prague's first Baroque palace and was built between 1624 by Italian master-builders supervised by Pieroni. It's got five interconnecting courtyards and a wonderful garden."

She returned to her seat, "Wallenstein was a Czech, wasn't he? How did he find the money to build that place?"

"War! The Thirty Years War made him a multi-millionaire."

203   "How?"

"Wheeling and dealing. Wallenstein came from a Czech Protestant family but was converted to Catholicism and offered his services to Ferdinand before he became Emperor and while he was still Archduke of Styria. Wallenstein married a wealthy widow which gave him his first step up the money-ladder. He raised his own armies and became a brilliant general. His business ventures in war-supplies and loot brought him a fortune and he lent Ferdinand vast sums, half a million guilden in 1623, and in return wrung land and titles from him. After the Battle of White Mountain, he increased his wealth by confiscating the property of exiled Protestant nobles and he built that palace. But it wasn't his only property, he controlled a quarter of all the land of Bohemia. After the Emperor, he was the most important man in the Empire and his power seemed unlimited..."

"Entrepreneurship!"

Blažej nodded, "He was the archetype of the successful entrepreneur — tough, ruthless ambitious... a gigantic risk-taker in the very centre of the power-politics of the time."

"So what went wrong?"

"He turned traitor and conspired with Ferdinand's Protestant enemies. He wasn't willing to bet everything on a single card."

She smiled at him, "Are you?"

He hesitated, "Well, I'm sitting with you in the Three Storks when I could be working in an office and getting a guaranteed income."

"I've got a feeling you're a little Wallenstein! I think you've got some more cards up your sleeve"

"Perhaps. Now I'd like to show you one of Wallenstein's favourite spots."

They walked across the square and down small streets to Letenská Street and through an inconspicuous doorway into formal gardens.

"How quiet it is!"

"Most tourists miss this spot."

She looked down an avenue of statues of classical and

hunting scenes flanked by formal, box-edged beds brilliant with flowers, to the beautiful three-arched loggia.

"This is where Wallenstein liked to sit. In his lifetime these graceful statues were the original ones designed by Adrien de Vries."

"Where are they now, the originals, I mean?"

"In Sweden. Towards the end of the Thirty Years War the Swedish army looted Prague's art-treasures."

They sat down on a stone bench in front of the bronze fountain with its statue of Venus, "The fountain was made in 1630," he took out his cigarettes.

She put her hand on his arm, "In Shakespeare the hero's always brought down by some fatal flaw in his character, what was Wallenstein's?"

He laughed and put the packet back in his pocket, "More than one flaw in this case! Kepler worked as his astrologer and commented on Wallenstein's erratic character, greed for power and suspicious nature. Wallenstein looked on most human beings as pathetic characters and perhaps his colossal arrogance destroyed him. He failed to see the strength of the opposition."

"Tycoons sometimes have bad luck!"

"I'm not sure if it was bad luck but Wallenstein had lost his health by 1634. He was fifty-one years old and crippled with gout and looked like an old, sick man. When his assassins came for him they found him standing at his bedroom window unarmed..."

"Who were his murderers?"

"A group of English, Scotish and Irish mercenaries under the command of a Colonel Butler. The murderers led by Captain Devereux, an Englishman, broke into Wallenstein's lodgings at Cheb where he'd arrived the day before with a few loyal supporters and kicked open his bedroom door. Wallenstein turned to face them, muttered a few words and stumbled forward onto Devereux's sword. An Irishman picked up the corpse and was about to throw it out of the window but Devereux stopped him and rolled the body roughly in the blood-stained carpet. It was pulled out of the room by its heels and down the staircase, the head knocking against every stair. Then it was thrown into a coach and taken to the castle."

"Wallenstein wasn't left to moulder peacefully in his tomb," Blažej continued. "He was regarded as a traitor by the Catholic Emperor and the Protestant Swedes and his corpse was drawn ignominiously by a yolk of oxen to the Carthusian monastery in Valdice. The Carthusian Order was very austere. It was a silent order and the monks walked barefoot, veiled their faces and even slept in coffins. But one day they were disturbed by an important visitor, John Banér, a Swedish general. In front of the astonished monks, he ordered Wallenstein's tomb to be opened and the coffin removed. Then he commanded the monks to open the coffin and Wallenstein's rotting corpse was revealed. Banér ordered one of his soldiers to cut off Wallenstein's head and his right arm, and they were wrapped in a blanket and carried to the general's carriage. Then Baner had them conveyed to Sweden. The lime trees on these avenues must have quivered in shock!"

Alice looked closely at Blažej's face, "Is your story true?"

He avoided her question, "Jaroslav Durych, my favourite Baroque author, describes Wallenstein's dizzy rise and fall. Looking at the pages of Durych's book, 'Straying' is like looking into a dark oil-painting. There are pillaging armies, burning villages, squalor, mire, disfigurement and perversity — the horror and upheaval of the world."

"Reformation... Counter-Reformation..." Alice murmured, "Yet both sides had religious ideals."

"Yes, but as far as murder and robbery were concerned, they matched each other. Baroque is full of religious passion and human baseness. Sombre devotion in great cathedrals full of gilded statues and flickering candles and nobles in heavy brocades, skilled in deception and intrigue..."

Alice got up from the bench and wandered round the garden admiring the pools and grottoes. Bees hummed in the flower-beds and a dove flew down and perched on Venus' head,

"Wallenstein's end was terrible," Blažej reflected, "but for fourteen years his soldiers had ravaged and terrorized Germany, and Europe was strewn with his corpses."

She smiled, "But he left us his garden!"

* * *

As they walked into Loretto Square Blažej pointed to the gigantic palace looming over them, "The Černín Palace!"

"Where?" she looked round vaguely.

He burst out laughing, "How can you miss such a colossus? It's 150 metres long, a wonderful Baroque giant. Look at the facade with its thirty great columns between the windows.

Černín Palace

It was designed by the Italian architect, Francesco Caratti and built by Italian master-craftsmen over many years from 1669. It's had a strange history because it was deserted by its owners at the beginning of the 18th century and became a human ant-hill. Thousands of squatters moved in! They

Loretto

lived in state-rooms, parlours, on staircases and in corridors. For many years they ate, drank, quarelled, made love, reared children... Finally the Austrian monarchy took the place over and turned in into a barracks."

"Who lives there now?"

"It's our Ministry of Foreign Affairs."

As they walked towards the Loretto he looked at his watch, "We're just in time. The steeple's early Baroque and has wonderful bells."

She looked up at the steeple and listened to the peal, "How lovely! It's playing several tunes."

"The facade was built by Dientzenhofer in 1721 but the shrine was built nearly a hundred year's earlier in 1626 and is modelled on the one at Loretto in Italy. After the Battle of White Mountain about fifty of these shrines were built in Bohemia to lure people to the Catholic Church and the Loretto's a monument to triumphant Catholicism."

She looked at the building and then glanced back at the Černin Palace, "The Loretto's graceful... what a contrast to that great bulky thing!"

"Great bulky thing? The Černín's considered one of the most beautiful buildings in Prague!"

He showed her the painting of St Starosta in the Chapel of Mary of Sorrow.

"She's got a beard!" said Alice in astonishment.

"According to the legend, St Starosta was a Sicilian or Portuguese Princess, who was converted to Christianity. Her father who wanted an advantageous marriage for her found her a bridegroom, a heathen. In spite of her father's threats, she refused to marry him so her father put her in prison. Praying to God, the girl entreated Him to make her so ugly and repulsive that her suitor would reject her. A miracle happened! Overnight she grew a beard! Her father had her crucified."

"A holy lady with a bushy beard! I'm surprised she was accepted as a saint."

209   "It took a long time. In the late seventeenth century

St Starosta

learned men were arguing that she was really a Christ figure from Lucca. Today she could earn a fantastic living in a circus!"

210

"It's lucky she avoided the wedding-feast, she'd have had a beardful of noodles!"

"Czech Baroque pushed all passions to extremes. Look at St Magdalene, she's squirming with voluptuousness. And St Hata's exposing her bosom."

Alice smiled, "I can feel kisses in the air!"

* * *

Jupiter and Juno

As they walked down Neruda Street, Blažej pointed to the portal of Thun Hohenstein Palace, "The Gods were a favourite subject of Czech Baroque and these statues are by my favourite sculptor, Matyáš Braun. After a difficult flight, these two eagles brought Jupiter and Juno to this palace. If you listen carefully, you can hear their wings fluttering..."

"Juno wants to fly away from him! Look, she's turning away, she's angry."

"You may be right... they do seem to be conversing."

"Not conversing, arguing! He's trying to convince her of something, she's saying 'No'. I think he wants to overpower her." Alice looked into Blažej's eyes. "I certainly wouldn't let any man overpower me!"

He frowned, "Arguing? You're right, there's passion... infatuation."

Day

"Desire!" she said, firmly.

As they walked on she took his arm, "I've been thinking about the people who built these tremendous palaces. I can see them, small people — dirty, ragged, poor."

"The sweat and blood of the Czech people is in the mortar. These palaces were the houses of the conquerors," he replied.

They stopped in front of the Morzini Palace and he pointed out the two statues of Day and Night, "F. M. Brokoff did these sculptures and this is one of the most beautiful Baroque houses in Prague."

"I like Night best with the moon on her head," she said.

"Peace and quiet..."

"Dreams!"

"Before we move on you must touch the toes of the first Moor and your wish will be granted."

213

Night

Caryatids

She stared at the great straining caryatids supporting the balcony, bent down and then glanced quickly up at him, "I hope my wish will come true by the end of the week, only two more days to go."

He turned away, "These Moors were the emblem of the Morzinis and they were looked on as one of the wonders of Prague."

* * *

"This is a typical Lesser Town house, At the White Lamb. Look at the wainscotting round the windows! It probably belonged to a well-to-do craftsman, possibly a baker or tanner, who ran his business on the ground floor."

"I think these house-signs are my favourite things in Prague. You rarely see them in England, though we've got pub-signs, of course. This house reminds me of home, a village house in Herefordshire transported to Central Europe!"

"It would have been built by a master mason by rule of thumb — no drawings. He would have built it out of his head from long experience. Donna Flavia might have stayed in this house. She was a beautiful and famous Italian sculptress and she came here to see the wonders of Prague. On Charles Bridge, among the beggars, she saw a dreamy-looking young man, a student. His face fascinated her and she asked him if he would pose for her. She was working at the time on a statue of Christ. He refused at first but she convinced him he would be serving his country..."

"How?"

"She told him that Bohemia had fallen into darkness and despair and that her statue would symbolize the crucified

At the White Lamb

nation. The student went with her to her studio and she tied him to a cross. At first her work went well but then she had great difficulty with the face. Even with all her great skill and experience she couldn't capture the expression of the dying Christ. In a fury she stabbed the student and as he died in agony, she modelled his face,

'I give my blood for you, my beloved country,' whispered the student, 'receive it as my redemption.'"

"Joy and sensuality... and at the same time agony, wounds and suffering. There's a kind of relish in suffering and decay and it repels me, I hate it!" Alice said indignantly.

* * *

St Hubert
and
the Miraculous
Deer

216

"You said you liked house-signs," he said as they walked through Tomášská Street, a quiet Baroque lane, "I'll show you a statue on a wonderful Baroque house, probably a merchant's. It's a magnificent building with a double portal. Please, look up!"

She looked up at St Hubert with the Miraculous Deer by M. Brokoff. The saint, in armour, knelt on one knee before the deer which had a cross between its antlers. Mesmerized by the statue, she stared at it for a long time, "It's extraordinary! There's such intensity about it. Hubert is astonished, horrified, guilty!"

"And look at the deer, it's putting its hand, not its hoof on Hubert's breast. Look at its foot on the tree-stump, too!"

'The deer's got a human face. I'm trying to make out its expression. It's got sad, thoughtful eyes. It's reproachful, too," she replied.

"Compassionate eyes, they remind me of the eyes of Celtic statues. Its expression has an etherial quality. The sculptor was a genius, a master of stone."

* * *

"This bridge is a symbol of the Counter-Reformation," he said, as they crossed Charles Bridge, "Frederick of the Palatinate fled across this bridge and on the Lesser Town Bridge Tower twelve heads of the Protestant nobles and the right hand of Count Schlick were displayed after the executions in the Old Town Square. Behind these statues are the horrors of the Thirty Years War. Their bodies seem to shudder and their limbs twitch as though moved by a great wind."

They stood on the stone steps leading to Kampa Island and looked up at St Luitgarde.

"She longed so much for Christ," Blažej said, "that in a dream while she was praying before his statue, she saw his right hand come down towards her. Christ pressed her to himself, to his wound. He embraced his beloved and his head seemed to come closer... Her face seems blind with passion. She's smiling lovingly and touching his hot knee."

She looked at it scornfully.

"It's a celestial encounter," he said, noticing her expression, "I think it's depicted with great pathos."

She nudged him, "I'd love to be joined to someone celestially!"

"With great pathos," he repeated, pretending not to hear her.

* * *

"Now I'd like to see more of your Baroque favourites," she said as they left the bridge. "But please don't expect me to admire everything. I'am a tourist and it takes time for things to sink in! What did Baroque actually give Prague?"

218

"A vista for a cloudy day! A flowing tenderness in chiascuro, flying masses."

She stumbled slightly on the cobblestones and gripped his arm, "It's important to look up!" she said laughing, "otherwise I miss the statues on the roofs. I think the most essential thing in Prague is a comfortable pair of shoes."

Some demonstrators passed them, holding placards, "What's going on?"

"They're going up to the Castle, they want a clean-out in the administration. Too many communist fossils are still around!"

"It's a city of 'Happenings'. Defenestrations, demonstrations, street theatre, musicians on Charles Bridge, new cafés! It's fantastic, quite different from stolid old Britain! When I arrived here four days ago, there was a boring little shop near my hotel selling plastic bowls. Now its being turned into a Jazz cafe."

The walked towards the Klementinum and went into the courtyard.

"I don't know quite how I feel about this place," she said. "I like the feeling of quiet — an intense quiet. Yet there's something a bit sinister and severe about it. It makes me feel like a child in Church!"

"It has a terrifying geometry," said Blažej. "It was the Jesuit College — a Baroque fortress. It sent missionaries all over the world. It's a reminder of catastrophe, psychosis — the time of darkness. Yet for those who live and work in the centre of Prague it's just a daily sight. I think you get your feeling of quiet because the Klementinum has an undisturbed outer covering. You see, so much of Prague is engulfed by warehouses, half-finished panel-houses, rubble, abandoned buildings — to a far greater extent than Western cities."

"I've never been in a city with so much deserted scaffolding. It's odd, it props up buildings all over the place. Some of it has moss on it and it looks as though it is growing into the walls of the buildings."

219   "Money! We need money to preserve our inheritance. But

let me tell you about the Klementinum. It's interesting and not only for its size. It's colossal, of course. Six towers, two churches, chapels... After Prague Castle, it's the largest building constructed over a period of 160 years. The library has 5 million books. But you can read all these things for yourself. It has another significance. Czech intellectuals found a refuge here during the time of totalitarianism..."

Klementinum

"Strange!" she interrupted, "dissidents writing their books in the symbol of repression — the Baroque Fortress!"

"Thousands of people came here in the terrible housing crises in Prague; they had nowhere to go. They came here to read and study and then in the evening, they went off to sleep on a friend's floor. Also, let me tell you about the bulletin board in the Porter's Lodge. It's the best place to learn about cultural programmes in Prague. All sorts of events are posted here which will never be mentioned by the Press."

* * *

"For me this is a heavenly spot of Czech Baroque," Blažej said, as they walked back to the Knights of the Cross Square towards the Church of St Saviour. "I call it concentrated Baroque, it's as if church music had streamed across the square and had materialized in stone. The square is guarded by Christ, Mary and the Four Evangelists in front of this church."

As they stepped down into the church, she was amazed at the intense cold in the building, "It's like wading through cold water, it's a good place for sweaty tourists."

They sat down for a minute in the icy calm of the church.

"One of the most terrifying figures of the Counter-Reformation is buried here, the Jesuit, Andrew Koniáš. He was the scourge of Protestants and I imagine him going round Prague with a flaming torch. He was possibly the greatest book burner in history. No one knows how many books he destroyed but he boasted that he burned 60,000."

"I'll take you to the Church of St Francis, now," Blažej continued, as they walked across the square, "I want to show you the work of Vavřinec Reiner, I think he's the greatest decorative Baroque genius in Prague. Some of his work reminds me of Michelangelo."

She sneezed, groped in her pocket and produced her usual square of toilet paper. He looked at it in irritation and offered her his handkerchief but she ignored it.

"I wouldn't call Michelangelo decorative!" she said irritably, "I've seen his 'Last Judgement' in the Sistine Chapel. A lot of it has faded but you still get an impression of turbulance and whirling shapes."

"How I would like to travel," said Blažej quietly, "especially to Italy!"

Alice took his hand impulsively, "Yes, you must travel," she said warmly, "I hope you do." She looked at Reiner's painting of the Last Judgement, "Actually I do see what you mean about Michelangelo, everything here seems to be flying."

"Flying masses heading for the sun." he said. "Its rays are drawing the turbulent crowds from the darkness of the Church to freedom and light..."

"There's a kind of wild excitement about it, but I like things on a calmer, smaller scale, to be honest with you!" she released his hand.

"In that case I'll show you one of my favourite Madonnas," he said, as they walked towards the Church of the Knights of the Cross. "Baroque saints often have an erotic touch linked to the cult of the Virgin Mary. The Baroque artist lived an intense sensual life but concealed it behind a religious mask. The Queen of Heaven, often with a subtle smile and half-closed eyes, is telling us about the triumph of feminine beauty!"

"Wow, she's no saint!" Alice walked up to the stone Madonna and examined her closely. "Look! another one opening her robe to expose her bosom! She looks as though she is about to step into an invisible carriage."

"She's got a charming smile!" he said.

"And what delicate little feet! She's standing on a serpent's head. You find her smile charming — I think it's enticing!"

"How can I not succumb to your sensual wiles?" he declaimed, bowing to the statue.

Alice bowed to Blažej and laughed, "How not to succumb to your sensual wiles?"

Madonna, Knights
of the Cross Square

* * *

They paused in front of the Madonna in Celetná Street. Seeming to float in her draperies, she held her child in the crook of her right arm but her head was turned to the left.

"She's a pagan, she's smiling at her man! She's ready to dance and she's waiting for him to cross the room. She'll dance away with her child on her arm. There's nothing religious about her face, she looks like a girl at a village dance, a very beautiful one." She sighed, "I wish I was very beautiful!"

223

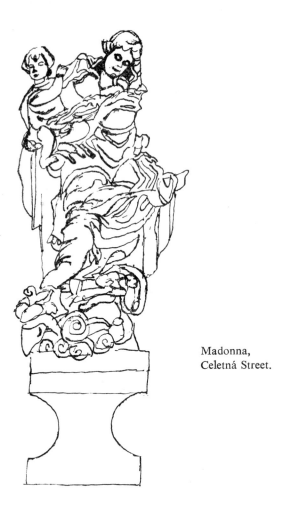

Madonna,
Celetná Street.

He removed a speck of dust from her cheek, "You're not so bad, a charming young English lady."

She burst out laughing.

* * *

Alice was silent as they walked across Náměstí Republiky towards the hotel.

Blažej looked at her, "You're very quiet!"

"I've been thinking about the Battle of White Mountain, the executions... the book-burning. Everything you've told me seems to be Protestant. Don't Czech Catholics see things differently?"

"I was brought up a Catholic and my Uncle Vilem's   224

a Moravian priest. He loves sitting in front of a glass of beer talking for hours about history. He thinks that Ferdinand's victory was the best possible thing for Bohemia. He hates the Hussites and looks on them as a troop of brigands and he says that Prague was a medieval Slavonic city before the Battle of White Mountain and that Baroque transformed it into a city of stately palaces, beautiful loggias, great court-yards and wonderful churches."

"But what about the persecutions?"

"He waves those aside! He thinks the Protestant nobles were a useless wishy-washy lot and not a bit patriotic and he thinks Ferdinand and the Jesuits brought unity and order to Bohemia after all the religious squabbles. According to him, Prague became a wonderful cosmopolitan city where German, Spanish and Italian could be heard in the streets."

"What do you think?" she asked.

Blažej hesitated, "I can't wave the persecution aside... What really interests me is how the three hundred years of darkness affected us Czechs..."

"How did they affect you?"

He groaned, "Another dreadful question and I'm not even trying to smoke! I think we were thrown back on ourselves. Forgotten by Europe and deprived of our language, we tended to regard ourselves as the centre of interest. By the way, there was none of that satire or refreshing irony which you had in England. We learned that later by reading English books. In our art we were always fighting for something, instead of just expressing art. Politically, we were under the heel of the conqueror so we saw politicians as being remote... on top of us, and because we felt helpless we fed on a lot of national myths."

"But national myths are important; how could you have survived without them?"

"We're Europeans, now! We shouldn't need them. We don't have to see all the Hussites as noble warriors when many of them became robbers and gangsters, and the Battle of White Mountain was a defeat."

225

"Yet out of the period of darkness came Czech Baroque, it expressed Czech identity."

"Yes, Baroque... a magic tomb over a murdered nation."

"I think it's got too much spirit to be called a tomb," she replied.

As they shook hands she looked into his eyes and smiled, "Someone or other called history a fickle whore! Who knows what's true and what isn't?"

He laughed, "You know, my job's a bit boring at times but I have to make a living. I've really enjoyed today, you make things come alive for me. How's your blister?"

She beamed at him, "It's gone!"

THE FIFTH
DAY·
REVIVAL

ALICE WAS IN A BUOYANT MOOD, beaming at passers-by and seeming to dance along with her curious half-skipping walk, as they went up Národní Street towards Jungmann Square.

"You look as fresh as a daisy," Blažej said, with a smile. All the same, he felt a bit puzzled. She was wearing white shorts and a baggy white tee-shirt with a huge Mickey Mouse on the back. Had she put in on back to front? Maybe it's a Western trend, he thought.

"We've had Primeval, Gothic, Renaissance and Baroque," she said cheerfully, "what's on today's menu?"

"Revival!"

"Revival of what?"

"The Czechs! You see, from the Battle of White Mountain to the end of World War 1, we were part of the Austrian Empire. Sometimes the Austrians let us be but at other times they showed an iron fist, as in July 1848, for example."

"Why, what happened in 1848?"

"Hell broke loose in Prague. There was an uprising against the Austrians, part of a wave of revolutions which swept Europe at that time. The Praguers built barricades in the centre of the town and there were five days of desperate street fighting. People were trampled to death as the imperial cavalry charged into the crowds and blood ran in the streets. Prince Windischgrätz, the imperial general and a stubborn reactionary, showed Prague no mercy, though probably the government in Vienna would have been prepared to negotiate. Windischgrätz had a personal reason for hating Prague for his wife hed been shot as she lent out of her window in Celetná looking down at the chaos in the street."

"Who shot her?"

"No one knows. It might have been a deliberate killing or the result of someone firing wildly into the air. Windischgrätz concentrated his troops on the Prague hills and gave the order for a cannon bombardment. Fires broke out all over Prague and on July 17th, the city was forced to surrender."

Blažej gave Alice a quick look and saw she was listening, "Women fought on the barricades and I've seen an engraving of one of them, a beautiful woman holding a gun. Almost thirty years after the uprising, a strange, desolate woman appeared in the Prague taverns. She was emaciated, barefoot and in rags. People called her Elizabeth of the Barricades because she told anyone willing to listen to her that she had fought in 1848."

"What happened after the rising?"

"There were political trials and many people went into exile. Hundreds lost their jobs and a policy of 'germanization' followed, with strict censorship."

As they walked into Jungmann Square, she looked with interest at a small market stall selling brilliant hand-made sweaters, "Fantastic colours!"

"One of the biggest problems for my people was language," Blažej continued, "the official language was German — it was the language of government, the civil service, the universities, the schools. Every official document, even a simple complaint or petition, had to be written in German, the language of a rich and powerful ruling class. Long before 1848, the Czechs had tried to find ways of expressing themselves in their own language…"

"The eighteenth century Singing Linden," she interrupted, "you never think I'm listening but I remember your lectures really well!"

He smiled, "At the beginning of the eighteenth century there was an unusual wooden theatre called The Shanty in Wenceslas Square which was a bustling horse market in those days. The actors performed plays in Czech about famous heroes of our history — John Hus, Jan Žižka, Wenceslas IV."

"Who was in the audience?"

"Servants, grooms, blacksmiths, tapsters… The actors had grandiose words about the future of the Czech nation and its future on the world stage which struck a chord in their listeners. The search for language gathered strength at the end of the eighteenth century when serfdom was abolished and people were no longer tied to the land. Thousands flocked into the cities looking for a better life and schools for their children. They needed a feeling of solidarity with other Czechs, a sense of belonging somewhere, and language was a key, probably the main one, to national identity..."

"Who's this?" she interrupted.

Blažej had stopped at a statue in the middle of the square, "Josef Jungmann, one of the linguists and scientists who re-created the Czech language. In the black years after 1848, scholars were trying to establish a separate Czech culture and Jungmann's books made a unique contribution. He transformed original Czech into a suitable language for scientific and cultural work."

Joseph Jungmann

She stared up at Jungmann trying to fathom his expression. He was staring down Národní, a pen in one hand and a scroll in the other, lost in thought. A sparrow perched on his shoe.

She chuckled, "I wonder what he's thinking about?"

"Words! He was sculpted by Ludvík Šimek and it's probably his best work. The statue was unveiled in 1878."

'I like the way his greatcoat ripples over his right knee," she said, walking round the statue, "but his pedestal looks clumsy, it's rather like a tomb."

Jungmann Square

"It was designed by architect A. Barvitius." Blažej took her arm and led her a little way down Národní Street, "He wanted it to be admired from a distance. It looks better from here."

Alice nodded, "The whole thing fits in well with the square."

"It doesn't dominate it and it's not overawed by the buildings," either, Blažej agreed, "there's a harmonious balance."

She waved to Jungmann as they walked down Národní street, "Do the Praguers like him?"

He laughed, "Hardly anyone knows who he was!"

* * *

"There's a story about the 1848 uprising which I really like," Blažej said, as they walked down Národní Street. "It's by a famous nineteenth century writer, Jan Neruda, and it's called Joseph, the Harp Player. Joseph was a picturesque vagabond who frequented the taverns in the Lesser Town where he played his harp and told stories for a living. His stories were strange, melancholy tales which touched the hearts of his listeners and his songs about freedom brought tears to people's eyes. He was a poor man and he lived very frugally but he had a wonderful black evening dress... what do you call it... coat-tails? He said that he'd bought it for a feast, a very special feast.

Jan Neruda was a student at that time and he often searched for Joseph in the taverns because he needed help with his studies, mainly with his translations from German to Latin. Joseph always corrected his work and handed it to him with a smile, 'There you are, tadpole!' he'd say. One evening the 'tadpole' hung around in the tavern waiting for the Harp Player to finish one of his sad tales and he saw that a sentence in Joseph's book had been underlined. It read, 'Can a neglected genius live better than the far-off suns?'

Then the revolution broke out in Prague and while the
233   soldiers were decimating the people on the barricades and the

ground was littered with corpses, the 'tadpole' saw a very elegant man approaching. He wore a top hat, immaculate evening dress and yellow gloves. It was Joseph, the Harp Player. He climbed in a dignified way onto the barricades with a pistol in each hand. A bullet hit him and he fell to the ground. His last words were, 'Thank you!'"

Alice chuckled.

Blažej looked at her in surprise.

She burst out laughing, "What an idiot!"

Blažej was silent for a while. Eventually, he began to mutter under his breath, "Cultural differences..."

* * *

"Isn't it all much ado about nothing, this fuss about language?" she asked, as they walked past the National Theatre towards the river. "After all, Czechoslovakia's only a small country."

Blažej reflected for a while, "Language is the bridge between oneself and the world, I'm a Slav and a thousand years of my history is contained in language. The culture of my people is in language; great things, small things, the enormous space of the subconscious; the variety of human emotions — anxiety, joy, fear, hope — everything's in language."

"Not necessarily," she argued, "what about images... painting...?"

He brushed her interruption aside, "Language is more than words, it creates reality by naming it. Also, the power of national spirit is conveyed through language, it represents the brain and character of a people. After Bohemia's defeat at the Battle of White Mountain in 1620, the German language was felt as the language of absolutism, the triumph of tyranny over the Czech Estates with their democratic constitution, at least, democratic for that age. Language became an important weapon in the long drawn-out struggle between the Czechs and the Hapsburgs and during the First World War when the Czech legions fought against the

Austrian armies on several fronts, they were fighting for identity, for language. Czechs working abroad at that time like Thomas Masaryk, succeeded in persuading America and its allies that the Czechs were a nation and should be recognized as such."

Alice shrugged, "You seem to be knocking the German language! What's wrong with it? I don't see..."

"German's a fine language," Blažej went on, unruffled, "But you see, at the time of the Hapsburg monarchy only a thin crust of the population here spoke German and it was mainly the language of bureaucracy. A bureaucrat thinks of a person in terms of his official file and if the file gets lost, the person gets lost, too! It was irrational that a huge Slav majority should have to bow to the language of a narrow ruling class. It created great tensions and it was absurd, a phantasmagoria..."

"But..."

"The Slavs reacted against the absurd world outside," Blažej went on, warming to his theme, "which is why so many Czech writers described their environment as dream. Prague was fulfilled by dreams — Rudolf II and his alchemists, the Rabbi Löw's Golem, the planets orbiting in Kepler's ellipsis, the sensual power of Czech Baroque..."

"So the Czechs dreamed away the centuries?" she said mockingly.

He looked at her ironically, "It's healthy to dream!"

* * *

They went up the ornate stairway of the National Municipal Museum, under its great dome and historic murals of Prague life, to the first floor.

"Nineteenth century inventiveness!" Blažej exclaimed. "This is Antonín Langweil's model of Prague. It's 5.76 metres long and 3.24 metres in width. It took Langweil eight years to make and I think it's one of Prague's wonders."

Alice walked round the model in its great glass case, entranced.

Antonín
Langweil's
model

"Langweil liked lithography," Blažej continued, "and he opened the first lithography workshop in Prague in 1819 but it didn't do well and he became an attendant in the University Library and devoted every spare moment to his hobby, finishing his model in 1837. What's so amazing about it is its meticulousness, the facades are absolutely exact with their house-signs, inscriptions, lanterns and numbers. He's even marked the ditches and the sewer inlets on the pavements."

"Look at the piles of wood and the ladders in the court-yards!"

"Look at the different roofs," he said, "red ridge-tiles, dark slate and tin, and grey shingle. He drew the facades and pavements on paper, then painted them and glued them on cardboard. The church domes and the chimneys and trees and shrubs were made of wood."

"Look at the tiny statues on Charles Bridge!"

Blažej nodded, "He carved them from ivory."

"Here's the Singing Fountain," she said, delightedly, "and look at that tiny duckpond!"

He pointed to St Vitus, "The Cathedral was still being built while Langweil was working away. Look at the little pathway from the Castle to the Belvedere Garden."

She smiled, "Rudolf II's private path... Look, there's washing drying on the Vltava beach."

"Yes, and look at the gutters and the tiny lanes. I came here once on a rainy afternoon with my telescope and imagined I was walking in those nineteenth century alleys..."

"Blažej," she interrupted, "a dwarf!"

"And look at Bethlehem Square with the former Bethlehem Chapel."

"What weird chimneys with holes on the sides. And there's the Powder Tower... but no Obecní Dům."

"It hadn't been built!"

"There are masses of trees in Hradčany Square and there's the Old Town Hall before it was damaged, it's got a beautiful little tower... I can see someone leaning out of a window
237   from At the Golden Unicorn."

Blažej smiled, "There's the entrance gate to the town. Look at the crumbling fortification walls."

"I like the balconies... and there's even a picture, probably a saint, on the wall of that mysterious little courtyard."

* * *

They strolled along the embankment in the warm sunshine and she looked across the Vltava River and up at St Vitus, a magnificent silhouette against the cloudless sky. She gasped as they went into Palacký Square, "What a statue, it's really over the top!"

František Palacký sat gravely on his plinth gazing at the trams passing and repassing on Masarykovo Nábřeží Street. Savage gods of war and destruction crouched below him and behind him supplicating naked forms crowded round a vast elongated figure of Death with hands like thorns. A figure on Palacky's right seemed to be tearing herself from the plinth as with cupped hands she shouted a warning to passers-by, and high above her the Muse of History raised her left hand triumphantly to heaven.

Blažej turned to Alice, "It's interesting to compare this monument with the Jungmann statue because there's a feeling here of something new coming in to sculpture, the spirit of Art Nouveau. It was sculpted by Stanislav Sucharda in 1898 and the monument was finished in 1912. There's furious energy in the wild figures and the composition's full of symbolism which tries to capture the spirit of a heroic past."

"Who was Palacký," she asked, smiling at his statue.

"Our greatest historian. He worked on his monumental book, The History of the Czech Nation in Bohemia and Moravia, from 1830 to 1876."

"Forty-six years on one book?" she looked incredulous.

"Yes, but what a book! Palacký studied whole libraries reading archives in eight languages in different countries. He was a brilliant scholar but our history didn't leave him in peace. Because he was contributing in a big way to the national revival here, he was looked on with great suspicion 238 by the Austrian secret police and was kept under constant surveillance. He used to avoid busy streets in Prague and even kept away from his friends because he didn't want to compromise them."

Alice frowned, "How can one book contribute to national revival?"

He reflected, "A nation without its history doesn't have much of a memory and I think Palacký gave us ours. The Nazis realized this when they occupied Prague so they took him away."

"One of these cranks lives next door to my parents," she said with a laugh, as they left the square, "he's been writing

František
Palacký
statue

historical novels for 40 years and his book-shelves are packed with them. He's about seventy now and he sits in his study all day reading his own novels."

Blažej smiled politely, "But Palacký wasn't a crank..."

"I know," she said quickly, "he was a historian, wasn't he? I know he wasn't a crank.

Blažej frowned, "Palacký wasn't a crank," he said firmly.

She stopped for a last look at the statue, "No, he certainly wasn't a crank," she said airily. "He was a historian after all, not a crank...," her voice trailed off.

* * *

As they went back to the embankment she looked dismissively at Palacký Bridge, "It's boring, it needs some statues."

"It had them at one time. Josef Myslbek, the artist who sculpted St Wenceslas made some mighty figures for this bridge. He had the broad flow of the Vltava River and the hills of Vyšehrad and Hradčany in mind and he knew there had to be something imposing and monumental to fit into this frame. He was fascinated by Slav myths and for forty years he sculpted tremendous figures, like Princess Libuše, from our legendary past."

"Where are they now?"

"The statues are up on Vyšehrad. They stood here until the end of the Second World War when the bridge was damaged by bombing."

Alice made a face, "Myslbek's St Wenceslas is certainly imposing but he's not my cup of tea."

Blažej laughed, "What's your cup of tea?"

"Something lighter... more graceful."

"Myslbek didn't want to express grace. His message was all about strength, enterprise and national potential. I think his statues are linked to another development at that time," he continued, "the invention of new machines and industrial expansion."

She looked at him doubtfully, "What a weird idea! What have machines got to do with statues?"

"Nationalism drives the human engine along," he replied, taking her arm. "While Myslbek was slogging away here carving his giants, a technical renaissance was going on in this country. In Mladá Boleslav, for example, Laurin and Klement set up a workshop similar to Henry Ford's and they began to turn out cars and motorbikes. The first plane motor in the Austrian Empire came from their workshop. There were other innovators, too. Jan Křižík, a cobbler's son, invented the predecessor of today's arc lamp, the tram and the first electric-powered locomotives. He became a factory owner and built electric power-plants throughout Austria. Another entrepreneur, Jan Škoda, set up a machine shop and a mammoth company emerged from it constructing bridges, cannons and locomotives. By the end of the nineteenth century, a class of Czech capitalists had grown up and the Czech lands became the most industrialized part of the Austrian Empire."

"What's all that got to do with nationalism?" she asked impatiently.

"Czech entrepreneurs were competing with Germans and they wanted to demonstrate Czech brain-power and initiative."

Alice looked at him provocatively, "Entrepreneurs are your heroes! You really admire them, don't you?"

He smiled, "Why not? They're risk-takers, ideas-people, adventurers."

* * *

Blažej pointed to the tall glass and concrete structure, "The National Technical Museum."

In the entrance-hall some children were sitting in front of a video-screen watching a Donald Duck cartoon. Donald Duck and Goofy were having a spot of bother with technology and Alice sat down chuckling to watch.

As they went into the section on Transport, she looked down from the first floor gallery at the vintage cars and locomotives on the ground floor. There were three galleries of exhibits and gliders, planes and a helicopter were suspended from iron girders which bisected the glass roof.

Blažej led the way down a flight of metal stairs, "It's a big museum, there are sections on Metallurgy, Sound Ecology, Astronomy and Mineralogy. I'd like to show you a few things from Czech workshops."

Alice looked at the 1912 motorbike from Laurin and Clement's workshop, "What a beauty!" she examined the spacious leather seat with its foot-rest in front of the machine, "I doubt whether the driver could see where he was going, though. I really like this car," she said excitedly, as she stopped to look at a Laurin and Klement two-seater in green and gold with a green leather seat, now slightly torn. "What a small engine, yet it could do 40 kilometres an hour!"

"It was the first car from their workshop," He looked at her curiously, "Do you drive?"

Vintage car

"Yes, a light motorbike, I'm going to bike repair classes in the autumn, I like engines. What brilliant Škodas!" she admired two 1924 models, one of them was a giant four-seater.

They wandered round the museum and stopped to look at some prints and photographs on the far wall.

He pointed to a photo of František Křižík, "Here's his first Prague tram!"

She smiled at the photo of the tram and its passengers. The tram was open at the sides. Two small girls in picture hats sat in the front seat and the driver and conductor, proud men with moustaches, posed for the camera.

"They had a right to be proud!" she compared Křižík's tram with the horsedrawn vehicles of 1875 and 1886.

"This 1903 locomotive was the first from a Czech factory," Blažej said, as they admired the trains, "There were horse-drawn vehicles long before, of course, like those on the Prague—Lany line."

She peered at the tiny wooden seats in the 1903 carriage, "Tough on the backside!"

He laughed, "Would you like a coffee-break?"

She nodded and they went up to the first floor.

She looked at the three small tables, "A miniscule cafe in a majesticule building!" Her coffee came with a tiny coconut biscuit perched on the saucer. There was a Czech folk singer on the radio. "The museum's brilliant," she said happily, "a really good atmosphere."

* * *

He showed her the building opposite them on Na Příkopě Street, "The Živnostenská Bank built from 1894—1896. I think it was probably more important for the Czechs than the building of the National Theatre."

"Why?"

"It was a saving bank and its branches grew rapidly in Czech cities. It owned factories and big companies and symbolized successful enterprise."

"The building's really trying to make an impression on me," she said, screwing up her eyes, "I like the corny attics."

"Look at the four panels on the facade designed by Jan Preisler in 1909. I don't think he's generally known in the West but he was an amazing artist, I call him the Czech Gauguin. He was a Modern Style painter in the Art Nouveau movement, a poet in paint. One of his favourite romantic motifs was a prince on a white horse riding towards his lady

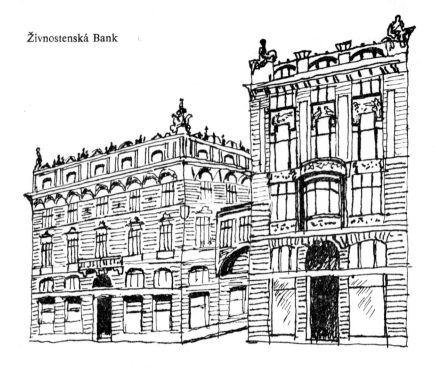

on the beach of a dramatic black lake. There's a monumental mosaic of his in the Palacký salon in Obecní Dům, all delicate greens, blues and mauves. It depicts a naked Venus accompanied by a peacock with dancing nymphs below."

"I can hardly believe it's a bank," she said, as they went into the lobby, "it's more like a theatre and I'm expecting the curtain to go up any minute!"

"It's Czech Neo-Renaissance, but it foretells Art Nouveau."

The huge banking hall had a ceiling of stained glass. In the centre stood a heraldic lion on a glowing orange background. Around him were stylized castles in a frame of delicate leaves, flowers and berries.

"It's really fantastic and emotional, isn't it?" she looked around enthusiastically.

"Yes," he replied thoughtfully, "a symbol of ever-changing life."

Under the ceiling, below coats of arms, graceful life-sized statues lined the walls — peasant-girls, hunters, ploughmen and a soberly dressed clerk. A few customers stood at marble   244 counters faced with oak under great archways. Leather semi-circular benches, solidly comfortable but elegant, were arranged in the middle of the hall. An armed guard watched from a first floor gallery flanked by two triumphant statues, a young man holding out a bunch of fruit and an elderly miner with a crystal. On the first floor there were great murals depicting rural life, Vltava boat-builders, and machine-tool makers before a smoking factory chimney.

"It's a riotous exhuberance! she said, laughingly.

"I don't agree," he replied a little stiffly, "it's certainly decorative but it's sober, too, it's a dedication to honest toil."

She nudged him, "I like it, it's a hymn to money!"

* * *

They walked past Charles University and turned into Kamzíková Street.

Blažej paused in front of an extraordinarily tall, narrow house, "Can you feel the atmosphere here?" he asked, "for me, it captures the spirit of fin de siécle, the last moments of the Austrian monarchy."

"The whole place seems a bit sinister," she replied, surveying the small enclosed lane.

"The biggest brothel in Prague, full of fallen girls, had its home here," he went on. "It was called U Goldschiedtů and it was the setting for Franz Werfel's novel, House of Sadness, in which he describes the feverish pace and the frenzied search for pleasure of a dying world, the world of decaying Empire."

She looked puzzled, "Why did he choose this spot?"

"Because he saw the decline of the Austrian monarchy as a long, drunken evening where whores and officers with moustaches and laced bodices, made merry. As they waltzed and laughed there was menace in the air — the old order was comining to an end. Werfel's story describes the night before Austria's fall and the fall of this house..."

Alice looked intrigued, "Long dresses, whispers... decadence?"

Blažej nodded, "This place has been a magnet for writers. You remember Egon Erwin Kisch, the famous reporter?"

She smiled and took his arm, "Very well! He lived in the Renaissance house with the two golden bears."

"One of his stories is called Tonka the Gallows," Blažej continued. "One night before the First World War, the police came to this brothel because they needed a whore willing to sleep with a condemned man. He was going to the gallows the following morning and he'd been granted his dying wish, a prostitute for his last night on earth. None of the whores in that house were willing to spend a night with a murderer but finally the beautiful Tonka agreed to go with the police as an act of mercy. But from then on she was doomed. Her former clients abandoned her, her luxurious existence disappeared overnight and she became a street walker. However, she couldn't make a living as a street walker because her story had spread through Prague and everyone shunned her like the plague..."

"What happened to her?" Alice interrupted.

"Sadly, she died of hunger. But she got her reward for her act of mercy..."

"How?"

"When she got to Heaven she found she was standing in front of a desk in a huge police-station. The police greeted her politely and handed her an admission slip which read, "Enter, dear Tonka, the Gallows.""

* * *

"They've got some really good salads here, you can help yourself to as much as you like," he said, as he led her into the buffet adjoining the Palace Hotel.

She looked appeciatively at the big bowls of salads and pulses with an array of sauces and mayonnaise. They took their plates over to the window where they sat on high stools at a marble table in a small room glittering with mirror-glass.

Blažej smiled, "I've got a colleague who's genius at building salad mountains. He's a lecturer here and rather hard-up, so he comes here for lunch and piles his plate until it looks like the Himalayas. It still only costs 40 crowns here, however much you take. But this is July 1992... who knows what it will cost next year."

"It's cheap for me, less than £1 for lunch. Are prices going up here?"

"They're shooting up, but it's necessary..."

"Why?" she interrupted.

"We're moving into free enterprise," he said briskly, "it's bound to bring teething problems."

"But..."

He cut across her, "I'd like to get back to nineteenth century enterprise if you don't mind. There were extraordinary developments in art as well as business, Art Nouveau, for example..."

"I love it!" she said enthusiastically, "I often go to Brighton for the day to do some drawing. It's full of Art Nouveau and there's a great little museum there but people often miss it because they're hurrying to the beach."

"Prague's sparkling with Art Nouveau! It was a style which brought new, young expression. Artists found inspiration in nature, in plants, animals, fish, and they took a lot from Egyptian and Japanese Art and Celtic ornaments." He hesitated, "Perhaps I'm telling you what you already know?"

She smiled, "I don't mind, I've probably forgotten anyway! When did Art Nouveau start and when did it end?"

He reflected, "The movement got going here in the Nineties of the last century and it flourished until the First World War. After the war, sterner styles took over. I'd like to show you two little Art Nouveau gems of mine if you're ready."

Alice laughed. "Do you own them?"

"Only while I'm showing them to clients!"

They walked down Kaprová Street and he stopped in front of a shop selling plastic kitchenware. High on the wall, bound with threads of iron, stood an Egyptian god with outstretched arms. A halo of intricate wrought-iron burst

behind his head like a sun and on either side of him were grey-green fish. Two more floated above his head.

"Look at his thick hair!" she said, "his arms are painfully thin, yet they're decorative at the same time."

Blažej took her round the corner and showed her a matching panel, a fish-bordered goddess, on the side of the shop. Alice got out her drawing pad and began to sketch her.

"Both panels are very decorative," he said thoughtfully, "and I think there's something spiritual in them, too."

She looked at him in surprise, "I wonder why the artist was so keen on fish?"

"We're standing in Carp street!"

* * *

He drew up at the main railway station and she looked up at the monumental glazed arch and the turbulent statues of men and women accompanied by eagles, on the towers.

She looked impressed, "It's a really bold building."

"It's known as the Wilson Station and it was built between 1901 and 1909. Josef Fanta who helped build our National Theatre, designed it and I think it's his best Art Nouveau work."

He guided her into the vast domed concourse ringed with statues. There was a stained glass window over the entrance arch and decorative white foliage against a vivid blue background on the walls.

"Wow! nothing's quite what it seems in Prague! A bank like a theatre and this place looks like a set for grand opera." She walked to the end wall and looked at two statues of semi-naked women with huge breasts reclining in a riot of foliage, "'Prague, Head of the Kingdom'," she translated, looking at the Latin inscription.

Blažej smiled, "It was a cheeky claim when this station was built because we were still taking our orders from the Austrians, but Prague was trying to equal Vienna in business and art. My town only had a population of about 400,000 at the time but it was a bustling place in the Empire rivalling Budapest and Cracow. It had its National Theatre and National Museum and a lively intelligentsia. The Modernist Manifesto came out in 1895 and the following year, the anti-establishment Art Nouveau Almanack was published. At the dawn of this century the time was ripe here for new artistic styles — a self-confident city willing to patronize the arts and new construction techniques based mainly on steel, cast-iron and glass. The techniques had been used in London half a century earlier to build the Crystal Palace and in 1887 to build Paris' Eiffel Tower. Also artists in Prague were getting impatient with heavy pseudo-historical buildings expressing national greatness and identity and people like Fanta wanted to experiment with new styles."

They went into the big, shabby station restaurant with its

high vaulted ceiling. People were drinking beer at tables with rather soiled red cloths and in one corner a group of middle-aged men were singing Beatles's songs. Alice looked at an elderly woman swathed in shawls, at the next table. She was taking a porcelain bowl covered with a white cloth, and an enamel kettle out of an immense black bag.

Blažej chuckled, "She doesn't trust the refreshment here! What would you like to drink?"

"Beer, please."

Two Romanies approached their table and stood looking at the vacant chairs. Blažej waved them away.

Alice looked concerned, "What's wrong with them?"

"They're Gypsies."

She looked at him sharply but he was staring at the table-cloth with a forbidding frown.

He looked up suddenly, "Please look at the mosaic panels, they're pure Art Nouveau."

Large, oblong panels decorated the walls and pillars. They depicted dark freen foliage and trees bursting with golden fruit. Girls in gauzy drapery seemed to float against a background of blossom and on the wall by their table a red-trousered huntsman with a bow moved through a dark green forest. On the mosaic facing him, a beautiful girl with a dreamy expression rowed her boat through water-lilies.

Alice smiled, "Her drapery's tumbling into the stream!" She got up and wandered round the restaurant examining the panels, "They're gorgeous!"

"I thought you'd like them but the whole place needs a coat of paint," he looked at the grubby walls with distaste.

"Things are better left alone," she said quickly, "in no time at all some entrepreneur will come along and tart the whole place up with lots of plastic and fluorescent lights and the atmosphere will be ruined."

He looked puzzled, "Tart up...?"

"I mean someone will give it a face-lift. Everything will be clean, modern and hygienic and the atmosphere will be ruined."

250

Blažej looked startled, "But Prague needs a face-lift, the town's crumbling."

She gulped her beer and stared up at the dusty metal chandeliers, "I like Prague as it is."

They sat in silence for a few minutes.

Art Nouveau panel,
Wilson Station

Suddenly she looked at him indignantly, "I've got no time for racial prejudice," she said. "We've got Romanies in England and we try to respect their nomadic life-style."

"England's not Czechoslovakia," he said mildly.

"I didn't like the way you looked at them," she said crossly.

"Perhaps you like thieves? Gypsies will rob you whenever they get a chance."

"I've never been robbed!"

He leaned towards her, "I'm not prejudiced, I have to protect my clients..."

"I can look after myself!"

"I'm not saying all Gypsies are dangerous but go to Wenceslas Square and have a look at the gypsy prostitutes and pimps and you should see some of the gypsy settlements in Slovakia. Their villages look like something out of the Middle Ages. There are more than three million Gypsies in this country and they're multiplying! They've got no documents and they can't read or write. No one knows how they make a living."

She got up abruptly, "They've got to make a living somehow!"

* * *

Blažej pointed to the house-sign, "The House At the Black Mother of God."

She stared frowning at the Mother, a black-faced doll swathed in a glittering golden robe, "It's an amazing house-sign and it rings a bell... yes, Kyork Arabian lived here with his skeletons, only a stone's throw from the Prague Witch."

He smiled, "It's Josef Gočár's first Cubist building. Along with other Czech architects, like Pavel Janák and Josef Chochol, Gočár was experimenting with a unique form of architecture, new for Europe and the world, and Prague was its home. Cubism only existed in paintings at that time..."

"Which time?" she interrupted.

252

"Cubist architecture began around 1895 and went on, alongside Neo-Renaissance, Art Nouveau and other styles, until about 1914. The Czech Cubists got their inspiration from painters like Picasso and Braque and they were fascinated by the way their paintings depicted geometrical shapes in space. Architects here wanted to create original architecture which would make a clean break from the past — an architecture for this century. They threw traditional decoration and design in the bin and replaced it with abstract form. They were delighted with Picasso' paintings of Spanish houses, small cubes in parched rocky landscape."

He led her into the house and showed her the staircase, "Circles and squares," he said enthusiastically, "it's decorative, isn't it?"

When they returned to the street, Alice frowned up at the

At the Black Mother
of God

facade, "It's a dreadful colour... that mustard yellow, it should be white. And the building's so severe..."

"You're caught up in Art Nouveau," he said with a smile.

"Why shouldn't I be?"

"I'm not trying to talk you into Cubism," he said mildly, "I just want to show it to you. Please, will you put up with me for a little while? I'd like to show you a house by Josef Chochol."

He parked the car in Neklanová Street and pointed to number 7, "Praguers must have found this house extra-ordinary at the time of the Austrian monarchy. Chochol and the other Cubists wanted to express Czech identity just

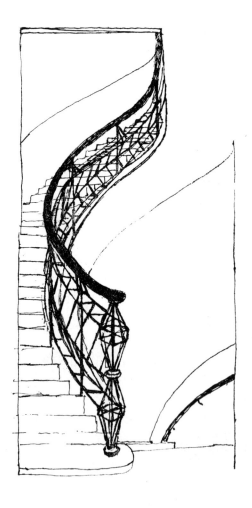

At the Black Mother of God — staircase

as much as their predecessors had done but they wanted to do it without delving into history. Their buildings were defiantly contemporary."

She looked unmoved at Chochol's house, "It's an exercise in geometry!"

No. 7,
Neklanova Street

"But why not? Chochol defined the cube as the basic shape of matter and gave it dynamism by adding diagonal planes. What really mattered to the Cubists was the artist's capacity for abstraction rather than the function of a building or the materials used in making it. The architect Pavel Janák said as much in 1910 in one of his essays."

She looked unconvinced, "What about the interiors?"

"There's interesting detail on windows and staircases but on the whole they concentrated on facades and their interiors were often rather traditional."

"But they designed some fantastic furniture, didn't they?" She smiled, "I've seen photos of it — sofas with backs like mountain peaks, cupboards with waists, wood which looks like pleated paper and a lot of crystal shapes."

Blažej nodded, "I think there's fantasy in their buildings, too. A new rhythm in matter and strange, mysterious space."

* * *

"I love this bridge," he said, leaning over the parapet and looking down at the broad river, "It's a modern poem."

The arches of the long bridge, faced with ribbons of stone, seemed to flow like waves across the Vltava River. The parapet was built of rectangular stone cubes, alternating with iron rectangles decorated with metal circles.

"This is the Hlávkův Bridge," he continued, "I came here once on a rainy day and it seemed more beautiful than ever. There was no one around and I could admire it properly. The bridge seemed to ripple away from me like a snake." He smiled, "It's got hidden violins in it, it's a song."

She lent against the parapet looking at the bridge's extraordinary length, "It's very dramatic, it seems to float! Who designed it?"

Pavel Janák with engineer F. Menzel and it was built between 1909 and 1911, "I think it's unique, probably the only Cubist bridge in the world."

She climbed down the grassy river bank and admired the massive three-quarter length decorative stone reliefs of naked men and women on either side of the bridge. She looked at one closely. He was a powerful figure in profile, his huge hands half-buried in stone.

"The figures seem to have something of Art Nouveau about them," she said, surprised.

"Prague's experiments in architecture, Art Nouveau, Cubism, Constructivism, influenced each other but the trend was towards pure geometrical form and peeling away inessentials."

She climbed up the bank and lent against him, resting her head on his shoulder, "I like masses of decoration."

"I prefer austere buildings."

Hlávkův Bridge

"Do you want to live an austere life?" she murmured.

"Maybe. I don't want inessentials in my life, they're boring."

She watched some swans walking awkwardly towards them looking for crumbs.

"What's essential for you?"

He considered her question for a while. Then he laughed and took her arm, "A good client. An enthusiastic one is like manna from heaven!"

Work
and Humanity

As they left the bridge, he paused before two groups of statues, "They're called Work and Humanity and they were sculpted by Jan Stursa just before First World War. There were times before our Revolution when I felt a bit low and I used to come and look at these figures. I found them cheering — full of joy and vitality."

Alice looked carefully at the groups of strong, lively men and women, "Yes, they're optimistic, I feel they're going places."

"There was quite a lot of apathy around in the bad old days," he said, "and these figures were a real contrast for me, light-hearted but proud and energetic at the same time."

"I like the incredible Cubist plinths, they're like pleated paper!"

He smiled, "Am I converting you to Cubism?"

* * *

"My feet are tired," she said, in a burst of irritation.

"I only want to show you a couple more places and then I've got a nice restaurant lined up for you."

He found a grassy patch by the river and went off to the car returning with a plastic bag containing lemonade, two beakers and some cakes wrapped in a white cloth.

He offered her one, "They're really Czech!"

She cheered up, "Did you make then?"

He shook his head, "Can you cook?"

"I know how to boil eggs!"

He sat down next to her, "Do you mind if I give you a short lecture?"

She smiled and took another cake, "They're good! Please steam ahead."

"The Austrian Empire split apart at the seams during the First World War and there was a spontaneous revolution here. The whole nation refused to take an oath of allegiance to the Emperor and on October 28th 1918, the independent Czechoslovak Republic was born. It's known today as our First Republic and it lasted 21 years. In France, the victorious powers were re-making the European map from the old, crumbling Empires and new states were created in Central Europe with scope for political activity. But their position was always precarious because they needed support from powerful friends. Tsarist Russia had been swept away in 1917 and America had retreated into isolation. Britain and France didn't take much interest in Central Europe because the unity of the Central European market had been broken when the Austrian monarchy collapsed. Many Czechs had high hopes of the Versailles Settlement but perhaps your historian, G. Barraclough was right when he called the post-war years' the era of illusion."

He paused and filled their beakers with lemonade, "By the peace treaties after the war, the Czech lands were united with Slovakia to the East, a country which had been under the Hungarian heel for a thousand years..."

"I've heard that the Slovaks want to break away and form their own republic," she interrupted.

"Some do... but we survived as a unified state during the First Republic in spite of tensions, so maybe we'll manage to hang together now. The First Republic had its problems in the years between the wars — the minorities for example. Three million Germans in the Sudetenland and other border areas, 500,000 Hungarians, 400,000 Ruthenians, 100,000 Poles..."

"And Romanies," she chipped in. "There were a lot of them in Slovakia at that time, weren't there? You seem to have left them out."

"Gypsies? They've got a different life-style," he said reluctantly.

She looked at him critically, "But your Republic survived a lot of differences, didn't it? At least, until Hitler came along?"

He nodded, "Czechoslovak politics consisted of a balancing act between different groups and although there was a lot of in-fighting, we managed to build up a democratic state. We were fortunate in our first president, Thomas

260

Garrigue Masaryk, or TGM as he's often called. He was a scholar, philosopher and a writer."

"You seem to have a habit of putting writers in the Castle!"

"Writers have been very important in our history, they've given our spirits a boost in bad times which is why the Nazis and the Communists wanted to silence them." He stretched himself out on the grass, "Masaryk set a good example in those years between the wars, he lived a frugal and moral kind of life and tried to keep above the dirt of politics. He wanted to encourage what he called 'Czechism' which he saw as humane, democratic politics, and a cultured life-style."

"You make him sound like a saint!"

"I'm sure he had his faults... he could be a boring old moralizer at times! But please don't quote me when you're talking to Czechs, you'd be trampling on a holy myth. Masaryk and our First Republic are still a big inspiration for us. When Václav Havel became President, he went all out to promote the Masaryk image, he even learnt to ride a horse like TGM."

"It's strange," she reflected, "I don't seem to have seen any statues of Masaryk."

"There were a lot at one time, even small towns and villages had statues of him and they named their streets after him, too. But we had the Nazi occupation and then Communism. The statues were destroyed to blot Masaryk out of our history. But the memory of the First Republic lived on. There were remarkable advances at that time, like the big boom in industry and trade, for example. We had a new national currency and the Czechoslovak crown became a sought-after commodity. We'd inherited roughly 70% of the industrial production of the former Austrian Empire and the Czechs were more hardworking than the other Slavs — the Poles and Croatians, for example."

She gave him a sidelong look, "Were the Czechs born that way? I mean, as hard workers?"

Blažej stiffened, "National characteristics do exist," he

said coolly. "During the First Republic we took tenth place in the world industrial league and we were famous for our engineering plants and our successful light industry; glass, shoes, textiles and our breweries at Plzeň and Budějovice. We produced all sorts of high quality goods from pins to locomotives. I think Thomas Baťa's store in Wenceslas Square, all glass, iron and concrete, symbolizes our success at that time. He was a Wallachian shoemaker who sewed slippers by hand and rose to be a great entrepreneur. Another place

Baťa Store

which showed our prosperity was the Lucerna-Barrandov complex, built by the Havels. It was a unique place for that time, combining urban life with the charm of nature. We had a cultured President, a prosperous middle-class and artists who wanted to move from Cubism to new experiments in architecture and design. There were more Constructivist and Functionalist buildings here between the wars than in Britain or France, or even America and artists came from all over the world to study our Modern Movement."

* * *

They sat at a table on the Barrandov terrace, perched on its high cliff above the Vltava River.

"This is the spot where middle-class people spent their Saturday nights and Sunday afternoons," Blažej explained, "Behind this restaurant is a dream factory, the Barrandov Film Studio which fed beautiful dreams to Cinderellas from working-class tenements, dreams of rich young men in sports cars."

Alice looked glumly at her ice-cream, "Didn't poor Cindermen dream about women in sports cars?"

He smiled.

She stared at him, "It's quite strange," she said, "I've never heard you speak admiringly about ordinary women. They're either whores or high up on pedestals..."

He interrupted her, "The motto of the First Republic was 'live now, pay later' and entertainment was the thing! Writers proclaimed that life should be a poem — five working days and Saturday nights and Sunday mornings for poetry."

"So that Cinderella could hook an entrepreneur?"

"Not necessarily. One of Barrandov's most successful films was about a little clerk who worked in a Travel Agency. Once a month, and only once a month, he dressed carefully and came here to Barrandov or went to a posh Prague night-club. He'd search for a lovely woman sitting on her own and sit down next to her. Then he'd look into her eyes and tell her tales of effervescent palm trees, blue seas, the cicada's song, strange towns, romantic ports and curious, colourful skies. Towards the end of the evening he'd ask his companion to close her eyes for a while, saying that he'd meet her outside in the starlight…"

"Did he?"

"No, he escaped. Then for another month he'd drudge away at his boring, everyday job as a clerk.

"What a con-man!" she said disdainfully.

Blažej laughed, "But he'd entertained her! Anyway, I haven't finished my story… After one of his romantic evenings his lady was so fascinated by his stories and his charm that she decided to hunt for him in the maze of Prague. Then the fatal day came… she walked into his Travel Agency and discovered that her elegant companion of the night was nothing but a grey little clerk."

Barrandov Terrace

Alice looked indignant, "What a snob she was! Does it matter what a man does for a living?"

"But she wanted to meet him again."

"Then why didn't she?"

"He felt that her high position in society was way beyond him. And he was happily married to a good little wife."

Alice spluttered.

As they left the terrace she turned to Blažej, "I'm beginning to think you're a chatterbox."

"And you're a left-wing nut!"

* * *

"It's a hive for office workers!" she exclaimed.

"Do you find it boring!" Blažej said in surprise, "I think it's a magnificent palace of modern architecture. It's a Constructivist building designed by A. Beneš and J. Kříž and was built between 1926 to 1935. It's always been known as the Electric Company Building but it's now the Transport Centre."

Electricity Building

She made a face, "You can certainly see it's function!"

"But look at its clean lines, there's nothing superfluous. And it's so clever. Look at the repeating patterns in the window design! On the first floor, long rectangles which are repeated on the fourth floor of the largest block. The windows below are divided into two vertical rectangles above horizontal ones."

One of the Directors, a genial man, came up to them in the lobby and offered to take them round. Alice stared up at the symmetrical, concrete balconies on three floors. A mellow light fell into the well of the building from the windows above.

"Constructivism grew out of Cubism," Blažej said, turning to her enthusiastically, "but the Constructivist architects believed that the form and appearance of a building must be determined by the materials used in building it and that its actual construction should hit the eye. Concrete permitted huge, simple, geometrical forms and Karel Teige, a Twenties theoretician, hit the nail on the head when he called Constructivism, 'Ostentatious Simplicity'."

The Director showed them a fine room with a parquet floor, "The clerks could come here at five o'clock and dance!" He pointed to another room, "And they could have dancing-lessons in there."

As they left the building, a small dog appeared from nowhere and sniffed at Blažej's heels. He turned round and kicked it irritably and it cringed away yelping.

Alice looked at him aghast, "How can you kick a little defenceless animal?"

"I'm not interested in animals."

"But I am," she said furiously, "If I'd known you were so horrible, I'd never have hired you as a guide."

He didn't reply and they walked on without speaking.

* * *

266

Blažej beamed at the building, "The Müller Villa!"

She admired the clean pure lines of the flat-roofed building which seemed to flow down into the hillside.

"It was designed by Adolf Loos and built in 1929. He had a lot of bother getting planning permission from the municipality but he persevered and got his way after eleven applications."

A burly caretaker opened the door for them and took them into the living-room.

Blažej turned to Alice, "Loos started his career as a theoretician and his book, 'Speaking into the Void,' caused a stir in intellectual circles. He built very few houses and I think this building's his greatest. His value for the world is in ideas."

She looked round the gracious, airy room, "What were his ideas?"

"He was the inventor of the Raumplan, meaning Space-Plan. It was the idea that the rooms of a house should flow

Müller
Villa

267

into each other in a creative way. His ideal was Roman and Greek architecture and he had a vision of unbroken inner space, creating a feeling of calm and harmony." Blažej took a piece of paper from his pocket, "I'll read you a quote from Loos because he puts it better than I can: 'In my house, a ground floor, first floor and other floors don't exist... In my work there is only correlative, continuous space...'"

The caretaker showed them the study with its fine window and took them up to the bedrooms.

Alice looked excited, "I can feel what Loos was getting at, its all up here and down there! It's bewildering at first, everythings on different connected levels, but it's refreshing."

Blažej had been feeling the weight of a week with Alice and her incessant questions, she was hard work. But looking at her enthusiastic face, his spirits rose. "The house is a cascade of different levels," he said, "and it's designed for creative living and good communication. Although it's austere in its way, it's a house to be lived in. At the time it was built, young Prague architects were rushing around with all sorts of flamboyant designs and Loos told them that there's a lot of difference between an architect and a painter. A painter can provoke, shock, disturb... but an architect should be a craftsman who should always remember that he's building for human beings. Loos once described the architect as a bricklayer who knows Latin."

They sat down on a leather couch in one of the smaller upstairs rooms and the caretaker walked up and down gesticulating.

"What's he saying?" she asked.

"He's telling us that this room was specially designed so that a lady and gentleman could get away from other people and have a quiet chat."

She giggled.

"And he says that there was an extraordinary mechanism here which regulated the room like a drawer. If the family of friends wanted fresh air, they pressed a button and were propelled onto the outer wall, into space."

"Can we press it?" she asked eagerly.

"No, he says it's broken. He says that Loos' fee for designing this house was 50,000 crowns, a lot of money in 1929. However, Loos wanted his Raumplan idea to benefit the less well-off, too. He realized that the future lay with smaller family houses."

Alice looked round the sober room, "Didn't Loos like decoration... ornaments?"

"No, he regarded ornament as a crime. He argued that a house would satisfy its owners by its proportion and design. He felt that architects at that time concentrated too much on facades and neglected the inner space of buildings and therefore the people who had to live in them. He believed that the right kind of house would encourage the right kind of life."

They went up onto the flat roof and the caretaker showed them the roofs on different levels at the back of the house. Alice lent over the parapet looking at the leafy surroundings. "It's a fantastic house, like music," she said happily.

Blažej smiled, "Loos was an eccentric genius who spent a lot of his life on trains — London to Paris, Paris to Vienna, Vienna to Prague... In the 1890s he created some ripples in Vienna with his lectures and articles and he was successful there. But he liked Prague and found it a favourable spot for developing his ideas. The government was investing money in buildings, there was an exciting intellectual climate and a public which was coming round to austere, experimental styles."

As the caretaker showed them out of the house, Alice shook his hand and slipped him a note.

"How much did you give him," Blažej asked, as they walked to the car.

"Two hundred crowns."

"Two hundred!" he burst out, "that's far too much!"

"Why, what should I have given him?"

"Ten crowns."

269   "But that's nothing... he was nice to us."

Blažej whistled, "Two hundred crowns, that's roughly £4 in your money. The average wage here is about £74 a month and many people have to live on far less. My friend Zdeněk, an architect, has to live on £60 a month and there's no way he can buy furniture for his new flat. Why didn't you let me advise you?"

She was silent and they walked along in mutual irritation.

After a while she looked at him provocatively, "Guides have to be tipped, don't they? So what should I give you when I leave?"

He turned to her haughtily, "You could try an apology!"

They walked on without speaking. Then she turned to him in mock contrition pulling such a grotesquely rueful face that he could hardly suppress a smile.

"Blažej, I didn't mean to offend you..."

"You won't have to give me anything," he said, "I'll spread my wings and soar into space when you've gone."

She looked startled.

"My bonus will be your departure," he chuckled.

* * *

"Mammoth hunters lived here!"

Alice stared down from the headland at St Vitus' Cathedral and the Prague panorama with its glittering spires, "What's that strange building down to the left? It looks a bit like a church."

Blažej smiled, "I call it a mad confectioner's dream!"

She looked at him enquiringly.

"I'll take you there tomorrow."

"Where are we?" she asked.

"We're in Nad Patankou Street, on one of Prague's seven hills and this is the Baba Colony. A group of inventive architects decided to use this site to build a Functionalist community."

"During the First Republic?"

"Yes, they designed the colony between 1928 and 1932 for well-to-do Praguers sharing the same interests and cultural   270 tastes. The houses were quite expensive, partly because of the stone blocks and other materials used in construction and also because the buildings had to be linked up to the city's water-main and power supply."

She looked at the white house on their left, "It's like a ship braving the ocean. It's got a passenger-deck and port-holes and there's a little deck for the captain, too."

"Pavel Janák who organized the colony wanted to build houses without traditional decoration so he used ribbon windows, port-hole windows, porticos and balustrades to humanize the sober facades." He took her arm and pointed to the other side of the street, "You see the gallery? It was designed for modern statues which would complement the severity of the building."

"It's a brilliant spot for a colony, really leafy," she admired the flowering shrubs and the trees lining the street and scattered over the hillside.

Blažej looked pleased, "This house on the edge of the headland belonged to Edvard Beneš, our second president,"

Baba Colony

he said, as they strolled down the street, "he had a wonderful view of St Vitus and the town from his roof."

Alice looked at the house critically, "It's a fine house but the bedrooms must be dark, the windows are tiny."

"They were only intended for sleeping. A lot of these houses have balconies leading off the bedrooms with access to the flat roofs. Although the rooms are quite small they were designed to give their occupants the feeling that they were flowing out into space..."

"The Raumplan idea?" she interrupted.

"There's a suggestion of Raumplan here," he replied, "because some of the houses have rooms on different levels. Pavel Janák was inspired by Loos and these homes were designed with people's physical and spiritual health in mind. Like Loos, Janák believed that the pure form of a building, the functional use of space and the large living-room windows would encourage a good life-style."

"I like the way the windows go up the walls in different sizes! And these fences are extraordinary, too," she looked at the metal fences, divided into small squares, which enclosed the gardens.

"They were used in the interiors as well," he explained. "The big challenge for the architects lay in keeping the purity of the stone cubes and providing some light, fantastic touches at the same time, like the ribbons of small windows just above the ground."

She looked at the port-hole windows dotted on the severe facades, "Joky cubes!"

Blažej nodded, "The colony has to be seen as a whole because the architects who were mainly left-wingers, had a vision of a complete community, a kind of intellectual collective. They planned a kindergarten and job opportunities for women. They wanted to avoid an exclusive image so they didn't built luxurious facilities like swimming-pools because they thought that people should use public ones."

Alice turned to him, smiling, "I think this is your spot, even though left-wingers designed it! It's austere but light-hearted at the same time. I can imagine you up there on one of the captain's bridgeheads surveying Prague through your telescope and giving a lecture to the crew."

He laughed, "When I'm a millionaire... I'm glad you like this place, very few tourists see it. It mirrors the intellectual climate of the First Republic — sophisticated, experimental, bold. The colony has influenced architects across the world, including Le Corbusier. I think the houses are Functionalist in the best sense because they were built to support and serve a way of life."

She looked at him critically, "What sort of life?"

Blažej put his hand on her shoulder and breathed into her ear, "Give people the right kind of architecture and they'll write poems!"

* * *

They went across a wooden veranda into a small restaurant overlooking the river.

"This is the Vltava Tavern," he said, leading her to a table, "It's known for its fish suppers."

"I'm not a total vegetarian," she said, looking at the generous helpings at the next table.

Blažej ordered trout and an omelette.

After a while he looked at her thoughtfully, her face was slighty freckled from the sun, "You'll have a lot to tell your family when you get home..." He hesitated, "And William, of course."

"William?" she said sharply.

"You told me you had a boyfriend..." He coughed, "Sorry... friend."

"If William was here he'd spend his whole time rushing around trying to do business. He's got about as much feeling for art as..." she stared moodily at the remnants of her trout,"... a goldfish!"

"Then why...?"

"Why what?"

273   He coughed again, "It's none of my business..."

"Why won't you talk to me?" she asked, her temper rising, "You never ask me any personal questions. You go on and on lecturing me about this and that but you don't seem interested in me at all." She leaned across the table, "I'm not just a client, I'm a person!"

"Yes, but a client first and foremost."

She glared at him, "Is that all?"

"Alice, I've got my living to make."

"I suppose when I leave you'll be talking to your next client in just the same way? One Alice is as good as another?"

"That's not what I said."

She glared at her plate, "You're as stiff as a frozen carrot!" she burst out loudly.

The group at the next table were staring at them.

Blažej felt prickles of irritation across his back and shoulders. He clenched and unclenched his hands under the table.

"I know you think I'm a pain," she said, leaning forward again so that their noses almost touched. "What I'd really like to do is explore on my own from now on..."

He got up abruptly, "If you're disappointed with your guide, then go and find another!" He strode to the door, "You'll get no more so-called lectures from me..." he searched for words, "unless you come after me in a golden chariot!" He walked out, then put his head round the door, "With six white horses," he added.

Shaking with rage, Alice marched up to the reception desk and got out some money. The waiter waved it aside, "The bill's paid, Miss."

She walked out onto the embankment and into a light shower. In spite of her fury, she noted the beauty of the river in the rain, its metallic surface punctured with a myriad raindrops. She walked past the moored boats, many of them floating restaurants packed with diners, and past the towering nineteenth century houses on Masarykovo Nábřeží Street with their ornamental stone balconies, and then turned right into Národní Street. Her anger ebbed away.

She wandered past the National Theatre and past the shop selling English tea and up to the Lucerna. I'll go and look at the Horologe again, she thought. She crossed the road and went down tiny cobbled streets towards the Old Town Square. The cafes and pubs were full and she saw two lovers kissing in a window. She felt the rain flattening her hair and cooling her face. I'm just an item in his itinerary, she muttered to herself but the thought didn't carry conviction. Snapshots flew through her mind: Celtic bards by a roaring fire... a green frog standing on its head... Wenceslas IV stumbling through the bushes with Zuzana... Golem lurching through the streets... Věk walking sadly down a country lane, his hopes shattered... A tear rolled down her cheek and she scrubbed it away with her fist.

She joined a group of tourists waiting for the Horologe to chime the hour and then she walked impatiently past the Old Town Hall and into the square. A row of swarthy men stood next to their carriages waiting for customers and she noticed that the horses were wearing curious white ear-caps. Impulsively, she jumped into the first carriage, a bright vehicle in yellow and white.

The driver cracked his whip and they moved swiftly past the Baroque splendour of St Nicholas Church and down Pařížská Street towards the river. She sat mournfully in her seat.

Suddenly the sun burst through the clouds and its dazzling light caught the decoration on the great Art Nouveau houses. The driver returned to his pitch by the Old Town Hall along Dlouhá Street and they trotted back into the square.

She had a flash of inspiration and fishing in her bag she found Blažej's card. She handed it to the driver and he looked at it doubtfully. She pressed some notes into his hand.

Her spirits rose as they trotted briskly past the National Museum. They passed tall houses, then rows of smaller houses and shops and taverns. At last, in the distance, she saw the dark apartment blocks of Prague 4. The summer wind blew into her face with a swirl of dust and she sneezed and got out her small roll of toilet paper. If he's not in, I'll leave him a note, she thought.

The driver began to rein in his horses in front of one of the concrete blocks but she leaped out impatiently. She rolled over, got up unhurt and found Blažej's bell. No one answered.

Then she tried the great metal entrance gates. They were locked. He lives in a fortress, she thought. A man carrying a shopping bag appeared and unlocked the gates and she slipped through quickly and took the lift to the sixth floor.

She knocked on Blažej's door.

Silence.

She sat down in the corridor to wait...

*

Blažej parked his car and walked, slightly stooped and with his habitual frown, down the long treeless street lined with concrete apartment blocks towards his flat. Suddenly, he was rooted to the spot. A carriage drawn by two white horses, a surreal vision in that sprawling shabby suburb, came swiftly towards him.

He raised his hand. Then he shouted, "Alice!"

She was sitting in the back seat staring glumly ahead and within seconds she was out of sight.

* * *

Blažej led her to a bench on the small green in front of St Wenceslas Church.

"I feel a bit tired," he said, with a faint smile, "Perhaps you'd like to take over from me for a while and be my guide?"

Alice looked alarmed, "But I don't know..."

"You can describe what you see and feel. Josef Gochar designed this church and it was built between 1929 and 1930." He leaned back on the bench and folded his arms. "That's all I'm going to tell you." He closed his eyes.

She stared in silence at the austere grey building which seemed to rise in giant steps to the presbytery.

276

"It's shocking," she said at last. "There's something stark and forbidding about it, even brutal... but I can see the point. It's not like any old church which people walk past without noticing. It wants to alert people to its presence... is it Functionalist?" she looked at him questioningly.

He nodded.

"Yes," she went on, "It proclaims its function all right, it's a menacing concrete structure threatening sinners! I don't know whether it attracts me or repels me... perhaps a bit of both." She leaned back and gazed up at the great tower, "It's amazing that a tower built of concrete and glass should

Church
of St Wenceslas

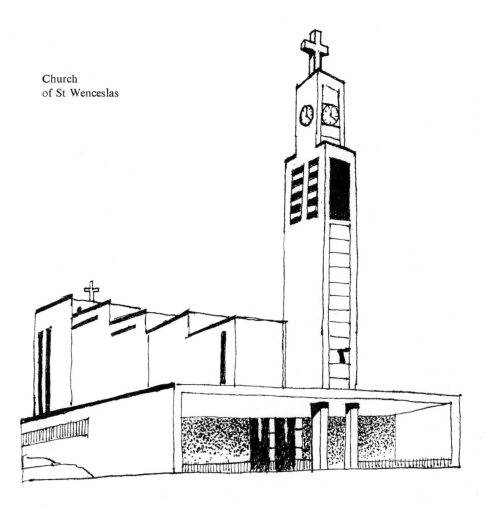

be so graceful. I think there's a touch of Gothic about it in the way it's straining up heaven."

They sat for a while without speaking.

Eventually, she turned to him with a smile, "Would you like me to guide you round the interior?"

* * *

"Can we look at the river?" she asked, as he drove back into the centre of town. "It's a nice evening, I'd like to see the sunset."

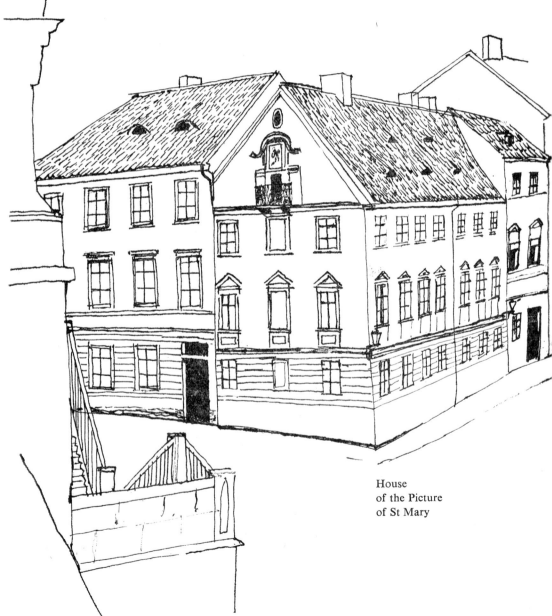

House
of the Picture
of St Mary

He parked the car on Seventeen Listopad Street and they strolled down to Knights of the Cross Square and across Charles Bridge.

He pointed to the first house on Kampa Island with its picture of the Virgin above a tiny balcony, "The House of the Picture of St Mary. Just before the First Republic came into being, it was the home of Josef Rousek, a shoemaker who lived on the ground floor. He was the owner of boats for hire too, and he made a hobby of rescuing people from the Vltava."

She looked at Blažej in surprise.

"He rescued about 200 people and fished out the bodies of something like 100 drowned unfortunates. Can you imagine a woman in long skirt jumping into the river in front of that magnificent view of Hradčany!"

"Why would she do that?"

"Poverty! Once a whole family jumped into the Vltava. They'd come to Prague from the country desperate for work and they'd just lost 50 crowns, their entire fortune."

Alice frowned, "You said that the First Republic had become a bit of a myth for Czech people but I think you've been spinning a bit of a yarn, too. You haven't said anything about the seamy side... didn't it have one?"

"Hush!" he said, jokingly, putting his finger to his lips, "the Praguers might hear you!"

"It was the time of the World Depression, wasn't it!" she persisted, "there must have been a lot of miserable people around."

"Yes, there were probably a million unemployed in the Thirties and a lot of people left this country to work in the steel-mills and coal-mines of Pennsylvanis, Ohio and Michigan. At the time the Baba Colony was being built for the well-to-do, destitute people were living here in derelict huts and caves. It was a sad time in the countryside, too. Thousands of small farmers ran into debt and lost their farms and in one year alone, 1936, 27,000 farms were auctioned off. After the Second World War, the millions

279

who'd suffered at that time dreamed of a more equal society."

She looked at him enquiringly, "Did they get one?"

* * *

"We're back where we started!" she smiled at the Jungmann statue, bathed now in a mellow evening light.

He led her towards the far end of the square, "I'd like to show you a gem... but first I'd like to say something about the collapse of our First Republic in 1938 to 1939. You know about the Munich Agreement, of course?"

"Yes, I've seen dreary, grey film-clips of it — Hitler and Mussolini standing at a table and Chamberlain and Daladier ready to sign on the dotted line. They handed part of your country, the Sudetenland, to Hitler on a plate. I remember Chamberlain saying something awful about a quarrel in a faraway country between unknown people."

Blažej lit a cigarette but she decided to ignore it.

"After Munich our country was torn apart. We lost our protective border areas and were left exposed..."

"Something surprises me," she interrupted. "You told me that the Praguers really like the British, have they forgotten how we betrayed them or have they simply forgiven us?"

He shrugged, "Your country fought against Germany. Besides, a great deal has happened since Munich, we've got a lot to forgive." He sighed, "The First Republic collapsed on March 15th 1939, when we were occupied by the Nazis and the following day Hitler came to the Castle. He had a bitter hatred for the Slavs and we felt the full weight of another era of darkness — the concentration camp at Terezín, the destruction of villages, terror, torture and execution. The amazing dynamism in art and industry ended and the enthusiasm generated by the fall of Austria and the heady excitement of independence were obliterated. Something was broken and once again the country fell into despair, something so common in this part of Central Europe."

"But not everyone despaired?"

"No, my people clung to the hope that the Allies would win the war and that deliverance would come." He turned to face her and began to recite:

'The city of factory owners, boxers, millionaires,
the city of inventors and engineers,
the city of generals, merchants and patriotic poets
with its black sins has exceeded the bounds of God's wrath:
God was enraged.
A hundred times he's threatened vengeance on the town,
a rain of sulphur, fire and thunderbolts hurled down,
and a hundred times he's taken pity.
For he always remembered what once he had promised:
that even for two just men he'd not destroy his city,
and a god's promise should retain power:
just then two lovers walked across the park,
breathing the scent of hawthorn shrubs in flower.'"

"What's the poem called," Alice asked.
"Sinful City, it's by the Nobel prizewinner, Jaroslav Seifert." He took her to a corner of the square and pointed to an extraordinary lamp with a trunk like a palm tree.
She beamed at it, "Amazing! It's Cubist, isn't it?"
"Yes, I call it Cubism in a cube."
She looked at him curiously, "Why's it so important to you?"
"It was probably put here at the beginning of this century and I love it! It's a symbol of uprightness and will-power but it's much more... Some palm trees exude dragon's blood but this one gives off dragon's light. This lamp's a witness! It's a witness to young Czech men joining the ranks in the First World War and it heard their death-rattle from the distant European fronts. It's a witness to the crazy, electrical Twenties and it heard black jazz-bands playing in Prague night-clubs.
It's a witness to the Thirties, too, when my country was growing pretty fat, padded by money from all corners of the

world for shoes, glass and machines. And it heard the cries of the unemployed...

It's a witness to the German occupation on March 15th 1939, a day filled with snowflakes. The Czechs clenched their fists and the lamp heard German war-drums and fifes. It witnessed communism, too, and communism's fall. In November 1989, it heard anti-communist slogans and the barking of police dogs."

Blažej smiled, "Its light is a beacon through history... I'm flying round and round this lamp like a moth drunk by its light!"

Cubist lamp

Alice had been studying his face, "I think I've been a bit..." she sighed, "maybe I've been a bit of a pain today, I'd like to kiss you in front of your lamp... may I?"

He frowned, "No!"

THE SIXTH
DAY·
COMMUNISM

BLAŽEJ GLANCED at Alice apprehensively as they walked to the car, she looked pale... withdrawn.

"You're not wearing your boiler-suit!"

She turned to him and smiled, "Don't worry, I'm not in a bad mood. Where are we going?"

"To the land of Winston Smith."

She looked puzzled for a moment, then she nodded, "I saw the film of Ninteen-Eighty-Four." She sighed, "It's my last real day here..."

He put his arm lightly round her shoulders, "Do you know how Orwell's Animal Farm found its way into Russia?"

She shook her head.

"The Soviet customs officials thought it was a book on agriculture."

She began to laugh as the little car rattled towards the main railway station. "I'm looking forward to a guided tour through communism! I've read the Communist Manifesto and I thought it was quite inspiring."

He frowned, "Inspiring?"

"Yes, a kind of utopia... everyone getting according to their needs."

He drew up in Washingtonová Street but made no effort to move. He stared ahead, still frowning. Following his stare, she noticed that the windscreen was dotted with tiny insects. She looked at him closely. As always, there was something fresh and spruce about his early morning appearance. He was wearing jeans and a spotless white tee-shirt. His black hair stood up spikily in spite of his efforts to flatten it.

He opened the car door but she caught his arm, "Have you read Orwell?"

"I've brought something to show you, you'll find it in the glove compartment."

She pulled out a battered book.

"It's an illegally printed version of Nineteen Eighty-Four," he said, "I read it when I was twenty-one. I was sitting in a cafe in the Františkánská garden trying to improve my English and the waitress took a bit of a fancy to me. As I was leaving she gave me a conspiratorial look and put Orwell in my pocket. Actually, she winked at me! She was risking interrogation by the secret police but I suppose she felt I was a trustworthy type. Some people weren't so lucky that year — the writer Milan Šimečka, for example. He'd been a university professor but he'd been turned out of his job like so many others and he'd become a labourer. In his spare time he was writing an afterword for the Czech version of Nineteen Eighty-Four but someone turned him in and the secret police arrived. When they searched his apartment they found his translation..."

"What happened?"

"He was given a one year prison sentence."

"Where had he hidden Orwell?"

"In his pantry, under the noodles!"

* * *

"You said you wanted a guided tour through communism," Blažej said, as they walked through Vrchlického sady Park. "I'd like to explain how the communists gulped this country in the late 1940s, so you're going to get a brief lecture."

She clapped her hand to her forehead and groaned exaggeratedly.

He turned to face her and saw that she was smiling.

"There was a feeling of bitterness and betrayal here after the Munich Agreement," he continued, "and Edvard Beneš who became president of the First Republic after Thomas Masaryk, began to turn away from the West and towards the Soviet Union. In 1943, he signed a treaty of friendship with Stalin which had a big influence on this country's future. Beneš felt he couldn't expect much from the West after the trauma of Munich and he probably believed Stalin's promise that he wouldn't interfere in Czechoslovakian politics but there's no doubt that his pro-Soviet attitude pushed us into the communists' arms."

Alice frowned, "Perhaps people didn't need pushing. I've

heard that there was a strong communist resistance here during the war so I expect the communists were popular."

"He nodded, "They'd won a lot of respect as resistance fighters. They'd hung out for years in the forests and mountains and 25.000 of them had lost their lives during the war. When their representatives went to Moscow in March 1945 to discuss the political future of this country, they demanded a leading role in shaping events and when the new Czechoslovak government was formed in Košice in liberated Slovakia in April 1945, the communists entered government for the first time and had a decisive influence on its programme.

Alice could see a huge statue looming ahead, "What was its programme?"

Statue of Brotherhood

"Sweeping proposals for nationalization," he replied. "All coal mines and businesses with more than 500 employees would be state-owned. The programme also included land distribution which meant breaking up the great estates and giving land to the small farmers and the dispossessed in the countryside. The Košice programme's tax proposals were popular, too. There were about 35,000 millionaires in Czechoslovakia at that time and the programme hammered them." He paused and frowned.

She looked at him expectantly.

"The Košice programme left a lot of headaches for the future," he continued, rather reluctantly, "The Sudeten Germans were forced to leave this country and their land and property was confiscated. Over two million of them were driven from their homes after the liberation and the evictions were cruel..." He sighed, "But in the aftermath of war and occupation there was a lot of popular support for the decision."

They had entered a small square lined with park benches and Blažej paused in front of an immense statue.

"Big Brother!"

She stared at the powerful, armed figure of the Russian, cap on head and military greatcoat slung round his shoulders. He was locked in fervent embrace with the slender bareheaded figure of a Czechoslovak private, a supplicant enfolded in the protective paternal arms of his saviour."

Blažej lit a cigarette, "The kiss of death! A crushing hug from the Russian bear. Bears are strange animals, once they hug you, they rarely let go."

"But the Russians liberated your country from the Nazis... well, most of it, at least".

"They didn't liberate Prague..."

She interrupted quickly, "How many Russians died in the Liberation?"

"I don't know exactly, perhaps 120,000."

"That's a lot!"

"Yes, but they didn't liberate Prague."

"Who did?"

"The Praguers! The streets in central Prague were bloody in May 1945. Barricades went up and people were scrabbling at the cobblestones with their bare hands. Weapons were brought out which had been hidden for years — in mattresses, in sofas, under floorboards and even in coffins."

"But I thought the Germans had lost the war by then," she said, surprised.

"The German armies were retreating and the military capitulated on May 8th, he replied, "but the fighting was carried on here by the SS and the Gestapo. The first foreign troops to arrive in Prague on the afternoon of May 6th belonged to General Vlasov's army. He was a renegade Russian general who'd gone over to the Germans and he was doing his best to keep out of the clutches of the Russians. When he arrived here in the Prague Smíchov district he was probably trying to worm his way into America's good books by giving the Praguers a helping hand."

"When did the Soviets arrive?"

"Soviet tanks reached northern Prague early in the morning on May 9th 1945, just as the shortage of guns and ammunition here was getting critical. During the clean-up operation the Russians only lost one tank and thirty soldiers but thousands of Czechs had died by the time the Soviets got here."

Alice looked at him critically, "I saw a film about it... tanks with red stars rolling through the torn up streets, flags flying..."

Blažej stared silently at the statue.

"People were milling around cheering," she persisted, "and girls were covering the tanks with flowers and hugging and kissing the soldiers."

"I expect the images on your film were true enough," he said slowly, "but I daresay a lot was left out."

He took her arm and they walked slowly down a tree-lined path towards Washingtonová Street. People were strolling under the trees with their dogs.

289   "Prague was left to bleed for days in that May of 1945,"

he said. "Our allies didn't turn up! The Americans were nearing Plzeň and the Soviets were taking Olomouc... Some American soldiers wanted to help the Praguers but they weren't allowed to because deals had been done behind the scenes. At Yalta and other conferences, spheres of influence were mapped out for the post-war world. There were a few untidy ends but it was understood that the Soviets would need a cushion of states between the Soviet Union and Germany so Stalin was allowed to dig his claws into Eastern Europe. Western Europe would be under America's protection."

She looked at him mockingly, "Didn't Truman have claws, too?" She tapped his arm, "Was Czechoslovakia an untidy end?"

"In a way. We'd had a democratic state between the wars and Stalin couldn't gobble us up without rocking the diplomatic boat but he was determined to embrace us just the same!"

Alice turned to him as they reached the car, "People must have had a tough time here after the war," she said thoughtfully. "Was Prague badly damaged?"

"The town escaped the terrible bombing raids which wrecked most European cities so its historic glories have survived. But some buildings were badly damaged, like the Old Town Hall. The building was shelled and then a great fire raged through it and the whole of the eastern and northern wings were gutted. Miraculously, the fifteenth century Council Hall survived... The war left a lot of scars here. The late Forties were bad years because there was very little food to be had and there was a dire housing shortage. People spent day after day in queues outside the Housing Authority's offices. Then, in 1947, there was a murderously cold winter which became a nightmare in Prague. The factories and power-stations would have collapsed without supplies of coal so the government commandeered twelve express trains and some local trains as well for coal deliveries to factories. Class-rooms in schools were empty and people shivered in their flats yet war profiteers were sitting in posh, heated night-clubs eating

290

delicacies. Many of them had fine apartments, too, when partisans who'd been sleeping rough for years were homeless. I met a man from a Moravian village who told me that when he returned to his family home after the war, his family had disappeared and the ground-floor of his house had been divided by a partition wall which cut across the family name on the tiled floor. In the entrance hall hung his grandfather's portrait, it was being used as a pin-board."

Memorial
to Prague uprising,
1945

* * *

Blažej parked the car and guided her into Anděl Metro entrance hall, "Please stand here where you'll get a good view!"

He walked past the escalators and stood against the opposite wall. She stared at the stone blocks painted in swirling pink and grey and saw two giants, a man and a woman, holding a sickle aloft. In the distance was a line of tower blocks and on their right, the Red Square and the Kremlin.

Alice laughed, "Communist kitsch?"

"Socialist-Realism!" He stood in front of the Kremlin with his arm across his chest in a Napoleonic gesture, "The Kremlin was delighted when the communists scored a great success in the 1946 election here, the last free election for forty-four years. Nationwide, the communists got 38 % of the votes and Klement Gottwald became the first communist Prime Minister. The communists had 114 Deputies out of 300 and they controlled important ministries in the new government, the ministries of the Interior, Finance, Information..."

"I suppose most people wanted a better deal?" she interrupted, "you told me there was a grey side to the First Republic."

"Yes, millions of people had bitter memories of the world depression in the Thirties. The communists had rallied the unemployed at that time and had organized demonstrations and strikes. There were clashes with the police... deaths. Capitalism had failed to live up to its promises.

Alice became aware that a group of young Americans were standing nearly and listening intently.

"You're giving a public lecture, Mr Guide!" she said, teasingly.

Blažej ignored his new audience and walked over to her earnestly, "I think there was something else that attracted people to communism at that time. My father was eighteen when he went to vote in 1946 and he says that fighting for communism was bound up with his optimism and youthful energy. He says it was an unforgettable time, you could feel the enthusiasm in the air. He felt a tremendous relief that the war was over with the killings, the concentration camps, the Gestapo... there was new hope, a very special hope that a completely new world would be born. Everyone would have enough to eat, the right to a job, free medical care, a roof over their heads. Like so many communists at that time, he was utterly unselfish and made great sacrifices. The Party workers went without pay and did shift-work in the mines, on building sites and in the fields. They worked at night, on Sundays and in the holidays. Thousands of young people in the Czech Youth worked for wages which were below the average workers' wages at that time. They really believed that the grinding insecurity of capitalism and the grim years of the Thirties would go into the dustbin of history..." He paused for breath.

"Was your father a Party member?"

"He joined in 1951".

"Is he still?" she asked.

Blažej shook his head, "He says now that it's amazing that he swallowed all the official propaganda but the slogans at the time had a wonderful simplicity. He feels he was gripped by a dream, a powerful dream of equality and a world freed from economic crises. He had a grandiose vision of a brand-new world. There was something lyrical in the air and the songs about building utopia had bewitching sounds. He felt that after years of poverty and fatalism, the lowly Czech worker would no longer be an object of history, but would actually mould the future."

Two of the Americans began to mutter to each other.

Alice stared at the giant sickle-waving workers on the wall, "Was your father working-class?"

"He was a miner's son and had to struggle for his education. He says workers flocked to the Party after the war and they made up 58 % of the membership. One in four Czech workers joined the Party. They believed in a People's Democracy where the working-class, led by the Communist Party, would shape the politics of the future instead of big capital. They thought they would be the conscious creators of their own destiny..." He paused, "In a way, they became noble..."

She began to fidget, "What do you mean... noble?"

"The Party told them they were the salt of the earth whereas bourgeois intellectuals were lazy good-for-nothings. The intelligentsia here were looked down on more than in any other country in the Eastern bloc at that time and they felt intimidated. They gave up wearing ties and went to work in blue overalls, open-neck shirts and cloth caps and I've even

293

heard that when they went to a canteen they used soup-spoons instead of knives and forks."

She burst out laughing, "It sounds like comic opera! I can see theatres and concert halls packed with people in blue boiler-suits."

Blažej waved to the Americans as he conducted Alice out of the Metro.

She was looking thoughtful, "I almost feel I'd like to have been one of your father's generation..."

He looked at her in surprise.

"He had something to believe in passionately, capitalism's so hollow..."

She felt him stiffen, "It's only well-to-do Westerners who have socialist dreams."

Her face reddened, "You're being patronizing..." she checked herself quickly, "I'm thinking about all that optimism and euphoria when communism started here. Your father had a kind of faith."

"Communism was a faith! It had its saints — Lenin, Stalin and Gottwald were embalmed. It had its martyrs, its dogma and its rituals. For a true believer, joining the Party was like joining a holy order, rather like a monastery with military discipline. People who were thrown out of the Party found themselves in limbo. They didn't belong anywhere, they'd lost their Church: Four or five years ago, I used to talk to a police-man, one of the few old faithful, in the pub on my housing estate. When he was fairly drunk I'd ask him:

What's the most important thing in your life?

'The Party,' he said.

I'd persist, What do you really live for?

'For the Party.'

What's the main goal in your life?

'To serve the Party,' he replied.

If the Party ordered you to kill people, would you do it?

'Yes,' he said.

Even yourself? I'd ask.

'Even myself.'

Alice jumped. She had come face to face with a statue on a small pedestal near the exit. It was an angel with fair hair and a small nose and it was looking across at the Kremlin with a puzzled expression. Blažej stared at the girl and the statue. The resemblance was striking; they were the same height, short-skirted and slightly mystified.

Angel —
Anděl Metro

He smiled, "Your twin, an angel in a mini-skirt!"

"Why's she here?"

"She's curious! She belongs to an Order of Watchers and she's staying here for a while to see how the paradise on Earth is getting along."

* * *

"The Kinský Palace!"

"Late Baroque!" she said happily.

"It's also a key spot in modern history. Klement Gottwald, our first communist Prime Minister, stood on that balcony on the 21st of February 1948 and addressed a wildly cheering crowd of about one hundred thousand people. He spoke of the promised land, a brilliant socialist future. It was a bitter day with flurries of snow and Gottwald was bareheaded. Clementis, one of his comrades, took off his fur cap and put it on Gottwald's head. The roaring crowd was celebrating the birth of communist Czechoslovakia and the country was

Kinský Palace — balcony

flooded with the famous photograph of Gottwald in the fur cap. But Clementis was wiped out of the photo."

"Why?"

"He was charged with treason and hanged. If you look at the photo today you'll see only the bare palace wall where he once stood. He was hanged four years after the putsch."

She frowned, "Putsch? You're going too fast for me!"

"Yes, putsch. But the communist putsch had to look democratic! The liberal traditions of the First Republic were still very much alive so a brutal coup was out of the question."

"So how did the communists do it?"

"They mobilized support in the army, the police and the trade-unions. A People's Militia was formed and Action Committees of staunch Communists were set up. Workers' delegations petitioned Parliament, large demonstrations were organized across the country and a smear campaign was started against democratic politicians who were accused of being in a sinister plot to overthrow the government. The atmosphere in Prague was electric that February of 1948. Workers poured into the town from all over the country and occupied key buildings, including the headquarters of the democratic parties."

"Didn't the government do anything?"

"The government was in disarray because twelve democratic ministers resigned on February 20th, creating a cabinet crisis. They were protesting against the dismissal of eight non-communist police chiefs by the communist Minister of the Interior. They thought that President Beneš would refuse to accept their resignations and that he'd seize the oportunity to bring down the Gottwald government and replace it with a more democratic one, less dominated by communists. But their political game didn't work. Beneš accepted their resignations. They'd played into the hands of the communists."

"Why didn't Beneš back them up?"

"He had the power to call out the army to defend democracy bu the was terrified of bloodshed and civil war. And he wasn't sure what the Soviets would do. Our borders were surrounded by Soviet troops — in Hungary, Poland, East Germany."

"Do you think the Soviets were ready to invade?"

"Possibly. The communist Prime Minister, Gottwald, hinted as much two months after the putsch when he said, 'We were prepared for another solution'. But Stalin preferred the Czechs to carry out the coup themselves. After all, the Americans had the atom bomb at that time and the Russians didn't, and if Russian tanks had rolled into Prague there could have been a nasty international situation. However, Beneš couldn't be sure what Stalin had up his sleeve."

"What about the West... America, Britain?"

"I think the communist putsch suited the Americans!"

"She looked at him in amazement, "What do you mean? The Americans hated communism."

"They needed communists to hate!"

"I don't understand..."

"They had a huge military-industrial complex after the war and unravelling it would have meant unemployment, social tensions, depression... and a huge loss of profits for the arms manufactures, of course. To justify their massive arms build-up there had to be an enemy."

She looked at him mockingly, "Communist bogeymen? It sounds far-fetched to me. You make the communist revolution here sound like a puppet theatre with America and Russia pulling the strings. People make revolutions." She looked round at the holiday crowds in the warm July sunshine, "It's hard to imagine that icy February day in 1948. No one forced one hundred thousand people to stand here and freeze... they really wanted communism, didn't they?"

Blažej shrugged, "It's true the putsch wouldn't have happened without the powerful cries of the crowds but Russia and America had decided a lot behind the scenes.

She looked thoughtful, "Another betrayal... ten years after Munich?"

"The democrats here had a lot to answer for, too," he replied. "While the communists were preparing the putsch, the   298 democratic politicians were quietly campaigning for elections which were never going to happen and the liberal National Socialist Party was busy organizing a ball at the Lucerna Palace in that crucial February! Of course, the democrats had taken a lot of knocks here over ten years, the Nazi occupation had wiped out most of the Czech intelligentsia."

"What about President Beneš? Do people blame him for letting Gottwald get away with it?"

"He's been accused of being weak and gullible. On the other hand, he wasn't responsible for the Iron Curtain or the Cold War Game in which we were mere pawns. He was old and ill in 1948 and he faced a terrifying decision. He couldn't be sure if the army would be loyal to him and a divided army would have meant certain bloodshed. But if he didn't call out the army, he'd be tacitly accepting the putsch. Václav Černý, a well-known scientist, went to see him at Sezimovo Ústí outside Prague on March 12th 1948, and he said Beneš looked terrible. He had aged about twenty years and looked a wreck. He hadn't even bothered to tie his shoe-laces and his face was ashen-grey. His eyes were horrified and they were watering a lot and when he tried to speak thick white saliva filled his mouth and he was forced to spit into a bowl.

"Perhaps he was spitting at himself," she interrupted.

"He said he'd been caught off-guard by the resignation of the democratic ministers because they hadn't warned him about what they were going to do. He gazed at Černý in an anguished way and seemed helpless."

"I don't see what he could have done," she said, as they left the square, "I don't suppose many people would have taken to the streets to demonstrate for democracy if he'd called on them." She looked Blažej in the eyes, "People wanted a new society... a different model."

"They got the Soviet model, Prague became a city of red stars."

299   * * *

They crossed Plzeňská Street and stood in front of three giant figures, two factory workers and a miner carrying his lamp.

"Solid chunks of Socialist-Realism, the People's Militia!" Blažej said.

"They've got limbs like tree-trunks... and look at their thighs and colossal boots! Why are they looking so grim?"

"They were guarding socialism, it was no joking matter."

She looked glumly at the grotesquely contorted faces and then brightened, "Well, they make a change from kings and queens, don't they? What was the People's Militia?"

The Communist Party called it their "armed arm". It was the Party's private volunteer army which could always be

The People's
Militia

300

counted on in a crisis. These workers genuinely wanted socialism and their feeling was probably as strong and spontaneous as that of the medieval Hussites. In 1948, the Militia were really only extras in uniform. Many of them had only just learnt how to load a gun and they knew nothing about elementary military tactics. Yet they were prepared to go into battle against the professional army if necessary. Most of them came from poor workers' families which had suffered during the First Republic and had witnessed wartime profiteering while their children went hungry. These volunteers were enormously enthusiastic and they really thought that socialism would bridge the age-old divide between rich and poor. Of course, they didn't know socialism, they only knew the bleak side of capitalism..."

"Capitalism's always got a bleak side," she interrupted.

* * *

"This is the National Memorial," Blažej explained, as they stood on Žižkov Height, "It was built during the First Republic by Jan Zázvorka."

She stared at the severe monumental building faced with granite. The bronze doors were decorated with revolutionary figures.

"The memorial contains the grave of the Unknown Soldier and various working-class leaders, and it was a shrine to Klement Gottwald, our first communist president. His embalmed remains were preserved here."

"I'd like to look at him," she said eagerly.

Blažej laughed, "He flew away in 1962 and I expect he's still searching Red Square for Stalin's ghost. After the communist putsch in February 1948, Gottwald became Stalin's stooge. Although I've heard he hated the Russians and always kept his hands clenched in his pockets when he had to speak to the Soviet ambassador, he took great care not to upset them. With Soviet approval he was elected president of this country on July 14th 1948 in the Vladislav Hall..."

301   "Was he the only candidate?" she interrupted quickly.

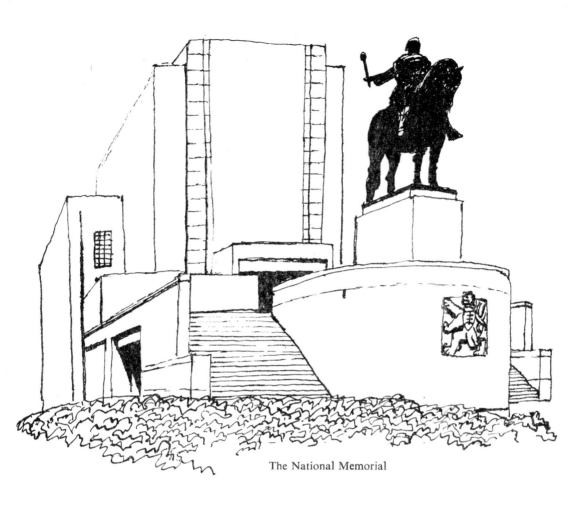

The National Memorial

"Yes, like all our presidents from that day to this, he was elected unanimously! The National Front, a grouping of parties in which the communists had a leading role, elected him. We had a closed political system under communism because the Front concentrated all power in its hands and it was impossible to form any party unless it agreed to the Front's programme."

"So Gottwald was the most important man in the country?"

"He seemed all powerful but he was dependent on Stalin's whims and all his moves were monitored by the Kremlin. Like other public figures, he had to fill in detailed personnel forms and the story goes that on one occasion he tried to

302

conceal the fact that he'd had syphilis. A serious mistake trying to conceal things from Big Brother's watchful eye! He knew the Soviets could blacken his name any time."

Alice began to chant, "Class enemy! Imperialist agent!"

Blažej nodded, "Gottwald could have found himself in front of a tribunal on a treason charge. When his nerves were bad he took to booze and was sometimes paralysed and flat on his back for days. Important state decisions had to be made without him. In the photos of him taken towards the end of his life, he looks like a heavy drinker — a soft fatty face with strange eyes. There's fear in his eyes, a fear that not even the most powerful man in the state could throw off. He'd unleashed some terrible witch-hunts and could never be sure that the hunt wouldn't be on for him."

* * *

"Pankrác prison!"

"She stared at the high white wall, above it she could see a narrow clock-tower,"

"Why are we here?"

"One of the bravest women in Czech history died here, Milada Horáková. Have you heard about her?"

She shook her head.

"She was a lawyer and during the First Republic she was a member of the National Socialist Party, the party of Dr. Beneš. She joined the Resistance during the war and in August 1940, when she was 39 years old, she was arrested by the Gestapo. She was on holiday with her husband, Bohumil Horák at the time. She was chained up in one of the cellars of the Petschek Palace and the chains sank into her flesh leaving deep scars..."

"Stop!" Alice put her hands over her ears.

He took her wrists gently, "The Nazis couldn't break her down, even in Terezín concentration camp. She was imprisoned in a bunker in the Little Fortress and kept in solitary confinement. Her interrogator used to stick needles into her hands when he thought she was feigning a fainting fit. She probably only survived Terezín because she knew her trial was coming up in Germany in October 1944. She saw her husband in the courtroom for the first time for four years and she took him some bread which she'd managed to save in prison. Horák said there were some terrible moments when the judges went out to consider the verdict but the result was better than he expected because Milada 'only' got eight years."

"What did he get?"

"Five years, but after seven months in different German prisons they were both freed by the Americans and returned to Prague. Milada went straight back to her legal and political work, she was a campaigner for the Women's National Council and various other organizations, and after some persuasion by Beneš she stood for Parliament. She was a successful and popular deputy but she resigned on March 10th 1948.

"The day Masaryk died... why did she resign"?

"She felt she wasn't getting anywhere. She was one of the very few democratic politicians to take a strong line against the communists and she'd been to see the Chairman of Parliament shortly before February 25th 1948, to beg him to call Parliament to work up resistance to the putsch. According to Horák, the Chairman was wishy-washy about it and during the conversation his son intervened dramatically and in an emotional outburst begged Milada not to rob him of his father."

"Was his father really in danger?"

"Possibly. The atmosphere in Prague was menacing and more and more people were being arrested each day. Milada stuck her neck out in her last speech to Parliament urging the democratic deputies to enter Gottwald's government and prevent a complete communist take-over. She made her last public speech on February 22nd and warned her audience that a communist dictatorship would ruin the country."

"February 22nd, that must have been the day after Gottwald's speech to the crowds in the Old Town Square. How many people turned up for Milada"?

"I don't know exactly, one or two hundred perhaps. She

ended her speech with an passionate appeal to Beneš in which she said that the majority of the nation stood behind him."

"But it wasn't true was it?" Alice asked.

Blažej sighed, "During those February days very few people supported her and she was kicked out of all the organizations she'd worked for. She was remarkably brave because she went to visit Prokop Drtina, the disgraced Minister of Justice, in hospital. He was being guarded by State Security at the time, but she wanted to show her support for him. Her own arrest was only a matter of time and she was dreading it because she was still bothered by the scars on her wrists which hadn't healed properly."

"When was she arrested?"

"On September 27th 1949. Her husband described how the secret police came to their house. He was sitting on the balcony when two men in shabby raincoats came through the garden gate and rang the bell. He managed to escape from the balcony and the following day when he was wandering through Prague trying to find a way to get to the frontier he heard that Milada had been arrested in her office."

Blažej pointed to a large and rather ugly Thirties building across from the prison, "The Palace of Justice! Her trial was held there and the building was completely surrounded by soldiers who were guarding the doors and windows with machine guns. A show trial had been organized and twice a day bus-loads of workers' delegates arrived from various organizations all over the country. There were mounting piles of papers on the courtroom tables; letters, resolutions, telegrams, demanding the death sentence."

"What was she accused of?"

"Along with the six other defendants, she was accused of 'espionage committed over a long period of time, on a large scale and in a particularly dangerous manner!' One of the defendants said it was difficult to sit silently listening to the prosecution's lies and innuendos. At one point he caught sight of Milada's face and said he'd remember it until the day of his death. Her eyes were glassy and vacant, no longer hers..."

"Drugs?"

"Probably. Great efforts had been made to break her down before her trial while she was in Ruzyně prison. The Report on Admission of Prisoners still survives and states that between her arrest in September 1949 and her sentence in June 1950 she'd lost 11 kilograms in weight during repeated interrogations. She was tough, clever and incorruptible — a very difficult person to destroy. The colonel who tried to get her to confess admitted as much. He also said quite openly that the secret police weren't interested in evidence, they wanted her 'to bow her head under the pressure of our communist ideas.' On June 27th 1950, ČTK, the Czech news agency, carried the terrible report that she'd been sentenced to death along with three other prisoners including Záviš Kalandra, the well-known writer. The news shocked the West and there were pleas for mercy from Albert Einstein, Bertrand Russell and many others, but the official press here didn't print them. For the first time in the history of our Republic a woman was sentenced to death for political reasons after a monster show-trial that set a precedent for many more."

Alice stared at the long white wall surmounted with barbed wire, "And she was executed in there?"

"It was in the early hours of the morning of June 27th 1951, a few minutes after 4 a.m. The guards went past the cells and made sure that the peep-holes in the doors were covered with tin so that the terrible show which was about to take place wouldn't be witnessed by the prisoners. The hospital wing was shrouded in darkness and all that could be heard were muffled steps in the courtyard..."

Blažej pulled a thin paper-back from his pocked and opened it at a photograph.

Alice studied the strong, handsome face, "She was incredible... fearless." She looked again at the ugly prison complex, "No, I expect I'm quite wrong, she must have been afraid, terribly afraid... it makes her all the braver."

* * *   306

"Forty-four years ago, Jan Masaryk, the only son of our legendary first president, Thomas Masaryk, fell or was pushed from that window." He pointed to the fourth floor of the Černín Palace, "His broken body was found in this courtyard on March 10th 1948."

She stared up at the window, "Was it murder?"

Černín Palace — window

"No one knows, a lot of detective work still needs to be done. The trouble is, a lot of clues have disappeared. The Gottwald regime said it was suicide but most Czechs believed and still believe, that he was murdered. He was a popular foreign minister, the last true democrat in the government and a cheerful, witty man who mixed with ordinary people. They really loved him and two hundred thousand turned out to mourn him at his state funeral. There were supicious circumstances surrounding his death. It's said, for example, that it couldn't have been suicide because when his body was discovered, all the windows of his apartment were tightly closed. An enquiry was opened on his case but it was suppressed after the Soviet invasion in 1968. Maybe there are some clues in Moscow in the Secret Police archives. At that time the NKVD,

307

the predecessor of the KGB, were monitoring every move in this country and there may be a report on Masaryk's end. People say that the documentary photos of his funeral show a bunch of snowdrops behind his ear which may have covered a bullet wound. Others claim he was killed at the airport just as he was planning to leave the country and that the Soviet Ambassador was involved."

"You think the Soviets killed him?"

"Possibly, or it may have been one of our liquidation groups..."

"Liquidation?"

"Secret Police jargon for executing people!"

"But why would the communists want to kill him? After all, they'd got into power."

"Perhaps they were afraid he'd get to the West and stir up trouble for them. He was a symbol of the First Republic, a living reminder of democracy."

He paused and fumbled for his cigarettes.

"Your fourth!"

He groaned and put the packet back in his pocket, "Some time after the 1946 election, Masaryk was sent a parcel bomb and Prokop Drtina, the democratic Minister of Justice, got one too. However, the bombs were discovered before they exploded. No one really knows who sent them, though some people say that Alexej Čepička, a communist diehard, was responsible. But maybe he was merely an agent... for American intelligence, for example."

She looked stunned, "Another of your off-beat theories?"

"Masaryk could have been a fly in the American ointment. He was almost certainly planning to flee to the West and he had a lot of contacts and maybe the potential to undermine the Gottwald government. That was the last thing the Americans wanted."

"Communist bogeymen again! Masaryk hadn't exactly taken a strong stand against the communists during the putsch, had he? So I don't see how he could have rocked their boat after it. He must have been in a very low state after the putsch and I expect he blamed himself for not being tougher in those February days."

"Yes, he was certainly depressed... a few days before his death, his fellow-democrat, Prokop Drtina, had attempted suicide by jumping from a window of his house."

"Attempted suicide? What happened to him?" she asked.

"He was carted off to hospital and then jailed by Alexej Čepička for slander."

"How could Čepička do that?"

"He'd become Minister of Justice!"

* * *

"It's a fortress!" Alice said.

"We're in Thákurova Street and this is the former StB headquarters."

"StB"? she looked at Blažej inquiringly.

"State Secret Security — Státní tajná bezpečnost, in Czech."

The enormous, many-storied building filled half the street. The lower windows were barred.

She looked up at the dusty windows, "Kafka's Castle! Does anyone live here?"

"I think it's empty," he replied.

She went to the door and pressed the bell. It rang with a hollow sound.

"There's no street number!" She peered through a glass pane and saw a shabby empty hallway, "Where've they all gone?"

"They were disbanded after the November 1989 revolution. Some went into the Intelligence Service, some joined the police, some retired on their pensions. Where do 20,000 StBs disappear to? No one knows! A lot of their files have disappeared, too.

She whistled, "20,000!"

"The StB network was like a poisonous spider in a sordid web with threads throughout the country," Blažej said, staring at the building with distaste. "They had a vast army of paid and unpaid informers and there were special riot police units, too, over 10,000 of them. If the People's Militia are included, 120,000 or more, then maybe there were about 150,000 people in the whole grisly network — that's one policeman to every hundred citizens! By the late 1970s, it's possible that the number of Czechs and Slovaks checking up on each other amounted to between 2% and 5% of the population."

She looked shocked, "Why so many informers... I don't understand..."

"During the terror of the Fifties, the communists built up a police state and the StB became a state within the state. The Communist Party was supposed to run the Security Forces but they took on a terrifying life of their own and were answerable to no one."

She sat down on the grass in the small park in front of the building, "Tell me about informers!"

"Some people thought it was their duty to turn in class enemies but the ideological motive faded away after a time. Other motives for turning people in were personal and family quarrels, hope of some profit or privileges, fear of punishment... Some people became informers because they fell under the spell of individual StB officers who got up to all sorts of tricks to trap susceptible people."

"What you're saying reminds me of something," she said excitedly, "I've got a story for you! About a year ago I was on a train going from London to Wales to join my parents on holiday. There was only one other person in the compartment, a middle-aged woman, and we got talking. After a while, I told her I planned to go to Prague and she immediately invited me to the restaurant car for a drink. She bought me a glass of wine and while I was drinking it, she gulped down at least three whiskies! She told me that she knew Prague well and that she'd been an employee at the British Embassy and had met up with one or two strange adventures. After a bit of prodding, she told me a fantastic tale..."

Alice looked at Blažej, "Are you listening?"

He smiled and sat down next to her.

310

StB House

"Apparently the Secret Police decided to set a trap for this woman and the officer in charge of the operation was an StB Major. The woman didn't tell me her name so I'll call her Vera. The Major found out that Vera liked good-looking men, preferably younger than she was, and he sent one of his agents to take her out on the town. Vera told me she really liked this man and even fell a little bit in love with him but she didn't talk to him about her work. She said she didn't like mixing up work and love. This infuriated the Major and he came up with an idea. He had a life-size rubber figure made of an old man, fully dressed with a hat on its head. In its chest there was a plastic bottle containing several litres of liquid which looked like blood and a spring mechanism had been designed so that the dummy could walk a few paces in a normal way. On the 'critical day' as she called it, Vera went off to meet her boy-friend in a hotel outside Prague. However, he didn't show up. After a while, a handsome man appeared on the scene, got into conversation and bought her one drink after another. Then he disappeared into thin air. Vera staggered to her car and raced back towards Prague. She told me she liked fast cars at the best of times and had been stopped for speeding more than once. Suddenly, she skidded badly on a sharp bend. In the car headlights an old, bent man appeared and before she could react, she had run him over. The car bonnet and windscreen were spattered with red. She accelerated at once and drove like mad through all the traffic lights towards Prague, ignoring police sirens. The traffic police tried to stop her on the outskirts of Prague but she got away and reached the Embassy."

"What happened to her?" Blažej asked,

"Within 48 hours she was on a plane to London, possibly with the help of the British Ambassador."

"Was she fooled by the rubber man?"

"No! She realized he was a fake when she hit him but she decided that if the StB had those sorts of tricks up their sleeve, she'd be better off back home."

312

"It sounds like science-fiction," he said thoughtfully, "but the StB set all sorts of traps... blackmail, forgery, slander. The techniques of terror were fantastic and the technique of the lie reached a very high level. We were in such a maze of lies that it's almost impossible now to know what's true and what isn't. The StB had brilliant techniques for putting a mask of treachery on an innocent face."

She plucked at the grass absent-mindedly, "How?"

"In the 1950s there was the case of the Čihošťsky Miracle. The StB wanted do discredit the churches."

"Were people forbidden to go to church?"

"Anyone could go to church," he replied, "but it was risky because it could get you a poor political profile. No one knew who was watching. The Christmas midnight mass in St. James Church here in Prague was packed with people but they knew that the StB were there, too! In the case of the so-called Čihošťsky Miracle, the unsuspecting victim was a priest, Josef Toufar. While he was preaching, the blue and green statue of St. Joseph on the altar moved several times. The 'miracle' had been staged by the Security Forces to persuade people that the Church fooled believers. Toufar was forced to take part in a reconstruction of his 'crime' and a film was made showing the whole elaborate system of wires and pulleys which made the statue move. It's said that there were traces of torture on Toufar's face, his fingers had been broken and the soles of his feet had been beaten so badly that he had to be carried to the pulpit. A Czech film director made his career on that film!"

Blažej stretched himself out on the grass. The StB were a byword for brutality in the Fifties. One officer killed people with his bare hands. The StB used karate, stamped on people's hands and feet, pulled out their hair... People were hauled off for questioning like animals with bags over their heads and were beaten until they fainted. Their teeth were knocked out and their testicles crushed. In StB circles this was known as 'roast veal' or 'tomato puree'."

313   "Stop!"

"Sorry," he put his hand over hers, "I want to explain how their techniques changed over the years. Their methods got more refined and sophisticated. I could quote you cases of terrible brutality right into the Eighties, but in most cases psychic torture replaced physical torture. The StB's aim was the destruction of personality and mental collapse. One of the oddities of communism was that in a system where a lot of people goofed off and things fell apart and complete idiots were running the economy, the StB recruited some of the best brains in the country and they often appeared very sympathetic to dissidents. The friendly StB officer would say he was only doing security work because he had to make a living and he'd put unbelievable energy into getting the dissident to like him. As soon as the dissident felt friendship for the StB officer he was destroyed. One of my father's friends, a priest, was investigated for a long time by a charming and exceptionally well-educated man with a delightful smile who talked to him on a high level about spiritual matters. Over a period of time the officer extracted all the information he wanted. He found out where secret meetings took place, who was there, what their attitude was to the regime and so on. There were an awful lot of false smiles under communism. Maybe that's why clerks and shop assisstants were so incredibly rude and morose, it was one of the few ways to be authentic!"

"Did the StB really believe in the system? Communism, I mean."

"Probably very few believed in it by the Eighties but the system still seemed to function perfectly." He got out his cigarettes and laughed, "Once I was on the Metro travelling from Kačerov station to Museum, it's about six stops, and I got into a conversation with an StB officer. He was quite open about his job and told me that the people on the Communist Party Politbureau were a bunch of mužhics!"

"Mužhics?"

"Village nobodies."

Blažej got up and giving Alice his hand, he helped her

314

to her feet, "Communism was built on fear. When I was working as a guide I knew that the StB were tapping telephones, bugging hotels, shadowing people and breaking into flats to install listening devices. I've heard that just before the Revolution in 1989, they had about 10,000 agents working as hotel porters, caretakers, managers, doctor's receptionists and so on, but it wasn't something I could talk about to foreigners..."

She interrupted quickly, "Aren't you exaggerating? Not everyone was afraid, surely?"

"I'm not saying that everyone went around quaking with fear. The shoppers on Na Příkopě Street probably looked much the same as the crowds in your Oxford Street, though shabbier and less well-fed, and probably most people lived their lives without coming up against the Security Forces. But they knew they were there! The StB were an invisible menace and most people adjusted to it in one way or another. It wasn't that they were afraid of trials, torture, executions... It was more a question of what you could lose if you didn't keep to the rules. I mean, obey the law and keep quiet! Teachers could lose their jobs if they stepped out of line, parents were afraid of damaging their children's chances of higher education, students were anxious in case they got a poor political profile. Everyone has something to lose and even the most humble factory worker could be shunted into a worse job. So people were cautious and they turned out to vote even though they knew the elections were a farce. They took part in boring Party activities, shouted the right slogans on May Day marches and filled in humiliating questionnaires. The StB could intervene in a person's life without warning and people knew it. It took naturalness away from human life."

Alice looked at him intently, "Were you afraid?"

"Not really, but looking back on it I realize I was rather anxious. I didn't want to lose my job as a guide which I liked and which brought me quite a good living and I was afraid I might put my foot in it by saying the wrong thing..."

"Even with friends?"

He hesitated, "I could be open with my friends. I used to sit in the Slavia cafe near the Vltava River and crack jokes about the regime. Then I'd look at the next table and wonder if anyone was listening and I'd think, Oh what the hell! I think I censored myself a lot of the time and I despised myself for it but I didn't want to come up against officialdom and I felt I couldn't change anything so I switched off politics and concentrated on other things..."

"What things?"

"Helping my parents build their little country house, improving my English, repairing my car. I wanted to improve my material existence. But I felt bored, a terrible, heavy kind of boredom, really oppressive. Time seemed to drag along and nothing seemed to have much point. And I wanted to throw up when I heard the great mountain of official garbage on TV. You see, by the Eighties hardly anyone of my generation believed in communism. An independent opinion poll was carried out in 1985, outside the official structures, of course, and it showed that for 99% of young people communism was as dead as a dodo. And we realized that the old Party fossils weren't communists either! They just went on mouthing the old slogans in public and then went home to watch Western videos and the wives of some top Party officials were queuing up outside a certain establishment for Little Robert..."

"Who was Little Robert?"

He avoided her eye, "Maybe I'll tell you later. As far as my life was concerned I felt I was living in a kind of greyness... I lost interest in chasing girls and dancing. Finally, in 1988, I began to go on demonstrations. I didn't stick my neck out too much, just a bit. It made me feel better." He looked into Alice's eyes, "I'm not a hero, you know. Only about one percent of people here were dissidents. I'm just an ordinary man."

She threw her arms round him impulsively, "You're not ordinary to me!"

He studied her radiant face and put his cheek against hers. Then he disengaged himself gently, "We're being watched!"

A very small toddler with a bright blue bow on top of her head had appeared from nowhere. She had her thumb in her mouth and was watching them with interest.

He drew Alice to a space between the trees, "Please look up!" he pointed to the nineteenth century tympanum on the StB fortress.

She smiled, "How odd, Jesus Christ with two beggars!"

* * *

They walked past the Loretto and down a narrow cobbled street between high walls.

"It's lovely here, I feel I'm in a medieval village!"

"This is Kapučinská Street. I don't want to spoil your mood but I've brought you here to show you the Little House, it was part of the former military prison. You'll get a glimpse of it if you look through this gateway."

She noticed that the top of the wall on her left was smothered in barbed wire. She peered through the gateway and saw a low, white building in a neglected courtyard.

"In 1950, Western radio began to broadcast reports about sinister goings-on in that house and the Presidium of the Central Committee set up a commission to investigate the place. However, it concluded that the radio reports were merely Western propaganda and that everything in the Little House was in perfect order."

"What were the sinister goings-on?"

"It was Bedřich Reicin's torture-chamber. I call him the bloodthirsty Richard III! He was appointed by Gottwald as head of the notorious counter-intelligence unit in the Defence Ministry — the Fifth Department. He'd worked in intelligence in Moscow and climbed the security ladder quickly under Gottwald, becoming a general at the age of forty. He was a gigantic man weighing about 120 kilos, clever, vain and power-mad. Every order of his, however

The Little House

trifling, had to be carried out meticulously and he couldn't stand the slightest opposition."

She peered through the gate again at the empty building in the bleak courtyard, "Who was tortured here?"

"Mainly army officers and people associated with them. In February 1948, a great purge of the army began and within ten months something like 60 generals, more than 200 colonels, 1000 lieutenant colonels and 1.500 lower-ranking officers were forced to leave the Czechoslovak army. Many of them were sent to the Mírov forced labour camp or brought before merciless military tribunals. Some of

318

the trials were held in secret and we're only just beginning to learn about the death sentences meted out at that time. Stalin had a pathological hatred of 'class enemies' who'd had contacts with the West — old communists who'd fought in Spain, members of the Resistance and officers who'd fought in the allied armies."

"Why?"

"He saw them as potential rivals and secret agents, contaminated by Western thinking and customs. In 1940 many Czechs volunteered to help the British in their struggle against Hitler. There was the 310th Fighter Wing near Cambridge for example, and the 312th Fighter Wing near Liverpool. Czech pilots were liked and respected in Britain and many of them were decorated for their bravery. One British squadron, the 68th which employed Czech pilots on night flights, even chose a Czech device for their coat of arms — 'Vždy Připraven.'"

She repeated the words, stumbling over the pronunciation.

Blažej laughed, "The British had a lot of difficulty with 'Vždy Připraven!' It means, 'Always Prepared.' In another age, at another time, the Czech airmen would have been welcomed home as heroes but here they returned to prison camps and torture. The main torturer in the Little House was František Pergl, a primitive sadist who rose to be a staff captain. It's said that the spent most of his evenings designing torture instruments. His office on the first floor was decorated with bulls' whips, batons, manacles and iron hoops used to crush prisoners' heads. On the wall was a poster with the slogan, 'No compassion for traitors, now or ever!' One of his interrogators boasted to his victims, 'You'll go straight to court from the Fifth Department or straight to the cemetery.' A flogging platoon was at the ready to beat people into submission in the dark, dirty cells..."

"I don't want to hear about tortures..."

"I promise I won't describe them but I'd like to tell you about General Janoušek. He fought for the British as an

Air-Marshal in the RAF and he was highly decorated

but when he returned to this country after the war he was immediately put under surveillance. The Security Forces watched his home night and day, tapped his telephone and opened his mail. He was followed by Security wherever he went and began to feel terribly depressed. One day a young man turned up and said he'd been expelled from university, hated the communists and would like to offer the General his services. He was one of Reicin's agents but only one of several informers around Janoušek. One woman in his neighbourhood reported on him regularly and even turned up at the General's funeral many years later wearing a large black hat! The young man who seemed sympathetic and intelligent, offered to help Janoušek leave the country..."

"But why would he do that?"

"At that time the Security Forces had a policy of luring their victims towards the frontier and then arresting them. It was called Operation 'Kameny' or 'Stones'. Tens of thousands of Czechoslovak citizens were trying to escape abroad at that time and agents made contact with selected individuals and offered them their help. The operation was so elaborate that they even set up West German customs offices and had people masquerading as American military guards. They were questioned in detail by an 'American' officer who asked them about their attitude to the régime, their activities and their friends. One StB officer played the part of the American perfectly, he'd been in Britain during the war and had mingled with American officers. After being questioned, the would-be exiles were seized by a Czech frontier patrol. Sometimes they were brought to trial but many were massacred on the spot."

She looked at him in amazement, "How do you know all this?"

"Reports on what happened in the Fifties like The Report on Organized Violence by Vilem Hejl have now been published here and many of the crimes of that time have been documented. Janoušek was trapped in the way I've described, he was stopped by a patrol and thrown into the local jail. 320

On May 1st 1948, people from Reicin's Fifth Department came to get him and he was brought here to the Little House. He was chained up in a cell and for a time an iron ball was fastened to his legs. Immense psychological pressure was brought to bear to make him break down but he managed to hang on to his sanity mainly because he believed the truth would come out at his trial. After all, he'd committed no crime unless helping to defend Britain against the German airforce could be considered a crime! His only offence under communist law was that of consenting to leave the country illegally and he pleaded guilty to that. The turning-point in his trial was when Reicin appeared as a witness. He shouted abuse at the airmen in the dock. They were traitors, hirelings and reactionary lackeys of imperialism who wore RAF buttons on their uniforms. During the war the British and Czech airmen had often swapped buttons out of friendship."

"What was Janoušek's sentence?"

"Eighteen years of penal servitude. He was freed in the amnesty of 1960 and immediately began a battle with the authorities for his pension. He was eventually granted 400 crowns a month — about £ 4 in today's terms which was later raised to 600 crowns. But he wasn't left in peace. After the Soviet invasion of 1968, a slander campaign was mounted against him and the rumour was spread that he'd participated in a counter-revolutionary and anti-socialist conspiracy and had aimed to be Minister of Defence. He died in 1971 and his former rank of General was only restored to him in 1990.

"What happened to Reicin?"

"The regime devoured its comrades! He was arrested in 1951 and charged with treason, the charge he'd brought against so many others. He was hanged in 1952. No mention was made at his trial of the Fifth Department or the Little House."

* * *

"A mad confectioners dream!"

"It's a cross between a cathedral and a wedding-cake!"

she stared up at the huge twelve storied International Hotel.
It was surmounted with vaguely Byzantine arches and something which looked like a funeral urn out of which a starred
stalk reared.

"It must be one of the few red stars left in Prague," she
commented.

Red friezes of soldiers on gold backgrounds alternating
with odd heraldic motifs, decorated the walls.

He pointed to the sculptures of war heroes above the three   322 great entrance arches as they went into the large, dim lobby in browns and greens with pillars of mottled marble.

"Real Fifties!" she said looking pleased, "I feel I've gone back in a time capsule. It's like being under water with seaweeds," she added, looking at some contorted plants, "it's a bit of a museum!"

"It's got one fine exhibit," he led her to a table where she could get a view of a tapestry which covered most of the far wall, "'Prague, the Queen of Music' by Cyril Bouda."

"It's lovely!" she admired the panorama in mellow greens and reds with its meticulous little houses. A swan flew over the Vltava under dancing violins, Yellow birds perched in the foreground and to the far left a tiny figure with a pram was walking away from the town.

"The hotel looks quite pleasant on tapestry! It's odd that the communists built it like a weird church," she said.

"Especially as bishops were being thrown into prison at the time and something like 8000 monks and nuns had been arrested, along with tens of thousands of churchgoers," he replied.

He translated the menu for her and ordered omelettes and coffee. Three men were talking quietly at the next table and there was a hushed atmosphere in the lobby.

"This was a high-life spot in the Fifties — balls, receptions, conferences... And while Gottwald and the communist bigwigs were cavorting here a merciless terror was going on."

"The coffee's better than the decor!" she sipped it appreciatively. "I want to hear what happened in the Fifties, so please go on."

"After the 1948 February putsch, State Security got to work and thousands of people were thrown out of their jobs. Action Committees of staunch Party members were set up all over the country and were responsible for purging the Press, the professions, the Syndicate of Czechoslovak writers, orchestras, theatres, offices and institutions. University professors, secondary school teachers and thousands of students were dismissed. By April 1949, many of them were being rounded up and sent to prison or to execution."

"Where were they sent?"

"Mainly to forced labour camps. Some accounts say that there were as many as 422 camps and prisons to contain 'the forces of reaction'. Czechoslovakia had the biggest purges, the highest number of mass trials and executions in the whole of Eastern Europe."

"Why?"

He gave her a rueful glance, "Your questions aren't easy! Stalin insisted on absolute obedience from his empire and Czechoslovakia, in the strategic heart of Europe with its industrial power-house, was particularly important to him. Anyone whose loyalty was doubtful or even remotely doubtful had to go to the wall. The purges here with their interrogations, torture, phony confessions and show-trials were run on the Soviet model with the Czechoslovak security forces under the direct control of the Russians. In 1948 many Czech Communists had genuinely believed that Stalin would allow the Eastern bloc countries to choose their own road to socialism but they were quickly disillusioned. In the autumn of 1948, the first wave of arrests of highly-placed communist officials took place and a series of show trials were being prepared with the full backing of Gottwald and his right-hand man, Rudolf Slánský. Slánský had been a pillar of support to Gottwald during the putsch and had organized the first prison camps. It was he who had ordered the arrest of the foreign minister, Vladimír Clementis and his deputy, Artur London. Thousands of lesser Party officials were arrested and tortured, hundreds were executed and others got life sentences like Gustav Husák, the communist Party chief in Slovakia."

"Darkness at Noon?" she looked puzzled, "Surely, purges would weaken the Party?"

"They did in a way because good apples were thrown out with the rotten ones but Stalin's main concern was absolute power. He'd been in command in the Soviet Union for   324 nearly a quarter of a century by 1950 and his paranoia was gigantic. He not only killed his rivals but anyone who might conceivably be a threat to him in the future."

"Slánský was purged too, wasn't he?"

Blažej caught the waiter's eye and ordered more coffee, "Our lunch will get here eventually, people in time-capsules sometimes have to wait! In the summer of 1951 Slánský didn't know what was in store for him. His fiftieth birthday was celebrated by Gottwald and his cronies and he was showered with praise. But in November he was arrested and a year later he was put on trial here in Prague with Clementis and twelve others."

"What were they accused of?"

"Being Trotkyists, Titoists, capitalist spies, bourgeous traitors and Zionists!"

"But why Slánský, surely he'd been useful to Stalin?"

"He went the same way as Stalin's own police stooges, Menzhinsky, Yagoda, Yazhov... They all knew too much and once they'd done their dirty work they were expendable. After hours and hours of interrogation, sometimes sixteen hours a day, the defendants were forced to learn their confessions by heart so that they could recite them in court. Their trials were a mockery but afterwards the public was told that they'd been saved from a dreadful conspiracy by the clear-sightedness of Comrade Gottwald, the guide of the Czechoslovak people."

"What happened to Clementis, Slánský and the others?"

"Eleven of them were sentenced to death and the other three defendants got life imprisonment. A driver and two interrogators were given the job of disposing of the condemned men's ashes and they spread them on the icy roads. The driver made a gruesome joke saying that he had never carried fourteen people in his little Tatra before — three living and eleven in the sack."

Alice shuddered, "Some sense of humour!"

"There was an atmosphere of hysteria in the early Fifties, as you'd expect during a great witch-hunt. Apparently one of the defendants lost his trousers during the trial, they fell down suddenly and the whole court, including the judges and prosecutors, began to laugh uncontrollably. The session had to be adjourned."

The waiter arrived with some steaming dishes, "At last!" she helped herself liberally, "It looks good."

"People suffered in all sorts of ways at that time", Blažej continued, "entrepreneurs, farmers and small business people were looked on as class-enemies and their children were excluded from higher education."

"When did the purges end?"

"They petered out towards the end of the Fifties but arrests were taking place here even after Nikita Khrushchev's famous anti-Stalin speech in 1956. Writers, painters, engineers, technicians, manual workers... anyone suspected of anti-state activities ended up in prison."

"How many died?"

"We still don't know for sure. According to estimates made in the Prague Spring in 1968, 130.000 people were sent to prisons, camps and the notorious Jáchymov uranium mines North-West of Prague. But other estimates are much higher, claiming that there were at least 240.000 prisoners by 1955 and that the majority had been jailed for political reasons. The poet, Zdeněk Rotrekl was one of those sent to the uranium mines. He was a Catholic who'd always quarrelled with the official line whether it was under the First Republic or under Gottwald. After the war he was working as a deputy editor on Akord, a well-known literary journal. The editor tried to avoid official functions and preferred to send Rotrekl off to Party meetings and conferences. Rotrekl soon got into trouble at one of these gatherings by criticizing the censorship and the pea-brains who were sitting in judgement over what could or couldn't be published. On November 17th 1949, at the age of twenty-nine, he was condemned to death in Brno."

"What was the charge?"

"The usual thing; diverting the masses from the class-   326 struggle, supporting the Vatican and hostility to the proletarian revolution. The verdict was commuted to life-imprisonment and Rotrekl spent thirteen years in the uranium mines. On his release he saw the place where his family home had once stood. There was a brand-new building with two titanic busts in front of it and an inscription over the door: 'All the strength of the Party and People for building the fully developed Socialist society!'"

She sneezed and got out her usual paper square, "These communist slogans get up my nose! I've read about Stalin's show trials in Russia but I didn't know the same kind of thing happened here." She stared in silence at her empty coffee-cup, "What about women?" she asked eventually, "were there many women prisoners?"

"Thousands!" He took a notebook from one of his sagging pockets and studied it, "this is part of a letter written by Eva Seibertová to communist President Gottwald:

'On October 9th 1948 at six in the morning I was assaulted in my flat at U smaltovny 25, by two men and a woman. They bound me, covered my eyes and took me to an unknown place by car. I found myself in some sort of bungalow where they tied me to a bunk, began to beat me over the head and whisked a hot object up and down the soles of my feet... After every torture, they threw me into a box where I lay bound and blindfolded. On October 25th 20th, late in the evening, they wrapped me up half-dead and carried me to a car.'"

He glanced at Alice, "I won't go on reading if you'd rather not."

"Please go on."

"'On October 8th 1948, former partisan, Feitová, was carried off to a State Security bungalow, now known to be in Velká Úpa district and was kept for twelve hours in a box.'

'Hlinovská, the warden at Pankrác prison, assisted the investigators and placed VB naked in a correctional cell and forced her to walk until she fainted. She was woken up by kicks and curses from Peček, the investigator. The results

327

of interrogation: double pneumonia and vaginal infection.'

'The Deputy Minister of Justice, Karel Klos, told the women prisoners at Pankrác that until they scraped the whitewash off the walls and ate it, they weren't having such a bad time.'

'There was one non-flush toilet for 80 women in the provisional wing of the women's prison at Pardubice 1954. Women in Písek were only allowed a bath once in five weeks in a single wooden tub.'

'It was customary to put women prisoners in cells where the inmates had infections diseases or were aggressive psychopaths.'

He looked at Alice's serious face and closed his notebook, "Shall we go?"

Outside, she squinted up at the blue sky and got out her dark glasses, "I don't suppose there are any memorials to all the people who died in the purges..." "I know its rather a horrid question but what happened to all the corpses?"

"Some were buried and it's said that others were incinerated in the Martin blast-furnaces at Kladno. Workers were told that secret documents were being burnt."

"What about the survivors of the Fifties? Some must still be alive?"

"Some of them are in their seventies now and the Confederation of Political Prisoners is trying to get justice for them. The Prague branch is known as KPV-231 after a law of 1948 which was used to jail thousands of people. One of the survivors, Václav Horký, spent ten years in prison at Bohunice where Slánský was interrogated. He had the job of cleaning out the 'Pavilion of Terror' which was part of the prison hospital and he says that anyone who went into that place was doomed. He works for KVP-231 and says that he wants criminals brought to book, but above all he wants to keep the memory of those dark days alive."

* * *

328

"This is the Ministry of Industry, formerly the Ministry of Foundry, Metallurgy and Heavy Engineering. It was built in the First Republic by Josef Fanta who designed the main railway station."

"It looks a bit traditional for a Thirties building."

"A blend of old and new..." He took her through the lobby, "Please look at the staircase!"

She admired the grand Art Nouveau circular stairway and the small windows on the landings, "A touch of Cubism!"

"I've brought you here because in the Fifties this building became a power-house in Stalin's empire. He forced us into the role of an engineering satellite and metallurgy and engineering had to take first place in our economy while other things went by the wayside. Our whole economy had to change direction within a few years."

"And now you're changing again!"

"Stalin wrenched us away from our traditional roots..."

The Ministry of Industry

"What roots?"

"Our ties with the industrialized West and our successful branches of light industry. We became his heavy industry workshop in the Eastern bloc. To push through this change, central directives were needed. After the Nationalization Decree of October 1945 and during the first Five Year Plan which began in 1949, our economy was completely nationalized and most small businesses disappeared. A few were left — tailors, cobblers, village blacksmiths — but by the end of the Fifties the number of small businesses was negligible compared with East Germany, Hungary or Poland. We were tied to Stalin's chariot which meant high expenditure on the army and armaments. By 1955, over 10 % of our national income was going to the military. Economically, we became dependent on the Soviet Union for our supplies of raw materials and the Soviets dictated the prices of our exports. By 1953, 35 % of our exports were going to the Soviet Union and over three-quarters to the communist bloc, a huge jump from the First Republic when the figures were just over one percent for the Soviets and just over 16 % for the other comrades."

"At least you were certain of customers in the Fifties!"

"We became lazy! A lot of our exports were shoddy but many of our companies didn't care about quality, they knew our comrade neighbours would gulp whatever we produced."

"Most people were really enthusiastic about state-ownership after the war, weren't they?" she asked. "They wanted to get rid of private capitalists, unemployment, slums, beggars... that's why the communists got votes."

"The enthusiasm died away. It's true that people had security in old age and enough to eat but when they looked across the borders to West Germany and Austria and saw that workers there could earn in one day what they earned in a month, they lost enthusiasm for the glorious proletarian revolution."

"So you were ruined by capitalist neighbours!"

"People seemed to go into a kind of half-slumber and only

came alive at weekends when they went off to their country cottages. Prague was like a city of the dead by Friday afternoons, the only people on the streets were East Germans!"

"Having a planned economy seems logical to me," she said obstinately, "leaving everything to market forces only seems to make the rich richer."

"But the Plans didn't work! Probably no branch of industry fulfilled the Plans by more than 35% and the working week seemed to get shorter and shorter. Prime Minister Černík complained in 1969 that the whole country had a three and a half day working week. At noon each day people stopped working and went to lunch even if customers were waiting. One of my clients who used to come here regularly on business, told me that the clerks in the airlines offices would start making out tickets for people, look at their watches, see it was noon and walk away without a word. They'd go off for lunch leaving the half-written tickets on their desks. The Plans existed on paper but the reality was absurd. At the new Klement Gottwald Steel-Works, for example, the blast furnace had to be ready for the completion of the Plan but only half of it was built. When Gottwald arrived there was an official celebration to mark the firing of the furnace and the usual speeches were made praising the glory of socialist labour but the reality beneath all the fine words was a furnace stuffed with cardboard and small pieces of wood. When I took a Swedish industrialist to a textile factory in North Bohemia five years ago, we saw the workers wandering around chatting and drinking beer and my client thought they were on strike! He was shocked by the lack of investment here, too. We saw workers mixing a solution for coating textiles with wooden spoons in large kettles, it looked like something out of Charles Dickens. We're only just discovering that our technology and machine plant are years behind the West…

She looked at him sceptically, "You want to convince me that everything under communism was out of date and falling to bits But you must have had some successful industries.

After all, you've told me there was quite a good standard of living here."

"There was enough in the shops if you were prepared to search for it, though no one knew why the Plans didn't ensure a supply of vinegar in the summer months! But our economy was marching backwards from the tenth or eleventh position in the world industrial league to something like the fortieth. And there was a big price to pay for keeping up a bearable living-standard — it meant raping the environment. We're still frighteningly dependent on brown coal which produces large amounts of sulphur dioxide. The regime kept people reasonably content in the short-term but we're facing the long-term consequences now."

"Most Western governments think in the short-term, too. They only seem to start worrying about the environment when elections are coming up!" she said.

"Another problem in our centralized economy," he continued firmly, "was our jungle of bureaucracy, a jungle swarming with crocodilian clerks. Under communism, paper work was a god! There were was a menacing flood of orders, decrees, directives, political questionnaires and reports which swamped production. There were endless regulations and tons of paper piled up on the tables of factory managers, clerks and medical practitioners. Communist utopia was a weird place where vast piles of paper were shifted from table to table! For most Czechs, communism was an unbearably rude clerk and half an hour in any office was enough to make you feel murderous. Yet the same clerk went to a shop to buy something in the lunch-hour and came up against a bored and unwilling sales-person and had to queue two or three times while receipts were written out and checked. Some repairmen walked the town with their big repair bags and then sat in the pubs and wrote up pages of paper-work about the jobs they hadn't done! You see, no one could ever be sacked unless they stepped out of line politically."

"Wasn't that a good thing? At least you didn't have dole

queues. And if things were really going so badly wrong with the economy surely the government would have done something about it?"

"The regime knew the Plans weren't working and they knew that the new generation of technicians which had grown up since the war were fed up with all the bungling and red tape and their low wages which in no way corresponded to their qualifications. Critics in the Party drew up plans for reform on several occasions, in 1958 and 1965 for example, but there was always the problem of Party dogma. The Party looked on itself as the sole centre of political and economic life and if it loosened its grip on the economy, it might lose its grip on everything else."

As they left the building and walked towards the car, Blažej began to laugh, "One of our writers, Karel Michal, has some great stories about the bureaucracy here, I particularly like the one about Houska's hard-working chicken..."

She looked at him in surprise.

"One day after his customary visit to the pub, Houska, a fifty year old paver, found a huge speckled egg lying by his door. He took the egg to bed with him and was amazed next morning to find he'd hatched out a miraculous chicken. The chicken accompanied him to his job and worked like a fury on the building site and all Houska had to do was carry water, lime and sand around. He earned far more money than usual for the day's work but he was exhausted by the end of the day. The chicken wouldn't even allow him to go to the pub for his ten o'clock break."

Alice smiled, "I suppose written complaints began to pour in?"

"Houska's workmates were purple with rage. They complained that the chicken's unheard of output was showing up their own efforts and it wasn't long before they sent an angry delegation to complain to Management. A whole army of deputies, standardizers, rate-fixers and secretaries descended on Houska. After a great deal of form-filling, the Head of the Works & Wages Department asked the Personnel Department to regularize the unusual situation by registering the chicken as a piecework employee. However, the Personnel Department couldn't register the chicken until it had produced a document cancelling its previous employment."

"So what did they do?"

"The Head of the Works and Wages Department, shocked by Houska's soaring wages, went to see the Chief Engineer who'd been a confectioner by profession. He called an emergency meeting, but the meeting was hamstrung because no allowance for the chicken's activities had been made in the Plan. There was also the problem that it couldn't be paid according to the usual rates because of the furious pace of its work. The firm's Legal Adviser came up with the ingenious suggestion that the chicken should be taken on as a mechanized unit and this proposal was adopted with the important proviso that special papers would have to be prepared registering the chicken as a machine..."

"Wasn't that insulting to the chicken?" she, interrupted.

"Houska fought against the proposal, pointing out that the chicken ate regularly and sometimes even slept and could not therefore be categorized as a building machine. He was reproved by his lawyer for defending the bird because he was putting himself in a dangerous position by exploiting labour."

"Could the chicken talk?"

"Yes, but it hadn't got time for conversation, it was much too busy! The Head of the Machine Department was angry about the proposal too, and lodged a formal complaint saying that his department could not be designated as a zoo. That evening Houska pleaded with the chicken and asked it if it couldn't work at a slower pace. The chicken briskly refused to listen to such an idea and Houska went to bed depressed. In the morning he was so desperate that he tried to strangle the chicken..."

"How horrible!"

"It wasn't helping him! He was killing himself with work   334 and upsetting all his mates. Of course, it's impossible to strangle a magical creature and the chicken advised him to say a few words if he wanted it to go..."

"What words?"

"The words usually said on such occasions, 'Fie, fie, I don't want you!' The chicken flew out of Houska's life and he worked happily ever after."

"But the chicken had earned him a lot of money!"

"He preferred his little comforts!"

* * *

She lent over the low parapet on Letná Height and gazed at the view, "Brilliant! There's unusual view of Hradčany and the Belvedere and a great view of the Vltava." She stared down at the river, a ribbon of silver-grey with miniature barges.

Site of Stalin's statue

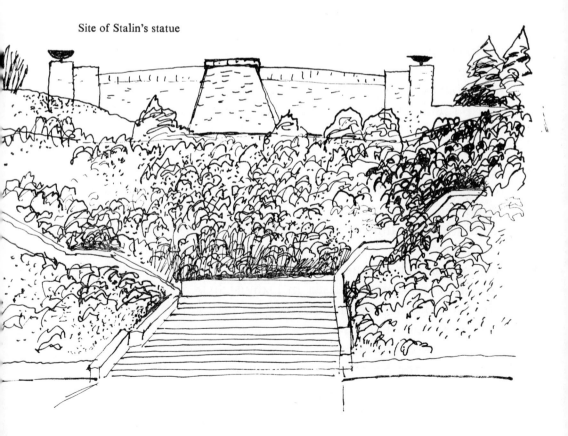

Stalin & the Meat Queue

Blažej edged behind her and lit up surreptitiously.

Her shoulders shook, "I know what your up to!"

He stubbed out his cigarette on the stone parapet, "Please turn round, I want to show you where the Meat-Queue stood!"

"Meat-Queue?" she stared at the strangely truncated concrete structure.

"It was the Praguers' name for the biggest group statue of Stalin in the world, a gigantic granite monument showing Stalin leading three men and a woman: a worker in a beret manning the barricades, an intellectual, a soldier and a socialist mother. There was a great shortage of meat in Prague at the time and Joseph Vissarion Dzhugashvili was first in line! He looked out over Prague from his pedestal here on Letná Plain for almost seven years and there was a grand unveiling in 1955 in commemmoration of the so-called liberation of Prague by the Soviet army." He handed her a photograph, 336

"This will give you some idea of what the statue looked like. It was the most dominant feature of my hundred-spired town and it was meant to be indestructible. Stalin was to be immortal! The designs for the monument covered four metres of paper and the communist big-wigs praised the designers to the skies. One of the designers came up with the mad idea for a rotating Stalin so that Big Brother could turn round and keep a watchful eye on the military May-Day parades up here."

She studied the photo and burst out laughing. "What a waste of paper! How big was the monument?"

"The giant structure was over 30 metres high and Stalin measured over 15 metres, his granite head alone measured two metres."

"What did he measure in real life?"

"About 1,60 metres! He was a small thickset man with red hair, an insignificant-looking fellow. The amount of granite needed for the colossus was staggering, over 14,000 tons of it. Hundreds of stone-masons laboured in the quarries of Ruprechtice and Rochlice hewing the granite and it was brought to Prague in specially designed waggons. The stone for Stalin's head alone weighed 52 tons. The paving-stones and masonry supports came from quarries all over the country and 600 people worked here, including the sculptors and masons, for 495 days."

"Who paid for it? It must have cost a lot."

"The long-suffering taxpayers, I suppose. A discreet veil was drawn over the cost and it still hasn't been lifted. Some estimates reckon with 160 million crowns, in today's terms about 2 billion. But apart from the problem of finding such a gigantic sum, there were a host of other hitches. There seemed to be an ill-omened cloud above the Generalissimo's head: Švec, the principal sculptor, didn't turn up for the unveiling ceremony. For some time he'd been getting anonymous letters saying things like, 'You traitor, building a monument to the murderer of the Czech nation!' By all acounts Švec was an abstemious, hard-working sort of person, apparently happily married to a beautiful and elegant woman who was the model for some of his allegorical figures. He was overwhelmed with grief when she died in the early Fifties. It was a bitter winter and as the heating had failed in their apartment they'd moved into a friend's studio. One day his wife stretched herself out on the couch and gassed herself. She'd left Švec a note which he carried everywhere in his pocket. About three years after her death in April 1955, Švec also gassed himself. He was sixty-two years old and he died just sixteen days before the elaborate unveiling ceremony. Everything had been prepared but where was Švec? Two weeks after his suicide his body was discovered under a blanket in his studio. The street was packed with State Security, police and Ministry cars and the police went into the house and broke up everything in the studio including his valuable models."

"Why?"

"Possibly they wanted to see if he'd hidden anything or they might just have felt vengeful. Švec had left all his property to the Klárov Institute for the Blind but it was all destroyed."

"It's a tragic tale," she said thoughtfully, "but he didn't have to sculpt Stalin, did he?"

Blažej considered her remark, "He had a living to make and great pressure was put on people in those days..."

She nodded, "I don't know what I would have done if I'd been an artist at that time... What did other sculptors feel about the Stalin statue?"

"I can only quote one of them, Hugo Demartini. He was a young sculptor in his final year at the Academy and he worked on the figure next to Stalin, the worker on the barricades. He said it was absolutely nauseating having to build such a gigantic stupidity! Although he had two excellent stone-masons working with him he said he had enormous problems sculpting the worker's face because of the statue's great height. To make it seen lifelike from the ground, he had to hew the Liberec granite in sharp contours otherwise the face would have looked like a potato! He described how the

338

sculptors and masons were organized into work platoons with supervisors who gave them personal assessments. Model workers had their photos plastered up around Prague but Demartini avoided this honour by pointing out that it would have upset the masons who were working long hours. He was relieved to get out of the dubious honour of doing Stalin's head, claiming that he had to get back to his studies."

"When did Stalin vanish?"

"In the thaw of the early Sixties. Khrushchev had criticized Stalin's personality cult in 1956 and the Generalissimo's crimes were coming to light, but our leaders were as quiet as mice for a while because they didn't know what to do with the Meat-Queue! The thought of destroying the monstrosity was even more mind-boggling than putting it up. What to do with thousands of tons of granite and reinforced concrete? If the structure was blown up and collapsed on the Čech Bridge or fell into the Vltava it could do enormous damage. However, something had to be done... An unobtrusive but insistent directive came from the Kremlin in 1961 — Stalin must disappear! Some experts came up with the idea that Stalin should be replaced with an allegorical metal lady holding a floral bouquet but they didn't get a response from Hendrych, the Party ideologist!"

Alice stretched herself out on the warm parapet and he sat down next to her, facing the concrete plinth, "Various explosive experts from the Baraba Company were told to solve the problem and they decided the only way to demolish Stalin was to break him down gradually. The whole monument was fenced in and this hillside was covered with a gigantic wooden structure which extended over the Čech Bridge and the surroundings. As soon as the Generalissimo and his inscription 'To our Liberator — the Czechoslovak People', had been fenced in, another inscription appeared on Stalin's gigantic side, 'JOSEPH, WATCH OUT, THEY'RE AFTER YOU!'"

She burst out laughing and Blažej began to splutter. It was a few seconds before he took up his story, "The first step was to cut off Stalin's head. It was broken up into pieces the size of paving-stones and thrown into the hollow skeleton of the statue. However, one enterprising worker managed to secure one of Stalin's ears..."

"Whatever for?"

"He needed a duck pond! For several weeks, holes were bored into Stalin's body for the dynamite. Unfortunately, the explosion only opened up his belly. More explosions followed in the next few weeks but Stalin wouldn't yield. Only after a final huge effort did they manage to blast Big Brother off his pedestal. Then stone-masons turned up to hew paving-stones from the first-grade granite. Grotesque tractors, nick-named 'Camels' by the Praguers arrived to tear down what remained of the monument but the surrounding border stayed put for a couple more years and then it was broken up and sold as building-stone.

"What happened to all the rubble? she asked curiously.

"A lot of it was carted away and some of it was thrown into the giant hollow below the monument. Originally, the area around the statue had been raised so that the monument would dominate Prague and the Letná Plain. This left a yawning cavern and the original plan was to fill it up with earth but construction specialists said that every metre of earth would take a year to settle and as President Zápotocký was absolutely insistent that the unveiling should take place on May 1st 1955, a reinforced concrete platform on pillars was built under the monument."

They began to walk down the steep flights of steps towards the river and Alice looked with pleasure at the churches and palaces on the opposite bank.

"Stalin's baleful influence went on even during the demoli-tion work," Blažej continued, "his statue was hollow with ladders inside and one expert had to go in and inspect the Generalissimo's innards before the detonations began. He went in with a lamp in one hand and his bag in the other, slipped on the steps and fell on his head."

They paused on the bridge and looked back at Letná 340

Height. Blažej began to chuckle, "Stalin would have fallen off his perch if he'd known about some of the goings-on under his nose. There was even a strike here in 1953. The workers were protesting against the government's currency reform which hit working people hard. President Zápotocký, who became President after Gottwald's death in 1953, arrived personally to talk to the workers and he got on with them rather well. He'd been a stone-mason himself and the old-timers greeted him in a familiar way and listened to his arguments. There was no unpleasant aftermath to the strike which was remarkable at that time."

"Were there any other goings-on?"

"I've heard stories that a shady sort of establishment opened under Stalin's feet at one time..."

"A brothel, you mean?"

"Not exactly, but a rowdy spot with some rough types and their molls. There was jovial singing and some winks and nudges under Big Brother's boots."

She laughed in a bemused way as they walked back to the car, "It's weird, it was difficult enough building Stalin but hell trying to get rid of him."

"He was very reluctant to leave us!"

* * *

"The Sixties brought a wind of change," Blažej said, as they strolled up Masarykovo Nábřeží Street along the Vltava embankment.

"The end of Stalin and the great Prague Meat-Queue?"

He smiled, "By the mid — Sixties there were critical rumblings in the Communist Party itself as well as outside it, particularly as the unwieldy centralized economy was going into terminal decline. Antonín Novotný, a hard-line bureaucrat who had become Party Leader in 1953 and President in 1957, found he was sitting on a volcano. He was forced out of office in January 1968 and Alexander Dubček, the Slovak Party leader, replaced him. Dubček bowed to the clamour for change and his government brought out an

Action Programme in April 1968 promising cautious political and social reforms. But Dubček was in a difficult position because although many people in this country wanted sweeping changes by 1968, he had to tiptoe through the tulips with the Soviets."

Blažej stopped in front of an elegant eighteenth century house with a fine oak portal and wrought-iron balconies. "This is where the most influential paper in the Prague Spring had its offices. It was a weekly paper called Literární Listy, meaning Weekly Leaves, and it had a circulation of something like 300,000. It provided an important platform for the intelligentsia and many well-known writers contributed to it. On June 27th 1968, it published Ludvík Vaculík's 2000 Words Manifesto, signed by 70 leading writers, artists, sports personalities and other public figures. Although the Manifesto expressed loyalty to Dubček, it left his Action Programme far behind and proposed radical

Offices
of Literární Listy

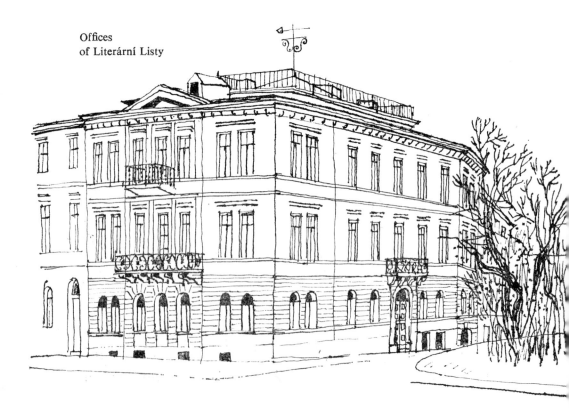

reforms. The people who signed it were worried that if reforms weren't pushed through quickly they'd be blocked by hardliners in the bureaucracy with backing from the Soviets. It was an appeal to the public to stand behind reforms like freedom of speech and assembly and it was immensely popular..."

He led her across Masarykovo Nábřeží and down Novotného Lávka Lane to an outdoor cafe overlooking the river. They sat at a small white table on a circular cobblestone area overhung with an ancient willow. She stared at the broad sweep of the river with its foaming weir and across at Charles Bridge and then up to the soaring bulk of St. Vitus.

Blažej ordered coffee and ices.

She smiled, "Let's go on with 1968! The 2000 Words Manifesto must have got up the Soviet nose."

"Some very menacing noises had been coming from the Soviets for some time," he replied, "and from March 1968, Dubček had received a torrent of reproaches from the Polish and East German leaders as well. They ran a big smear campaign in their newspapers and some papers even reported that American tanks had arrived in Prague and that special American units disguised as tourists were on their way to this country on buses from West Germany! But it was more sinister than that. About 30,000 troops from the Soviet Union, Poland and East Germany staged military manoeuvres here between May and August 1968 — a hefty bit of military blackmail. Ten days after the 2000 Words Manifesto was published, Dubček was summoned to a summit meeting in Warsaw and when he excused himself saying that he had previous engagements, the Warsaw Pact sent their most ominous warning. Their letter said that imperialist forces were taking Czechoslovakia away from socialism and that the events here were a threat to the whole socialist system. The letter went on to say that the Warsaw Pact countries had no intention of interfering in the internal affairs of this country..."

343   "Meaning exactly the opposite!" Alice plucked at his sleeve,

"I still don't really understand what the Soviets were getting so steamed up about. After all, Czechoslovakia was still a socialist country, wasn't it?"

"The Prague Spring was poison to the Soviets. It wasn't just a matter of ideology, though the idea that the Party should have the leading role in society was holy dogma. It was all to do with power. Leonid Brezhnev was determined to hold the Eastern bloc together for strategic and military reasons. If the Czechs and Slovaks slipped out of the Soviet net, then who knows how many East Europeans might want to do the same."

"It's almost as though the Czechs were a bit drunk in 1968," she mused, "and I'm not thinking of your good Czech beer... I mean boozed up on freedom!"

"It can be very addictive!"

* * *

"1968 blew people's lives apart," he said, as they walked down Vinohrady Street, "and personal dramas faded into insignificance. My mother's cousin, Marie Wágnerová, went to visit a friend of hers in Prague the day before the Soviet invasion and she heard an odd story. Thirty years before, her friend Lena had met a handsome young Czech pilot who'd arranged to leave this country to fight with the British airforce. They parted with great emotion and he said he would telephone her whatever happened and she should wait for his call. Lena was pregnant at the time and she quickly found a man to marry her and be a father to her child. The years slipped by... the war, the Nazi occupation, the putsch, the grey Fifties... Then in July 1968, she got a phone call. It was her former lover! She ran to meet him in a small tavern on Mikulandská Street but when she got there she couldn't believe her eyes. Where was her handsome pilot in his dashing blue uniform? She saw a hunched and haggard middle-aged man with a seamed face. He spoke to her in a faltering voice and during their conversation he got up and pulled up his shirt. His back was criss-crossed with scars from his years in forced labour camps. Lena drank her coffee and rushing home to her husband, she threw her arms round the man whom she'd thought of as dull for thirty years and she thought how good he was and how he'd looked after her and her son."

Alice looked at Blažej aghast, "Horrible, she's not my sort! How could she give her lover the push just because he looked old and ill? He was father to her child, too!"

Blažej looked surprised but went on with his story, "Wágnerová went to bed that night thinking about Lena's tale and in the early hours of August 21st she was woken up by a noise like thunder. She felt terribly afraid, dressed quickly and went out into the street. Outside the supermarket opposite her apartment she saw an enormous queue.

'What's going on?' she asked.

'The Russians have come!'

She hesitated, wondering whether to join the queue and stock up with food but then she turned away and hurried to the town centre. Up here she saw some Russian soldiers sprawled on the pavement. She said they looked like mere boys from Asiatic Russia, slant-eyed and grimy. Prague seemed to be shaking in a storm of noise and then she saw the Soviet tanks rumbling down this road, their tank-belts crushing the edges of the pavements. During the night of 20th to the 21st of August, about 400,000 troops had crossed our borders — Russians, Poles, East Germans and Bulgarians. Prague airport had been seized and huge An-12 cargo planes, one landing every minute, brought an armoured division into the town. Three columns of tanks arrived, one surrounded the Castle, one occupied the Party headquarters and another the Prime Minister's office. Prague Radio broadcast a statement from the invaders saying that they were responding to a request for help from the Czechoslovak leaders and that the armed forces of the Warsaw Pact were going to the support of the working people to defend the gains of socialism which were threatened by imperialist plots and counter-revolutionaries."

"Was there a request for help?"

"It was reported by Pravda on August 22nd, but three days later it was no longer mentioned and not even Soviet propaganda bothered with a possible begging letter!"

"What happened to Wágnerová?"

"She joined an enormous crowd blocking this street. It was jammed with people and the crowd stretched for several hundred metres forming a live barricade. The tanks advanced relentlessly towards it and some of the soldiers fired into the air and into windows. Then there was un uncanny silence and people seemed to press closer to each other for comfort. The driver of the first tank seemed to hesitate but then his tank slowly rolled forward again towards the unarmed mass. Suddenly, someone began to shout from a balcony, it was Emil Zátopek, the Olympic champion. 'Stand back! Put your backs to them' he shouted.

People immediately pressed onto the pavement and the human barricade divided on both sides of the street. Slowly, the tanks rolled through the human walls. People at the lower end of this street were feverishly building barricades using cars and lorries. The soldiers began to shoot wildly and there was a terrible noise of machine-gun fire. One woman was crushed by a tank. The window-panes in this building were shattered and crashed to the ground."

She looked up at the solid building, "What is it?"

"The Prague Radio building designed during the First Republic," he pointed upwards. "Zátopek was calling out from that balcony."

"Down here, people spat on the soldiers, threatened them with their fists or taunted them," Blažej continued, as they walked towards the National Museum. "One beautiful girl in a low-cut blouse, a mini-skirt and black stockings bit into a ham sandwich in front of a hungry tank-crew and then threw it away. Then she lit a cigarette, inhaled a few times and stamped on it. Some of the soldiers lost their nerve and fired at an ambulance. Then they started firing into the side of the National Museum. Dubček's colleague, Josef Smrkovský, 346 saw a Soviet parachutist shoot a young man almost under the window of Dubček's study and he immediately telephoned Červoněnko, the Russian Ambassador and said he held him responsible for the killing."

"Were many people injured?"

"Seventy-two wounded were taken to Vinohrady hospital during the day, mostly young workers. One of the first victims of the shooting near the Radio Building was Zdeněk Příhoda,

Vinohrady Street —
Radio Building.

a twenty-seven year old factory worker. His family went to pay their last respects at the Strašnice Crematorium and at 9.45 pm a deputation of young workers from his factory at Armabeton entered the crematorium hall carrying Czech flags adorned with black ribbons. In Bratislava there was the funeral of Eva Kosanová who'd been shot, together with other students in front of the Komenský University."

"And Wágnerová?"

"Her legs were shaking and she felt sick but she got back to her apartment and switched on the radio. At first there was a crackling noise and then she heard the government's declaration stating that they considered the occupation of this country an illegal act which violated international law."

"Didn't the Soviet take over the radio?"

"Yes, but radio stations stayed on the air by moving their studios around the country."

They sat down in the little square beside the National Museum and Alice sighed deeply, "I' don't suppose there was much people could do against four hundred thousand soldiers and tons of steel."

"There was an amazing passive resistance. People did everything they could to harrass and bewilder the occupying forces. Railway workers sabotaged the rail network. All the street-signs and house numbers were removed and telephone directories were removed from public booths. The names of villages and towns were changed and renamed 'Dubčekovo', 'Dubček's Place'. Signposts were carted off or turned round and some of them were repainted with the inscription, 'Moscow 2000 km.' Here in Prague the walls of houses were smothered in slogans and hand-made posters. Improvised monuments with flags and flowers appeared where people had been shot. Around the country shop-keepers and farmers refused to supply the invaders and when darkness came lights were turned off in small villages and towns... The Soviets weren't prepared for such a national resistance and they got worried about the morale of the soldiers. Three days after the invasion, the soldiers in Prague and other towns were replaced with different contingents! The free radio stations strengthened people's resistance and issued the Ten Commandments." Blažej began to chant:

"You don't know; you don't care; you don't tell; you don't have; you don't know how to; you don't give; you can't do; you don't sell; you don't show; you do nothing".

She lent against him for a moment as they left the square, "It's like a fairy-tale... brains against tanks!"

* * *

"The Soviet invasion was a punch on the nose for European Lefties," he said, as they walked towards the car, "very few of them could support the Russians after 1968."

"But it didn't mean the death of socialism," she said stubbornly, "I mean democratic socialism."

He gave her a sharp look, "There was even a pro-Czechoslovakian demonstration in Red Square."

"How many turned up?"

"Fifteen! At least four of them were arrested. The occupation of my country was even upsetting for crooks. When a thief in Venice stole a car and found it was a Czechoslovak model, he left it at a police station with a note of apology!"

"What about the government here, what happened to Dubček?"

"He was seized with his colleagues on August 21st and put on a Soviet plane in handcuffs. An air hostess tried to give him a bunch of flowers and lost her job because of it. The Soviets forced him to sign the Moscow Protocol which set out what the Soviets called 'normalization', in other words, silencing the opposition. Dubček had collapsed several times in Moscow and when he returned to Prague on August 27th and spoke to the nation over the radio he was in a highly emotional state and his speech was interrupted with long pauses and sobs. He appealed to the country to be calm and warned that there would have to be 'temporary' restrictions on freedom. His speech made an unforgettable impression and it was followed up by the studio announcer who said that the employees at Prague Radio all stood behind him because they knew he'd not had an easy time..."

"Did Dubček really think the reforms could go on?"

"Perhaps he thought they could go on discreetly but in reality they were doomed. Over the next eight months he had to make more and more concessions. Pro-Soviet stooges were edged into important government positions, the radio stations were closed and the Press muzzled. He was gradually stripped of his functions in 1969 and he was packed off to Turkey as ambassador in January 1970. The Soviets probably hoped he'd stay there! He returned at the end of May and in June he was expelled from the Party and became a lowly forestry worker in Bratislava for nineteen years. Communism with a human face had gone into the dustbin of history! Communism and democracy... it's like trying to combine fire and water. Anyway, if something has to be given a human face, it can't be up to much!"

"How do you know?" she said vehemently, "It didn't have a chance. It was a fantastic experiment and if the Soviets hadn't stepped in, it would probably have worked. There must be some alternative to capitalism or communism... capitalism's cruel."

"And communism's lethal!"

"I'm not defending communism" she said angrily. "but surely it must be possible to plan a society where people can get a fair deal? There was something wonderful and noble about the Prague Spring."

"We didn't defend ourselves, Dubček didn't call out the army."

"But that would have meant thousands of deaths!"

"1968 was an illusion," he said firmly, "the Prague Spring wasn't what it seemed..."

"What do you mean?"

"For twenty years the Soviets had wanted a permanent army and missile-bases in this country and their agents were working day and night with their friends the StB to create a situation which would give them a pretext to move in. The 350

Action Programme and the Two Thousand Words gave them their pretext but their planning had been done earlier. It takes time to manoeuvre a colossal army. The Soviets knew they could get away with their invasion in 1968; the Americans were up to their necks in Vietnam. They knew there would be a lot of pious hand-wringing in the West but they also knew the West would do absolutely nothing!"

"You're into your puppet-theatre again!" she looked at him indignantly. "The Prague Spring wasn't just a script written by the Soviets. What about all the brave people who stuck their necks out? Your people made the Prague Spring because they believed in socialism with a human face."

* * *

They walked down 17. Listopadu Street to the Museum of Decorative Arts and he showed her the bronze plaque by the museum entrance.

"Jan Palach!"

351   Jan Palach

She looked at the sensitive face, "I saw a documentary film about him" she said slowly, "There was a great procession... people going through the streets with candles."

"On January 16th 1969 at 3.p.m., Palach, a twenty-one year old philosophy student at Charles University, stood on the steps of the National Museum, took off his overcoat, put his briefcase down by the fountain and poured a can of petrol over himself and set fire to it."

Alice shuddered, "Wasn't there anyone to save him?"

"There was a tram station in Wenceslas Square at that time and one of the attendants saw a burning figure running towards him. Palach screamed, 'Throw a coat over me!' Then he tripped and fell. The attendant put out the flames with his coat and Palach was rushed to hospital. He had third degree burns over most of his body and died within four days. The TV announcer wept when she read the short news item about his death and our whole nation went into mourning."

"Only twenty-one... he was younger than me. I don't really understand... why did he kill himself?"

"He felt he had to make his lone protest against the Soviet occupation of our country. After the invasion we entered the 'lost years', the time of so-called normalization. Authenticity, struggle, purposeful work and effort faded away for most people along with the dream of a more open society. Palach touched a chord in our nation and on the afternoon after his death 200,000 people went to Wenceslas Square to put wreaths on the spot where he fell. Then they formed a great procession to the Philosophical Faculty of Charles University. Prague seemed to be numbed for days. On Friday 24th at noon there was a five minutes silence in the town. People stood silently and I've heard that even the police gave the salute. On the day of Palach's funeral the line of mourners stretched for three kilometres through the streets. My father was there and he told me that it was a cold damp day and he was shivering from the cold and a terrible feeling of grief. A man standing next to him shouted, 'What a country we're living in where the only bright future is the burning 352 body of a young boy!' The coffin, accompanied by the academic staff of Charles University in their medieval gold and brown robes, was carried to the Old Town Square where 100,000 people were waiting. The bells of Týn Church rang out and a choir sang a Hussite chorale from the tower of the Old Town Hall."

"Where was Palach buried?"

"In Olšany cemetary. People went there every year to put wreaths on his grave and light candles."

"I'm surprised the authorities allowed it."

"They did everything they could to try and wipe out his memory. His remains were dug up and cremated and taken away from Prague to a country churchyard at Všetaty."

She was silent for a while as she studied Palach's face. Then she turned to Blažej, "So young... was his tragedy really worth it? I'm thinking of all the things he could have done in his life, perhaps amazing things for his country."

"I think he did a great deal..."

She looked at the plaque sadly, "I don't really get turned on by martyrs. Maybe I got put off them when I had to go to church with my parents, all those wounds and agony... Some of them seemed to wallow in suffering like some of those miserable Baroque saints you showed me. I liked the ones full of the joys of life! Did Palach's death really change anything?"

Blažej pondered the question, "Perhaps not in an everyday sense, but there's more to life than the everyday. He gave us a kind of hope."

"How can such a horrible death bring hope?"

"He reminded us that normalization wasn't normal at all and that there's something more to life than being good adaptable citizens scrabbling after crowns. It's strange, Westerners are dismayed but not really surprised when Buddhist monks set fire to themselves because they think of it as an oriental practice but when a Central European student does it they find it very odd."

353   * * *

The prison was a five storied mustard-coloured building crouching under a great watchtower in a wasteland of decaying barns and sagging houses.

"This is Ruzyně!" Blažej explained. "Milada Horáková was jailed here in the Fifties and in the years after the Soviet invasion, Václav Havel and many others did time here."

He rang a bell at the porter's lodge and they were confronted by a furious guard, "Go away! Don't you know this is a prison?" he shouted.

They walked round the high walls, "What a strange silence," Alice said. "Not so much as a dog barking or a cell door slamming. I feel hundreds of eyes watching us..."

"Eva Kantůrková was in one of those cells and she could just get a glimpse through the small window of White Mountain and the Hvězda Summer Palace. Her book, 'My companions in the Bleak House' describes the conditions here during the 'lost years' after the Soviet invasion. She was investigated by the secret police along with other intellectuals when a French truck carrying foreign literature was seized on the border and she spent a year here in cells with common criminals. Her book's a moving description of their lives.

Ruzyně Prison

Soon after the Soviet invasion the doors of the state prisons began to close again, the StB crawled out of their holes and began to rebuild their secret town and pigheaded judges sat behind the tables of the vetting commissions. The Soviets insisted on a clamp-down after crowds had gone on the rampage in Wenceslas Square..."

"Why, what happened?"

On March 21st 1969, Czechoslovakia defeated the Soviets in the world ice-hockey championships in Stockholm and Prague went wild. Thousands of people left their TV sets and went to Wenceslas Square. Some of them wanted to climb St. Wenceslas' statue but it was surrounded by thorny bushes known as Štrougal's Park. Štrougal was the hard-line Deputy Prime Minister. I remember that ice-hockey match very well. I was playing outside our apartment block with some other eight — year olds and we shared some rather crude jokes about Tarasov, the Russian hockey coach. Then, on March 28th the Czechoslovak team defeated the Russians again and thousands of soldiers and students rushed to the centre of Prague, tore up Štrougal's Park and smashed the windows of the Soviet Aeroflot Office. They trampled on models of planes and threw furniture and pictures of Lenin onto a bonfire. Eventually five bus-loads of police arrived with tear-gas and truncheons." Blažej gave her a sharp look, "But perhaps the whole thing wasn't quite what it seemed..."

"Oh no!" she said in mock fury, "not another conspiracy theory?"

"Some say that the régime wanted to provoke demonstrations so that it could clamp down on 'anti-Socialist elements' and that the really important documents had been removed from the Aeroflot Office beforehand. It was odd that the police stood and watched the mayhem for some time without taking action and that a heap of paving-stones had been deliberately placed in front of the building... He sighed, "All we know for sure is that normalization began with a vengeance."

"Normalization?"

"Suppression of 'subversive elements'. Under Vasil Bilak, a Party hardliner, and Miloš Jakeš, his right-hand man, the Party was purged yet again and over 70 screening committees were set up. A lot of self-servers sat on the committees who were only too ready to denounce their colleagues to secure their own positions. Probably about 14,000 Party officials were dismissed and around 280,000 Party members. But the purges went far beyond the Party. Being an informer became a virtue once again and people like the Secretary of the Municipal National Council of Říčany sent notifications to employers when employees didn't turn up to vote at elections. The mass media was purged, 2000 journalists lost their jobs and a lot of newspapers offices were closed down. Literary and cultural journals were closed, too and by May 1970 there weren't any left. Many writers were banned and the purges went right through the film and theatrical worlds. Some actors were personally threatened like the well-known actress Chramostová, who was told that her left hand would be broken three times and that this was merely a 'warning', Heinrich Böll described Czechoslovakia as a cultural cemetery. Nine hundred university professors were dismissed and five departments in the Czechoslovak Academy of Sciences were closed, Employees in companies, publishing houses, schools, unions and many other institutions were forced to fill in humiliating questionnaires in which they had to describe their activities in 1968 and 1969. The army and police were purged, too, and nearly a third of army and police chiefs lost their jobs."

"I thought you said that Gustav Husák took over after Dubček, she interrupted, "He'd been in prison in the Fifties, hadn't he?" She looked up at the grim building, "So why was he sending people here?"

"It's true he'd spent years in prison and a lot of it in solitary confinement and he'd been looked on as a reformer in the Sixties but he was a skilful politician who bent with the Soviet wind!"

"What happened to all the people who lost their jobs?" 356

"They were forced to accept any job, usually badly paid physical work. There were probably more intellectuals stoking boilers, washing windows, cleaning railway carriages and laying bricks than in any other city in Europe! Some of them joked about their healthy lives on building sites but their careers were ruined, or at least interrupted, for a long time. For most people normalization meant passivity, apathy, hopelessness."

"I don't understand why people put up with it. There must have been some opposition, surely?"

"Some opposition, yes... but it's difficult to rebel with foreign troops on your soil. Also Husák's regime cunningly decided to permit more consumer goods to improve living standards and during the 1970s private consumption rose by over 36%. Many people were able to buy a car and weekend cottages. For those who did oppose the regime, life was unbearable. Eva Kantůrková describes how people were treated in this prison..."

Alice shuddered, "What happened to her, was she tortured?"

"She wasn't physically tortured though assaults on dissidents went on through the Seventies and Eighties. Zdena Tominová was physically attacked on May 29th 1979 and suffered from concussion. Zina Freundová was attacked in her home on October 13th 1981 her nightgown was torn off, her head was banged against the wall and she was beaten and kicked. There were sometimes appeals to Husák which needless to say, were ignored. On one occasion, for example, a worker, Radomír Hubálek, wrote to Husák offering to serve the sentence meted out to Otka Bednářová who was jailed in the autumn of 1979 and who was ill at that time. Eva Kantůrková was constantly interrogated and says that the prison regime aimed to humiliate people so that they would lose their mental bearings, make confessions and inform on their friends. In a bleak passage she says it was fatal to hang on to the hope of release. Like many others in her position, she was on remand and never knew when she'd be brought

357

to a court to be sentenced. Holding onto hope was dangerous because a prisoner could be drawn towards her interrogation officer. She writes that patience, not hope, was needed here."

Alice was listening intently, "What else do you remember from her book?"

"Smell! She describes the suffocating stench of prison life. She choked on the smell every time she was taken down from her cell on the fifth floor for interrogation. The reek of toilets, unwashed bodies, stale clothes and cigarette smoke that couldn't escape through the wire mesh on the cell windows." He pointed to the watchtower, "Then there was the horror of the exercise-yard deep under that tower. She called it one of the arseholes of the world. The prisoners were herded down the main staircase in track-suits with tattered blankets round their shoulders. They wore prison slippers with cardboard soles and they packed them with wads of cotton against the snow. Down in the yard all that the prisoners could see was a patch of sky and the high barred windows. Occasionally Eva got a glimpse of spring." He pointed to a water-tower in the corner of the yard, "From her interrogation cell, she saw a family of kestrels nesting there, they were teaching their young to fly."

* * *

"We're in Paneláks' land!"

She looked at the forest of grey apartment block which seemed to stretch on forever, "Alternative Prague... what are Paneláks?"

"High-rise apartment blocks for 400,000 Praguers. They're made out of pre-fabricated cement panels. This is Jižní Město, Prague's 'South Town', 100,000 people live here.

"What's the population of Prague?"

"About 1.2 million. A lot of people were grateful to get a modern heated apartment here in the early Sixties. There was a terrible housing-shortage after the war and the government hired architects to build the greatest number of apartments at minimum cost. Before these concrete monsters were

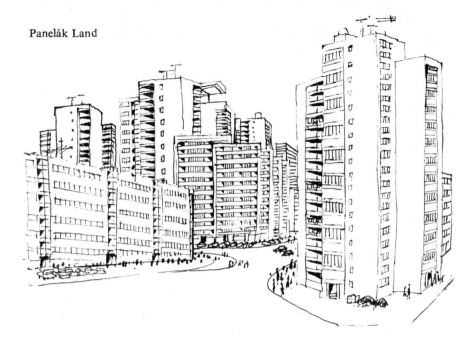

built it could take up to twenty years to get a flat. A friend of my mother's lived in a one-room flat for nine years with her husband and two children before moving into a ninth-floor apartment here. Even then there were rainwater leaks, the lift hadn't been built and there were no pavements, only a great muddy area criss-crossed with wooden boards. It was hell for mothers with prams, there was no landscaping of any kind."

She gazed down the long, bleak street, "There's not much now!"

"There's a park over there with tennis courts but most Paneláks just look onto each other without a tree in sight." He smiled, "A couple of years ago, I called on a friend of mine here and she had a surprise for me. When her parents moved to the country she made a park out of one of her rooms. There was artificial grass, garden paths and park bench and she'd even painted a sun on the ceiling!"

Alice laughed and nudged him gently, "So..., you sat with her on the park bench?"

"Yes, she told me she was getting plastic flowers for the small flower-beds. But it wasn't peaceful in her park. Panelák

359

walls are paper-thin and two lovers were having a quarrel next door."

She stared up at the concrete monsters, "I suppose you've brought me here to show me communist eye-sores, but the ones in London are just as grey." She sighed, "I don't know why they all have to look the same."

"Cost! The materials were cheap and automating the concrete panels cut down on labour-costs, but these flats are rather expensive for Praguers now. The poor insulation makes it very expensive to heat them and rents are rising rapidly."

"What's the average wage?"

"About 3,700 crowns which is about £ 72 and these flats cost between three hundred and eight hundred crowns a month, depending on the number of rooms. Most of the rooms here are very small, we call them 'Little Drawers'. The largest bedroom is usually about two metres wide and four metres long and people get very irritable living so close to each other. When I lived with my parents I used to lock myself in the bathroom with a book just to get a bit of privacy! Yet people switched on the TV and saw smiling comedies about life in Paneláks' land. Jolly people having a good time under socialism told us how lucky we were to have cheap housing, cheap heating, cheap food, in the socialist paradise. We heard that life under capitalism was cruel, hard and unbearable..."

"It often is!" she interrupted.

He gave her a keen look, "Not for you, surely?"

"But..."

"There were few jobs on these estates," he went on, "and people had to commute to work and they still do, packed into overcrowded buses. Originally, Paneláks' land was planned as a real community but the plans stayed on the drawing tables and there are few facilities for people here. There are some supermarkets and a couple of pubs... There's the cinema, it took ten years to build."

She stared at the shabby building, "It's closed!"

"It's waiting for a private buyer."

They turned to their left and walked down a Panelák-lined street towards an open space overgrown with weeds.

"The town hall!"

She looked at the small, drab building. "It looks like a tool-shed!"

"The block on our right is a home for divorced men and there's another down the street for women."

"How sad, blocks for divorced people."

"The divorce rate's always been high on these estates. Life was particularly hard for women under communism because they had two jobs, home and work. Shopping was a real nightmare because of the endless queuing..."

"Didn't men help them?"

"Some did, but Central European men... we're not very domesticated! We'll do jobs around the house, carpentry and so on but everyday chores aren't our scene. Naturally, women were tired and irritable and they felt drab. They couldn't afford nice clothes or anything to look glamorous and a lot of husbands walked out after a while and looked for a younger model. They usually found one but in no time at all the replacement started to look more and more like the original, tired, limp and droopy"...

Alice looked at him impatiently, "It's no different in the West! Lots of men look for younger models."

"But there was something different here under communism," he insisted, "Let's take advertisements, 'Handyman needed, car welcome.' Divorced women needed someone around when the toilet stopped flushing or the neighbour's bathwater came through the ceiling. Also sex played a special role under communism, especially during the 'lost years' of normalization. For most people, adventure and initiative had disappeared after the Soviet invasion and the sexual merry-go-round seemed to bring an element of risk and excitement into things..."

"It's no different..."

361   He cut across her, "A colleague of mine had an affair

with a married woman on this estate but the only time they could get together safely was in the lunch-hour when her husband was in his workshop. Her lover rushed from his architect's office in Prague 2, let himself into her flat, stripped off his clothes in the hall and then went straight into the sitting-room where they rolled around on the couch for half an hour without speaking. Then he dressed quickly and they both hurried back to work or to one of the endless pep-talks on the joys of socialist Labour. One day he couldn't get away from work on time, had to wait for the Metro and arrived late. He stripped off in the hall as usual and rushed panting into the sitting-room. Then he froze to the spot. The room was full of people including the lady's husband, talking and drinking coffee. They stared in amazement at the naked figure for a moment. He fled from the room, grabbed his clothes in the hall and rushed naked down the stairs. No one in the room ever found out who he was!"

She frowned, "You make it sound as though everyone was on a sex-spree. I suppose some people lived happily ever after?"

"Occasionally... I'd like to tell you about a former girl-friend of mine who lived in one of these Paneláks but I'm afraid the story's a bit..."

"Blažej!"

He coughed, "She lived in a tiny one-room flat and her next door neighbour was a rather lonely man who saw her quite often in the lift or in the supermarket. She was quite glamorous and he developed a real passion for her. Finally, he got really obsessive and bored a peep-hole in the thin partition wall so that he could see her in her bedroom..."

"Is that all?"

He coughed again, "His obsession grew with time and eventually he enlarged the peep-hole and stuck his penis through it. The poor girl would get back from work and see his member sticking through the wall! She felt too embarrassed to talk about it to anyone for some time but one day she got round to telling a couple of her so-called friends and they burst out laughing. Finally she got really desperate and went to her supervisor at work with the sorry tale. The supervisor was a tough, matter-of-fact lady, 'Go and see him', she advised, 'lodge a complaint!' That very evening the girl screwed up her courage and knocked on his door..."

"What did she say?"

"She invited him for coffee."

"What happened?"

"Within a few weeks they got married!"

Alice began to laugh, "There's a kind of Panelák madness!"

He shook his head, "Sometimes the sheer dreariness of life at that time and the general apathy snuffed out even the sexual sparks." He paused for a moment at the door of a small pub and she saw three men standing at formica-topped tables drinking beer under fluorescent lighting.

"Two men used to drink here most evenings for several years," he continued, "they were good mates and they used to discuss work and politics and so on. One day Milan invited his wife along and she took a fancy to his friend Robert. Within days they became lovers and she used to visit him regularly in the home for divorced men. After several months, lured by his sweet nothings, she decided after great heart-searching to leave her husband. It was a difficult decision because she liked Milan and it took her a long time to find the right moment to break things gently. One evening she packed a big suitcase and went into the sitting-room. Despite her husband's protests, she switched off the TV and amidst tears told him she was leaving him forever. Choking with emotion, she staggered out with her heavy case and dragged it across to the home for divorced men. She rang Robert's bell but no one came... After what seemed an eternity, she rang again and then a third time, Robert came to the door and stared at her. She could see the flicker of his TV set in the corner of the room. 'Go away!' he shouted, 'can't you see I'm watching TV?' Stunned, she picked up her suitcase and struggled back to her apartment. Her husband was still sitting in front of the television. 'Back so soon?' he commented."

"I suppose they were watching football?" she said acidly.

He laughed, "They were probably watching one of Jaroslav Dietl's TV serials. Everyone was hooked on them in the Seventies and Eighties. Dietl was a brilliant craftsman, probably the best propagandist the communists ever had. He was a superb scriptwriter who had his craft in his little finger, as we Czechs say. His serials covered more than ten thousand pages and he probably earned more than one million crowns a year. He could dramatize really banal events and hypnotize viewers with a dramatic story about a Secretary of a District Party Committee, bringing in all sorts of dramatic reversals and surprises. Dietl's serials were fairy tales in the socialist utopia, dreams within the dream."

"Your story about Milan and Robert and the poor woman with the suitcase reminds me of something," Alice said reflectively, as they walked back to the car, "you said you'd tell me about Little Robert."

Blažej looked resigned, "Little Robert was smuggled here from the West... Rumours circulated in Prague about his amazing sexual prowess and the wives of certain top communist functionaries were very intrigued. But where was little Robert to be found? Nobody knew. Eventually he was tracked down in an exclusive massage-parlour in a basement in a working-class district. Factory workers on their way home were surprised to see well-dressed women clutching leather handbags from the Tuzex shops standing in a long queue on the pavement in front of a shabby door..."

"Why...!"

Blažej continued briskly, "Although we lived in utopia, social classes soon developed. At the very top were communist millionaires who got rich through clever speculation in international trade. Western business men could buy goods or raw materials here cheaply if they knew whose palm to grease. Then there were Party functionaries who made profitable trade transactions by writing off machinery

364

as obsolete and selling it at a profit. These are the people who can buy a factory or a hotel today for millions of crowns! How they manage to be members of our Prague millionnaires' club is a mystery for most people. One or two rungs down from the top were various communist bosses who got high wages and all sorts of privileges. Under them came a kind of middle-class; university professors with opportunities to lecture abroad, artists collaborating with the regime, pop-singers, medical superintendents, generals. But so-called working people belonged to this class, too, and earned just as much. Taxi-drivers, waiters, petrol-pump attendants, money-changers. Taxi-drivers with access to foreign currency strutted about like turkey-cocks! I was sitting in a pub in the Old Town about four years ago reading my paper and sharing a table with a good-looking couple who were talking about art and literature and so on when a taxi-driver came in through the door. He stood on the threshold casually jangling his keys. The girl at my table looked at him for a moment and then went on with her conversation. The taxi-driver approached their table slowly and paused in front of the girl with his wallet open. Then he left. After a few minutes, the girl excused herself and went out..."

Alice made a face, "There are always some people who can be bought, even in the wonderful West! Who came below taxi-drivers'?"

"There was a kind of lesser elite — technicians with the Party card, journalists, managers of restaurants, heads of engineering workshops, directors of high schools, heads of agricultural combines, managers of work canteens."

"I don't see what's surprising about it, we've got classes in Britain."

"But we were supposed to have a classless society!"

"The girl who went after the taxi-driver... she didn't have to sell herself, did she?"

"It's hard for Westerners to understand the craving a lot of people had for Western things, a pair of jeans with a designer label or a nice sweater from one of the hard currency shops or maybe a bit of foreign currency to salt away for a longed-for trip abroad. I'm not defending the girl but things were very drab here and people wanted nice things so they could express a bit of individuality and stand out in all the greyness. Sometimes girls searched for foreigners just for the excitement of being with someone from the West, someone different... Some of the girls in my year at university used to hang around the international hotels on the look-out for foreigners. It was odd because they were studying Marxism for their exams!" He smiled suddenly, "A friend of my father's came here from Britain to teach English for a year on some sort of exchange system. He was middle-aged, fat and balding but he had the time of his life! He was besieged by young girls and felt like Prince Charming. He nearly wept when it was time for him to go home!"

She shook her head, "I think you're exaggerating, most college girls have plenty of things to think about... exams... careers."

He ignored the interruption, "Intellectual women often had a hard time under communism," he continued, "by the time a university graduate had finished her studies she was late on the marriage-market. Younger women who hadn't had to sit at home studying, had been out in a job and had saved up a bit of money to start up a home. The graduates went to dance-halls and coffee-houses looking for men but some of them never succeeded in finding a suitable partner which was sad, for an older woman only gets respect here if she's married."

"From what you've told me about some of the men, I'd say they were better off without them," Alice said caustically. "What did you think about all the sexual goings-on?"

"Maybe I'm an odd one, the merry-go-round doesn't appeal to me." He stopped and looked at her with a smile, "I'm looking for an Eve who doesn't want the apple!"

She looked puzzled, 'Doesn't the apple mean knowledge?"

"I'm talking about a different kind of apple."

She turned away, irritated, "You seem to have told me a lot about women selling themselves. What about men, didn't they sell themselves, too?"

"Often, and in various ways. To be successful, a man, or a woman for that matter, had to be part of a clan. It was best to have a party card but people without it could still get on in the world if they developed excellent relationships with those in their clan or mafia, brought them gifts when they returned from a trip abroad, invited them to their country cottages, took part in intrigues and helped trip up the undesirables."

She shrugged, "It happens everywhere!"

"But being part of a clan and toeing the Party line were crucial here because a person's working output really didn't matter very much, almost anyone could pretend to do the job! In the West you have to have some ability or you get thrown out..."

"Not necessarily, connections matter a lot too."

Blažej seemed not to hear her, "Marriage mattered a lot here on the way up the promotion ladder. I know of a very average journalist here who became a director of Filmexport because he married a prime minister's daughter. A mediocre actor who left school without taking the leaving exam landed a high prestige job in a film company through his father-in-law. When his father-in-law's star began to fade he got a divorce and married a TV director and secured his job when many others lost theirs after 1968. You see, once someone was securely in their clan, everything else followed; university places for their children, a good flat and so on — as long as he or she didn't step out of line politically."

"Aren't you exaggerating again, I mean did you know any of those go-getters really well?"

"Yes, I'll tell you about JK, a former friend of mine. He lived in a Panelák here and worked in the Academy of Sciences. However, he had a hard time of it fighting his way to the top and had to put up with rather an inferior job and low wages and no opportunity of getting a flat in the centre of town. He started to go to a lot of social functions and made careful enquiries about the girls he met and their circumstances. Eventually he got married to a girl whose father was a director of a building organization, so they got a good flat at once. However, JK wasn't satisfied, he wanted to be a director! His immediate boss was the Deputy Director of the company and JK offered to help him with his great hobby — gardening. He told his boss how he loved working in the open air and how interested he was in plants and so on. He worked in his boss' garden after work, at weekends and during vacations and for about a year and a half he tapped him for his opinions on the Director of the company, his habits and vices... Then he went to the Director and told him everything. In a fury the Director sacked his fifty year old Deputy and JK became Deputy Director at the age of thirty-five. After our Velvet Revolution in 1989, he quickly tore up his Party card, incriminated the Director and took over his job!"

She heaved a sigh, "There must have been a few honest people around who didn't sell themselves?"

"Yes, there were. During normalization some people withdrew with dignity into themselves and refused to co-operate with the regime. It was a kind of inner exile, they studied philosophy literature and languages and lived in poverty. Others became tramps like my history teacher at high school. He was a really nice man who tried to make the subject interesting but he got more and more distressed by the atmosphere in the school. A lot of the teachers lied to us a lot of the time and he couldn't bring himself to do it, so before the summer vacation he told the Director he was quitting and even told him why. Of course, there was no chance of him getting a decent reference after that, not even as a school caretaker. When he resigned his wife threw him out of the house, she simply couldn't understand his decision, so he spent the summer sleeping on a pile of leaves. Then he left our Moravian town and came to Prague where by some sort of miracle he got a job as a boiler-room attendant. Black with coal-dust — he told me later that the showers on the job didn't work — he went home everyday to a boarding house for divorced men. Sometime in the 1980s he signed Charter 77, the 1977 document for human rights. He was doing geological testing at that time, an awful job. It meant living in a caravan without hot water and working outside whatever the weather, often with former criminals who were sent to the job straight from jail. One day two men came to his caravan, told him he was suspected of distributing subversive literature and asked to see his typewriter. He was forced to go with them to the boarding-house and his room was searched. He'd hidden his typewriter and papers in the wardrobe but just as they were about to search it, he remembered to ask them if they had a search warrant. After the Helsinki Conference of 1975 the regime had to keep up an appearance of upholding the law and since the police had no warrant, they left the house."

She paused at the car door. A man ran past them down the street waving his arms and laughing to himself. He was wearing strange pink pants which looked as though they were made out of plastic.

"You seem to have some crazies here! Who's that?"

"He used to be a nuclear physicist but one day he told a colleague that he was thinking about signing Charter 77. The StB came to his apartment to question him and his sister panicked and threw him out. He couldn't find anywhere to live so he slept on park benches. One day he stood in the middle of the street and cursed the regime at the top of his voice. He was taken away to a psychiatric ward — anyone who criticised socialism was considered totally mad! He was forced to take strong doses of drugs for a while, then he was released with an invalid pension and given a tiny room on this estate. Some people here think he's crazy but I find he's got some interesting things to say and he's still got a sense of humour. There's something unbreakable and indestructible in some people. Every now and then he used to go into the restaurant over there and shout:

'The Americans are coming!'

The police who patronized the place would grab their caps and rush out as though they'd been shot from a cannon." Blažej chuckled, "It wasn't just a one-off thing, either, he played his trick several times with great success!"

* * *

Blažej led her up a small path through a leafy hillside cemetary to a plain headstone. On the grave stood small vases of summer flowers and ferns.

"Jan Patočka's grave!"

Jan Patočka's grave

"Who was he?" Alice asked.

"A well-known philosopher and the main inspiration for Charter 77. He died on March 13th 1977 at the age of seventy from cerebral haemorrhage after an eleven-hour police interrogation. He'd often been dragged to the StB headquarters for questioning."

"A simple headstone... I can hardly read his name," she said, wonderingly.

"He was a modest man and I don't suppose the regime wanted attention drawn to his resting-place. Along with Komenský and Masaryk, he made a big mark on European thought. He was a private scholar specializing in German and Greek philosphy but our history didn't allow him a peaceful life. He had to do a spell of forced labour under the Nazis, was banned from lecturing at Charles University after the communist putsch and was prevented from publishing his work after 1968. But he gave lectures in the 'private universities' which met in houses and flats in Prague. The StB had him under surveillance all the time but that didn't stop him from sticking his neck out and becoming one of the leading spokespeople for Charter 77 when it was formed in January of that year."

Alice began to pick some daisies and grasses, "What did the Chartists want?"

"They aimed to draw attention to individual cases where human and civil rights had been ignored and by 1977 they had a strong weapon against the regime because it wasn't respecting international agreements like the Helsinki Final Act of 1975 which upheld human rights. This is important today because it deprives the StB and their cronies of the old excuse that what they did was legal at the time they did it."

She arranged her bunch of flowers and grasses in a small jar at the foot of the headstone, "Did Patočka have a big funeral like Masaryk?"

"The ceremony for him in St Margaret's Church in Břevnov was a sinister affair. It was drowned by the roar of police motorbikes being driven round the church and by helicopters hovering overhead. After the funeral most of the mourners were detained and interrogated and later many of them lost their jobs."

* * *

They crossed Kampa Island and turned to their left down a small cobbled alleyway to the Devil's Brook.

"It's peaceful here: "Alice leaned over the bridge and looked at a little Renaissance house by the stream. Two small saints on the balcony clutched at their haloes. Above them was a row of tiny attic windows.

"That's my house! I'd like to see swans sailing under my bedroom window and I'd have the brook murmering through my dreams..."

"There's probably no central heating, it would be damp in winter."

They crossed to Velkopřevorské Square and he pointed to John Lennon's wall.

"It's wonderful and crazy!" she exclaimed.

"The huge, flaking wall overhung by a magnificent plane tree, was covered with drawings, slogans and scribbles in English and Czech. Near its centre, Lennon's huge bespectacled face, his blue and green hair streaked with yellow, looked solemnly over the square.

She walked up and down reading the inscriptions: 'Be free? Answer yourself!' 'One world!' 'Stop war toys!' 'This is not the end of the world!' 'Make love, not war!'

"People carrying flowers met here to protest against the regime," Blažej said. "They'd get to work painting the wall and they'd sing songs and shout slogans. Then van-loads of police would arrive and scatter them, trampling on the flowers and paint-brushes. They'd paint the whole wall green but the students soon came back."

She paused in front of a green and yellow butterfly, "I like this one!

'Go insane
Stand fight
And stay free'"

She came to the end of the wall and examined a black
and white painting of Lennon's face in a white frame. Below
the portrait lay some withered mistletoe and a yellow carna-
tion. "Life doesn't imitate Art, Life is Art," she murmered.
"It's an icon!"

Blažej sat down on a bench in the middle of the square,
"Communism contained a lot of paradoxes. The years after
the Soviet invasion have been called a cultural graveyard
and its true that official culture was corpse-like. But in the
Seventies and Eighties a lot of things were simmering under
the surface and the 'second culture' as Ivan Jirous called it,
became very important not only for rock musicians but for
other artists, too. Take samizdat, for example..."

She smiled happily at the wall, "Samizdat?"

"A group of writers would get together in someone's flat
bringing a dozen or so copies of their latest work, mostly
carbon copies because the police kept a close eye on photo-
copiers. The texts were put in blank cardboard folders so
that if the StB pounced they'd just look like miscellaneous
collections of typewritten pages.

She took her sketchbook and began to draw Lennon's face.
"What about music?"

"Rock groups like Plastic People of the Universe and
DG. 307 formed a musical underground and young people
used to travel half-way across the country for a concert which
might never take place. Husák's regime was particularly
tough on the Plastics and spread all sort of slanders about
the long-haired musicians describing them as drug addicts
and alcoholic layabouts!"

"I suppose they were banned?"

He nodded, "They still went on playing secretly in pubs
and barns and at weddings. The StB were kept busy going
through a lot of wedding invitations! In September 1976

John Lennon's
Wall

several of them were brought to trial and sent to prison."

"Did you listen to the Plastics?"

"I was crazy about them! It was such strong music...
moody atmospherics — and a far cry from all the bland
nothings on TV and May Day parades."

He took her arm as they recrossed the Devil's Brook, "At
last we were listening to music against something!"

* * *

"Are you tired?"

"Will you carry me?" Alice leaned against him, laughing,
"Where are we?"

"We're in Political Prisoners' Street. During the first three
weeks of August 1989, some weird protests were organized
here against communist President Husák's regime..."

"Who was protesting?" she interrupted.

"The Society for a Merrier Present! Their Merry Security
Patrol charged down this street wearing water-melon helmets
and leading plastic dogs on wheels. They beat up passers-by
with batons made of salame, cucumbers and french bread."

"Edible truncheons!"

Blažej nodded, "Most of it was eaten. The Society put on
grotesque shows parodying the way the police were beating
up demonstrators that year and to show their disapproval of
the Soviet invasion in August 1968, they constructed a whale
using chicken wire, paper and branches and sent it down the
Vltava River from Kampa Island using an inflatable mattress.

"What happened to it?"

"The police caught the huge creature and trampled on it."
Blažej began to laugh, "There were all sorts of Happenings
that August. A big, artificial duck suddenly appeared in
midstream..."

Alice looked puzzled.

"Mr Husák means 'Mr Duck' in English. The bird was
bearing a placard which read:

I DON'T WANT TO BE PRESIDENT."

375

* * *

As they walked up Národní Street on their way back to Alice's little hotel, Blažej stopped abruptly.

"November 17th 1989!"

She studied the memorial, a black wooden plaque with gold lettering. It was topped with supplicating hands and others giving the victory sign. On the pavement there was a thick coating of orange candle wax and on the walls on either side of the plaque there were blurred photographs of massed police, their white helmets blobs against the night.

"The massacre on this street was the spark which lit our Revolution," he said.

Alice looked at him questioningly, "The end of communism?"

Memorial
to November 17th,
1989

EPILOGUE

IT WAS A DAZZLING DAY and Prague lay in full sunlight. From her window seat Alice could see the spires and the roofs of the palaces and churches. Romanesque architecture around Husová, she said to herself, the Gothic cluster round the Old Town Square, the Renaissance Belvedere, the Baroque Church of St Nicholas, the modern, sober buildings of the Baba colony... She closed her eyes.

A huge red sun shone in a jungle of green vegetation and through it tramped a thick-set hunter with a stone axe and a bear slung across his shoulders.

The peaked roofs of the Gothic houses tore through the sky and on the Lesser Town Bridge she saw Wenceslas IV lift his sceptre and wave to her. Two eagles flew over the town bearing Jupiter and Juno in serious argument. On Charles Bridge, Christ brought his hand down from the cross and put it on St Luitgarde's shoulder. She swooned under its touch and quivered with love. Now a thin little man dressed in black with a large collar and a cone-shaped hat, ran onto Charles Bridge and jumped around on one leg like a stork, catching snow crystals in his hands and laughing madly. From the window of Prague Castle, Tycho de Brahe looked up at her through the Emperor Rudolf's telescope.

Gradually the picture clouded over... She opened her eyes and felt a lump in her troat. Her eyelids started to prickle. Two air hostesses approached with the inevitable trolley and she looked quickly down at her lap. She picked up Blažej's neat parcel and felt in curiously. What could it be? Excited, she unwrapped layers of tissue-paper. Whatever was it? Then she looked at her present with a smile. A handkerchief!

* * *

Blažej had a strenuous day with the Blunketts from Texas. They'd been off-hand about the Vladislav Hall and there were problems with their accommodation. 'A fistful of dollars and not even a double bed', Mr. Blunkett muttered ominously, staring at the two single ones. There was some-

thing wrong with the shower, too, and his wife complained that the water looked brown. After a lot of effort and a substantial tip to the hotel manager which he couldn't really afford, Blažej had sorted things out by 10 p.m. and went home. He walked across his small, cluttered room on the sixth floor, threw open the window and lent out. Far below him, he could see the lights of Prague. He felt curiously empty. The telephone rang and he listened to it irritably for a few seconds and then unplugged it. Eventually, he went over to his small writing-table and sat deep in thought...

In her bedroom in a leafy North London suburb, Alice was lying in bed. Her duvet was around her neck and her long, thin legs stuck out beneath it. Her hands were clasped behind her head and she was staring up at the ceiling. Somewhere, close by, an owl hooted.

Bird's — eye
view of Prague

Instructions

HOW TO GET TO THE SPOTS

Ancient and Romanesque times

DÍVČÍ HRAD (DĚVÍN)
(The Maidens' Castle)
You take line B from the metro station Můstek to Anděl (three stops) from where there is an exit straight to the bus station (autobusové nádraží). You take bus No. 231 to the stop Dívčí hrady (5 stops) and then walk up through Tetínská Street and then by path.

ŠÁRKA VALLEY
You take line A from the metro station Můstek to the terminal Dejvická (four stops). Take the exit to Evropská Street and from there continue by tram No. 2 or 26 to the stop Divoká Šárka. From the parking place you take the path that leads down the steps and at the crossroads turn left to Šárecký potok (Šárka Brook).

JESKYNĚ KONĚPRUSY
(KONĚPRUSY CAVES, Golden Horse Hill)
You take line B from the metro station Můstek to Smíchovské nádraží (Smíchov station) (4 stops), from where you take a train to Srbsko (about 40 minutes), then take the path marked with a yellow tourist sign. (This is a whole-day trip). The caves are open daily. Reservations can be made by telephone, No. 0311 2460, or 0311 29423.

A CELTIC SETTLEMENT
(Zbraslav - Závist)
You take line B from the metro station Můstek to Smíchovské nádraží (4 stops). There is a bus station right in front of the station and bus No. 245 goes to Závist. There is a signpost on the right. Follow the arrows up the asphalt path to the top of the hill.

OR

You can take line B from the metro station Můstek to Náměstí rebubliky (1 stop) where you take the exit marked Masarykovo nádraží, get onto a tram No. 3 to the terminal Nádraží Bráník, and from Bráník station go by train to Praha-Zbraslav, from where there is a tourist path up to the settlement.

LEVÝ HRADEC
(Roztoky-Žalov)
You take the metro (line B) from Můstek to Náměstí republiky (1 stop) and the exit to Masarykovo nádraží. Then go by train to Roztoky-Žalov and from there on foot up through the village of Žalov.

STATUE OF ST. WENCESLAS
Wenceslas Square
(Václavské náměstí)
You take line A from the metro station Můstek to Museum

(1 stop). If you take the middle exit you will see the statue straight in front of you.

STATUES OF SS. CYRIL AND METHODIUS
(Charles Bridge)
You take line A from the metro station MŮSTEK to STAROMĚSTSKÁ (1 stop). When you come out turn left, cross Valentinská Street straight on to Křížovnická Street, where you turn left, going down Křížovnická Street till you come to Křížovnické náměstí, which leads you to Charles Bridge.

BASILICA OF ST. GEORGE
(Prague Castle)
and THE MADONNA ENTHRONED
You take line A from the metro station MŮSTEK to HRADČANSKÁ (3 stops). From here you can take tram Nos. 1, 8, 18 or 23 to the stop U PRAŠNÉHO MOSTU.
The street of the same name takes you to the Castle. The Basilica of St. George is on Jiřské náměstí (George Square) behind the St. Vítus cathedral.

ST. MARTIN'S CHURCH
(Kozojedy u Prahy)
You take line A from the metro station MŮSTEK to ŽELIVSKÉHO (5 stops), going out by the exit marked BUS ČSAD. You go along the road till you see the bus station to the right in front of you. You take the ČSAD bus from

platform No. 3 that goes to KOSTELEC NAD ČERNÝMI LESY, route number 10920.
NOTE. Take care here, as there are two lines. We recommend you to write the name KOZOJEDY and show it to the driver, who will either give you a ticket or indicate that he doesn't go there.

THE CHURCH OF ST. JAN OF NEPOMUK
(Štěchovice)
You take line B from the metro station MŮSTEK to ANDĚL (3 stops). You should come out by the exit marked BUS DP and so get to the bus station Na knížecí. Look for platform 6 (towards the back) and take bus route 11670 Prague – Štěchovice – Slapy – Rabyně which will take you to your destination.

ROTUNDA OF THE HOLY ROOD
(Karolina Světlá street)
You take line B from the metro station MŮSTEK to NÁRODNÍ TŘÍDA (1 stop). From the exit you go round the department store MÁJ to Národní třída. You cross Spálená Street and continue in the direction of the National Theatre, under an arcade, crossing Mikulandská Street, and before you come to Voršilská Street turn right out of Národní Street into KAROLINA SVĚTLÁ Street, which will take you to the rotunda.

Gothic

RUINS OF THE ORIGINAL
FORTIFICATIONS AT MŮSTEK
Metro station Můstek,

GOTHIC ARCADES
(Havelská Street)
You walk through the metro
staion MŮSTEK, coming out into
the street NA MŮSTKU. Go straight
ahead, the third crossing you come
to is HAVELSKÁ.

GOTHIC SHOP WINDOW
Little Square
Malé náměstí
No. 12
You take line A from the metro
station MŮSTEK to STAROMĚSTSKÁ
(1 stop), from where you go along
KAPROVÁ Street to the crossroads,
taking the second turning to the
right in front of the house with the
wine cellar U zelené žáby (At the
Sign of the Green Frog). The street
U RADNICE will take you to Malé
náměstí.

THE HOUSE AT THE SIGN
OF THE GREEN FROG
(U ZELENÉ ŽÁBY)
U radnice Street
No. 8.

THE OLD TOWN CLOCK
(STAROMĚSTSKÝ ORLOJ)
Old Town Square
(Staroměstské náměstí)
No. 31.
From the metro station MŮSTEK
you go down the street
Na MŮSTKU, keeping leftwards

and crossing three streets till you
come to MELANTRICHOVA Street,
which comes out on the Old Town
Square. You will see the Old Town
Hall with the clock straight in front
of you.

THE HOUSE AT THE SIGN
OF THE STONE BELL
(DŮM U KAMENNÉHO
ZVONU)
Old Town Square
Staroměstské náměstí
No. 13
If you come out onto the Square
from Melantrichova Street the
house At the Sign of the Stone
Bell is on your right, in about the
middle of the upper edge of the
Square.

THE HOUSE AT THE SIGN
OF THE GOLDEN UNICORN
(DŮM U ZLATÉHO
JEDNOROŽCE)
The Old Town Square
Staroměstské náměstí
No. 20
This house is across the Square
from the clock.

GABLE OF THE HOUSE
Celetná street
Celetná ulice
No. 601
You take line B from the metro
station MŮSTEK to NÁMĚSTÍ
REPUBLIKY (1 stop). You come out
in the direction of the Art
Nouveau Municipal House
(Obecní dům) and going round it

come to the Powder Tower. Going through the gateway takes you into Celetná Street.

THE HOUSE AT THE SIGN OF THE BLACK SUN (DŮM U ČERNÉHO SLUNCE)
Celetná street
Celetná ulice
No. 556
This house is on your left as you go away from the Powder Tower.

TÝN STREET
Týnská ulice
No. 10
From the Old Town Square you go along DLOUHÁ TŘÍDA past the Tchibo-le Café shop and turn right into Týnská ulička (Týn Alley) which leads to TÝNSKÁ, where you turn left. (If the road is not blocked, you can go straight to Týnská from the Old Town Square, round the House at the Sign of the Stone Bell.)

SPIRE OF THE CHURCH OF ST. CATHERINE
You take line A from the metro station MŮSTEK to MUSEUM (1 stop) change to line C and go to I. P. PAVLOVA (1 stop). When you come up you should have the Hotel Kriváň on your left. You go straight down the road, cross Sokolovská Street into JEČNÁ. After a few steps fork left into Kateřinská Street, continuing along it until it crosses Viničná. You can see the spire well from here.

THE CHURCH OF ST. THOMAS
Letenská street,
CHAPEL OF ST. DOROTHY
You take line A from the metro station MŮSTEK to MALOSTRANSKÁ (2 stops). From the metro station you walk down Klárov Street, turning right at the traffic lights into LETENSKÁ Street. The Church of St. Thomas is on the right side. If you wish to go into the garden, turn right into a blind alley, where there is a door into the garden.

PUB U KRÁLE BRABANTSKÉHO
Thunovská street
No. 15
You take line A from the metro station MŮSTEK to MALOSTRANSKÁ (2 stops). From the metro station you walk down Klárov Street, turning right at the traffic lights into LETENSKÁ Street, which takes you into MALOSTRANSKÉ NÁMĚSTÍ (Little Quarter Square). From there you go past Smiřický's house and turn up the second street to the right. SNĚMOVNÍ, into THUNOVSKÁ. The pub (wine cellar) is on the left side.

STATUE OF CHARLES IV.
(Křížovnické náměstí)

THE CHURCH OF OUR LADY OF THE SNOWS
(Kostel Panny Marie Sněžné)
Jungmann square
(Jungmannovo náměstí)
You come out of the metro station MŮSTEK by the exit onto Wenceslas Square (VÁCLAVSKÉ

386

NÁMĚSTÍ) and take the nearest passage round the night-club Carioca to the right into JUNGMANNOVO NÁMĚSTÍ.

THE NEW TOWN HALL
(Nová Radnice)
Karlovo Square
Karlovo náměstí
No. 23/1
You take line B from the metro station MŮSTEK to KARLOVO NÁMĚSTÍ (2 stops). On coming out of the station you turn down the street so that the park is on your right. The Town Hall is at the end of the Square on the right.

THE BETHLEHEM CHAPEL
Bethlehem Square
(Betlémské náměstí)
You take line B from the metro station MŮSTEK to NÁRODNÍ TŘÍDA (1 stop). On coming out you go round the department store Máj, cross NÁRODNÍ TŘÍDA and continue along it till you come to NA PERŠTÝNĚ. You walk along this street to the crossroads, dominated by a Cubist house on the left, and a few yards further on turn left into Bethlehem Square.

PICTURE OF JOHN HUS IN THE ST. AGNES' CONVENT
St. Anne's Square
You take line B from the metro

station MŮSTEK to NÁMĚSTÍ REPUBLIKY (1 stop). From there it is best to walk, passing the streets Truhlářská, Soukenická and Klimentská, to the palace of the Czechoslovak Airlines (Československé Aerolinie), opposite which is the Ministry of Industry. You turn left past the Ministry into ŘÁSNOVKA, which takes you into HAŠTALSKÉ NÁMĚSTÍ. Turn right out of the square into ANEŽSKÁ Street, which leads straight to the picture gallery.

THE BRIDGE TOWER
(Charles Bridge)
SYMBOL OF THE KINGFISHER.

STATUE OF JAN ŽIŽKA
(Žižkov)
You take line B from the metro station MŮSTEK to FLORENC (2 stops). On coming out of the station cross the road to the bus stop and take bus No. 133 or 207 to the stop U PAMÁTNÍKU. You go a little way down HUSITSKÁ Street and turn right up the street U PAMÁTNÍKU (Near the Memorial).

JIŘSKÁ GALLERY
(Prague Castle)
George Square
Jiřské náměstí
Pictures by MASTER THEODORICUS.

Renaissance

WINDOW IN THE POWDER
TOWER
(Náměstí republiky)

THE TOWN HALL
OF THE OLD TOWN
(Staroměstská Radnice)
Old Town Square
(Staroměstské náměstí)
No. 3/1
Windows and doors.

HOUSE AT THE SIGN
OF THE MINUTE
Old Town Square
(Staroměstské náměstí)
No. 2/3

FACADE OF THE HOUSE
No. 5
Havelská street
You come out of the metro station
MŮSTEK into the street Na MŮSTKU,
and you go straight along it and
then slightly left, crossing Rytířská,
passing the narrow lane V kotcích
and the third cross road is
HAVELSKÁ. BRUNWIK'S HOUSE.

SWALLOW ROOFS
(Husova street)
Nos. 19−21
You take line A from the metro
station MŮSTEK to STAROMĚSTSKÁ
(1 stop). On coming out you turn
left and go to the crossing with
VALENTINSKÁ Street. Turn left into
this street and it will take you to
MARIÁNSKÉ NÁMĚSTÍ (Marian
Square). Husova Street leads out
of this Square. There is a gallery

on the ground floor of the house
with the swallow roofs.

THE HOUSE AT THE SIGN
OF FIVE CROWNS
(Melantrichova Street)
No. 11
From the metro station MŮSTEK
you go down NA MŮSTKU,
crossing Rytířská, passing the lane
V kotcích and also Havelská, so
that you come to MELANTRICHOVA.
The House at the Sign of Five
Crowns is on the left next to the
shoe shop.

TAYFL'S HOUSE
Melantrichova
No. 15
Going from the House at the Sign
of Five Crowns you should make
a stop in the Renaissance
courtyard of No. 15. Then
continue to the crossroads
Melantrichova and Kožná. Here
you will find a house with a
Renaissance portal.

PORTAL OF THE HOUSE
AT THE SIGN
OF THE TWO GOLDEN
BEARS
Melantrichova 475 − Kožná 1.

THE HOUSE AT THE SIGN
OF THE GOLDEN TREE
Dlouhá třída Street
No. 37
You take line B from the metro
station MŮSTEK to NÁMĚSTÍ
REPUBLIKY (1 stop), and from there

walk past the department store Kotva to the crossroads, where you turn left into DLOUHÁ TŘÍDA.

AT THE SIGN OF THE GOLDEN WELL
Karlova Street
No. 3
You take line A from the metro station MŮSTEK to STAROMĚSTSKÁ (1 stop). On coming out you turn left, pass Valentinská Street, go straight on to Křížovnická Street, turn left into it, and it will take you to Křížovnické náměstí, where you turn left into KARLOVA Street. Pass Liliové Street and at the crossing of Seminářské and Karlova Street you will see the corner house At the Sign of the Golden Well in front of you.

THE HOUSE OF THE FATHER, MOTHER AND CHILD
(Sněmovní Street)
No. 6
You take line A from the metro station MŮSTEK to MALOSTRANSKÁ (2 stops). You go down KLÁROV Street, turning right into LETENSKÁ, which will take you to MALOSTRANSKÉ NÁMĚSTÍ. The first street on the right is Tomášská, the second SNĚMOVNÍ.

STATUE OF ST. GEORGE
(Prague Castle – Third Courtyard)

THE VLADISLAV HALL
(Vladislavský sál)
(Prague Castle – Third Courtyard)

PICTURE GALLERY
(Prague Castle – Second Courtyard)
A Horse by Adrien de Vries.

BELVEDERE
THE SINGING FOUNTAIN
(Prague Castle)
From the tram stop U PRAŠNÉHO MOSTU you go up the street of the same name to the Castle. You pass the extensive building of the Prague Castle Riding School on your right, and on your left there is an entrance to the Royal Gardens, through which you can walk to the Belvedere.

THE SCHWARZENBERG-LOBKOWICZ PALACE
Hradčany square
(Hradčanské náměstí)
No. 185
After reaching Prague Castle you walk through from the second courtyard to the first courtyard and from there onto HRADČANSKÉ NÁMĚSTÍ (Hradčany Square). The Schwarzenberg Palace is on the left and it contains the Museum of Military History.

VLAŠSKÁ STREET
From Hradčany Square you go down the steps called RADNICKÉ SCHODY into Neruda Street. Then take the street Jánský vršek to the right down into VLAŠSKÁ.

SNACKBAR U RUDOLFA II
Meiselova Street
No. 5
You take line A from the metro station MŮSTEK to STAROMĚSTSKÁ

389

(1 stop). On coming out you turn right along Kaprová Street, pass Žatecká Street on the left and take the next left turn into MEISELOVA Street, before the Church of St. Nicholas.

THE TOMB
OF RABBI LŐW
(U Starého hřbitova)
Going down Maiselova Street you pass the Jewish Town Hall and reach the Old-New Synagogue. Turn left here and you will be in the street U Starého hřbitova, where there is an entrance to the Old Jewish Cemetery.

FAUST'S HOUSE
Karlovo Square
Karlovo náměstí
No. 40/502
You take line B from the metro station MŮSTEK to KARLOVO NÁMĚSTÍ (2 stops). On coming out you cross over to the park, from where you can see Faust's House (Faustův dům).

THE SWANS' HARBOUR
(U Lužického semináře)
You can see this swans' harbour from the Charles Bridge on your right as you go towards the Little Quarter. You go down from the bridge by the steps on the right, go round the hotel U tří pštrosů (At the Sign of the Three Ostriches), reaching a little square (Kampa) with a stream called Čertovka on the right. The street U LUŽICKÉHO SEMINÁŘE leads off this square and it will take you to a park and the harbour.

KEPLER'S HOUSE
(Karlova Street)
No. 4/188

Baroque

STATUE OF HOPE
(Malostranská metro station)
You take line A from the metro station MŮSTEK (2 stops).

MALOSTRANSKÁ KAVÁRNA
(Café)
Lesser Town Square
(Malostranské náměstí)
No. 28

THE CHURCH OF ST. NICHOLAS
Square of the Most Holy Trinity)
Náměstí Nejsvětější trojice
From the Malostranská metro station you walk down Klárov, turning right at the traffic lights into Letenská Street, which will take you to Malostranské náměstí. You cross the square, past Tomášská Street and Sněmovní on the right into NERUDOVA Street up the hill, turning left into NÁMĚSTÍ NEJSVĚTĚJŠÍ TROJICE with its Marian Column.

THE SUMMER PALACE THE STAR
(Hvězda - Liboc)
You take line A from the metro station MŮSTEK to HRADČANSKÁ (3 stops). From there you take a No. 8 tram to NA VYPICHU (10 stops) and going round the tram terminal to the right you cross the road and take the path to the gateway of Hvězda Park, which you can see from the tram. The path leads straight through the park to the summer palace.

THE VRTBA GARDENS
(Vrtbovské zahrady)
Karmelitská Street
(Passage through the House)
No. 25
From MALOSTRANSKÉ NÁMĚSTÍ you follow the tramlines into KARMELITSKÁ Street. House No. 25 is on your right.

THE VALDŠTEJN PALACE
Wallenstein Square
Valdštejnské náměstí
No. 4/17
You take line A from the metro station MŮSTEK to MALOSTRANSKÁ (2 stops). You cross the little park with the fountains by the station into Valdštejnská Street, which comes out into VALDŠTEJNSKÉ NÁMĚSTÍ.

THE LORETTO AND THE ČERNÍN PALACE
Loretto Square
(Loretánské náměstí)
No. 7/100
You take line A from the metro station MŮSTEK to MALOSTRANSKÁ (2 stops) and there take a No. 22 tram (up the hill) which will take you to POHOŘELEC. From there you go to the left downhill to LORETÁNSKÉ NÁMĚSTÍ.
STATUES OF SAINTS IN THE LORETTO CHAPEL

STATUES OF JUPITER AND JUNO
(The Thun-Hohenstein palace, the Italian Embassy)

Nerudova Street
No. 20/214
From MALOSTRANSKÉ NÁMĚSTÍ you
go up Nerudova Street. The Palace
is on your right.

STATUES OF DAY AND NIGHT
(The Morzini Palace),
AND THE CARYATIDS
Nerudova Street
No. 5/256
The Palace is on your left as you
go up the street.

THE HOUSE AT THE SIGN
OF THE WHITE LAMB
(Dům U Bílého Beránka)
Úvoz Street
No. 12
You take line A from the metro
station MŮSTEK to MALOSTRANSKÁ
(2 stops), go down Klárov, turn
right into Letenská, cross
Malostranské náměstí into
Nerudova Street, continuing till
the crossing Radnické schody
— Ke Hradu, where you take the
street ÚVOZ on up. The House at
the Sign of the White Lamb is on
your right.

STATUE OF ST. HUBERT
Tomášská Street
No. 4/26
You take line A from the metro
station MŮSTEK to MALOSTRANSKÁ
(2 stops). You cross the little park

by the station into Valdštejnská
Street and on into Valdštejnské
Square, which TOMÁŠSKÁ Street
leads out of.

STATUE OF ST. LUITGARDE
(The Charles Bridge)

THE KLEMENTINUM
Křižovnické náměstí
No. 4

THE CHURCH
OF ST. FRANCIS
Square of the Knights of the Cross
Křižovnické náměstí
The church of St. Francis is to the
right behind the statue of
Charles IV. (Not to be confused
with the CHURCH OF ST. SAVIOUR
(Svatý Salvátor).

MADONNA ON THE PORTAL
OF THE CHURCH
OF ST. FRANCIS

MADONNA ON THE HOUSE
Celetná Street
No. 23
You take line B from the metro
station MŮSTEK to NÁMĚSTÍ
REPUBLIKY (1 stop) and walk
through the Powder Tower into
CELETNÁ. The Madonna is on the
right, opposite the house At the
Sign of the Black Mother of God
(U černé matky Boží).

Revival

STATUE OF JUNGMANN
Jungmann Square
Jungmannovo náměstí

CUBIST COLUMN WITH A LAMP.

MUSEUM OF THE CITY OF PRAGUE
Na Poříčí Street
No. 52
You take line B from the metro station MŮSTEK to FLORENC (2 stops). You go through the hall to the Stardust fruit machines, turn left and take the exit marked Sokolovská — Museum hl. m. Prahy. The museum is just on your left in the park.
LANGWEIL'S MODEL

STATUE OF PALACKÝ
Palacký Square
(Palackého náměstí)
You take line B from the metro station MŮSTEK to KARLOVO NÁMĚSTÍ (2 stops) and take the exit to PALACKÉHO NÁMĚSTÍ. The statue stands in front of the Ministry of Labour and Social Affairs.

THE OLDEST ŠKODA CAR
National Technical Museum
(Národní technické museum)
Kostelní Street
No. 42/1320
You take line A from the metro station MŮSTEK to HRADČANSKÁ (3 stops), then go by tram Nos. 1, 8, 25 or 26 to LETENSKÉ NÁMĚSTÍ. Walk along OVENECKÁ Street,

turn right into LETOHRADSKÁ, then left into MUZEJNÍ, which leads to KOSTELNÍ, where the Museum is.

THE ŽIVNOSTENSKÁ BANK
(Na Příkopě Street)
No. 24/860 – 864
You can walk from the metro station MŮSTEK along the street NA PŘÍKOPĚ to the bank, which is on your right. Na Příkopě is known as Prague's Wall Street.

ART NOUVEAU EGYPTIAN FIGURES
Kaprova Street
No. 9
You take line A from the metro station MŮSTEK to STAROMĚSTSKÁ (1 stop), coming out in Kaprová Street.

THE MAIN STATION
(Hlavní nádraží) –
ART NOUVEAU PANELS
You take line A from the metro station MŮSTEK to MUSEUM (1 stop), change to line C and go to HLAVNÍ NÁDRAŽÍ (1 stop).

THE HOUSE AT THE SIGN OF THE BLACK MOTHER OF GOD
(Dům U černé matky Boží)
AND THE STAIRWAY
Celetná Street
No. 34/569
The house stands at the corner of Celetná Street and Ovocný trh (The Fruit Market).

CUBIST HOUSE
Neklanova Street
No. 7
You take line B from the metro station MŮSTEK to KARLOVO NÁMĚSTÍ (2 stops). You take the exit to PALACKÉHO NÁMĚSTÍ and RAŠÍNOVO NÁBŘEŽÍ (The Rašín Embankment). Here you take tram Nos. 3, 17 or 21 to VÝTOŇ. The main dominant here is the Railway Bridge, and the tram goes under it. Then cross Rašínovo nábřeží into VNISLAVOVA Street and take the second turning to the right, which is NEKLANOVA.

HLÁVKA'S BRIDGE
(Hlávkův most)
AND THE STATUE LABOUR
You take line A from the metro station MŮSTEK to MUSEUM (1 stop), change to line C and go to VLTAVSKÁ (4 stops). From there you can walk to Hlávka's Bridge past the Constructivist building Energoprojekt.

THE CONSTRUCTIVIST BUILDING OF THE FORMER ELECTRICITY CORPORATION
Bubenečská Street
No. 1
This stands at the head of Hlávka's Bridge, and is now Energoprojekt.

THE BAŤA DEPARTMENT STORE
Wenceslas Square
Václavské náměstí
No. 6
You come out of the metro station MŮSTEK into WENCESLAS SQUARE. The Baťa shop is on your right.

THE BARRANDOV TERRACES
Barrandovská Street
No. 1/165
You take line B from the metro station MŮSTEK to SMÍCHOVSKÉ NÁDRAŽÍ (Smíchov Station) (4 stops). There is a bus stop right in front of the station and bus No. 105 will take you to the Barrandov Terraces (BARRANDOVSKÉ TERASY) (2 stops).

ADOLF LOOS' HOUSE
Nad hradním vodojemem street
Ořechovka
No. 14
You take line A from the metro station MŮSTEK to HRADČANSKÁ (3 stops) and then tram No. 1 or 18 to OŘECHOVKA (4 stops). The house is on the left side of the street, where you have to go up some steps and turn left.

THE FUNCTIONALIST COLONY BABA
You take line A from the metro station MŮSTEK to HRADČANSKÁ (3 stops) and then bus No. 131 from BUBENEČSKÁ Street to U MATĚJE, from where you go up MATĚJSKÁ.

THE CHURCH
OF ST. WENCESLAS (Václav)
(Náměstí Svatopluka Čecha,
Vršovice)
(Svatopluka Čecha Square,
Vršovice)
You take line A from the metro
station MŮSTEK to NÁMĚSTÍ MÍRU
(Peace Square) (2 stops). From
there you can take tram No. 4 or 22
to NÁMĚSTÍ SVATOPLUKA ČECHA.

THE HOUSE AT THE SIGN
OF THE PICTURE
OF THE VIRGIN MARY
(Na Kampě)
No. 9
You can see the house from the
Charles Bridge. You can go down
from the bridge on the left and the
house faces you. The lane beside
the house takes you to the river
Vltava.

Communism

STATUE
OF BROTHERHOOD
(Vrchlického sady)
You take line A from the metro
station Můstek to Museum (1 stop),
change to line C and go to
Hlavní nádraží (1 stop). As you
come out of the station you see
the statue to the right in the park
opposite.

THE ANGEL AND MOSAIC
OF THE KREMLIN
(The metro station Anděl)
You take line B from the metro
station Můstek to Anděl (3 stops).
You take the exit to Lidická
Street.

THE KINSKÝ PALACE
BALCONY
Old Town Square
Staroměstské náměstí
No. 12/1002
You take line A from the metro
station Můstek to Staroměstská
(1 stop). Turn right into Kaprova
Street which will take you to the
Old Town Square (Staroměstské
náměstí). The Kinský Palace is
straight opposite you.

THE SCULPTURAL GROUP
OF THE PEOPLE'S MILITIA
(Ke Kotlářce)
You take line B from the metro
station Můstek to Anděl (3 stops)
and go from there by tram Nos. 4,
6, 7 or 9 to Kotlářka, where you
can immediately see the monstrous
statue.

THE NATIONAL
MEMORIAL
(Žižkov)
You take line B from the metro
station Můstek to Florenc
(2 stops) and from there take bus
No. 133 or 207 to U památníku.
You walk a little way down
Husitská and then turn right up
the street U památníku.

BUILDING
OF THE FORMER
STATE SECRET POLICE
Thakurova Street
No. 1
You take line A from the metro
station Můstek to the terminal
Dejvická (4 stops). You come out
in Evropská Street and take tram
Nos. 2, 20 or 26 to Thakurova
(1 stop). Thakurova Street is on
the right and the former State
Secret Police occupied the whole
vast compound of buildings.

"THE LITTLE HOUSE"
("Domeček")
Kapucínská street
No. 10
You take line A from the metro
station Můstek to Malostranská
(2 stops), then tram No. 22 to
Pohořelec. You then go down
the hill to Loretánské náměstí
and cross the square into
Kapucínská Street.
"The Little House" is not visible
from the street, only a wall with
the remains of barbed wire.

396

THE INTERNATIONAL HOTEL
Koulova Street
No. 15
You take line A from the metro station Můstek to the terminal Dejvická (4 stops) and then tram No. 20 or 25 will take you right to the hotel (also the terminal).

THE MINISTRY OF INDUSTRY
Na Františku Street
No. 32
You take line B from the metro station Můstek to Náměstí Republiky (1 stop). From there it is best to walk, passing the streets Truhlářská, Soukenická and Klimentská, to the palace of the Czechoslovak Airlines (Československé aerolinie), and opposite this, on the left of the Jan Šverma Bridge, is the Ministry of Industry (Ministerstvo průmyslu).

THE SITE OF THE FORMER STALIN MONUMENT
(Letná Hill.)
You take line A from the metro station Můstek to Malostranská (2 stops) and then tram No. 17 to Čechův most. Opposite the bridge there is a hill with steps up it to the peak where the Stalin Monument used to stand. Now there is a big metronome there.

THE FORMER EDITORIAL OFFICES OF THE LITERARY NEWSPAPER
(Literární noviny)
(Betlémská Street)
No. 1

You take line B from the metro station Můstek to Národní třída (1 stop). Going round the department store Máj you come to Národní třída, where you turn left towards the National Theatre, cross the street to the Slavia coffee house and go along Smetanovo nábřeží (The Smetana Embankment) towards the Castle which you see on the hill. At the crossing with Betlémská Street stands a corner house where, on the ground floor, there used to be the editorial offices of The Literary Newspaper, which triggered the Prague Spring 1968.

THE RADIO BUILDING
Vinohradská Street
No. 12
You take line A from the metro station Můstek to Museum (1 stop), coming out leftwards into Vinohradská Street. You go through the subway and on up to the right.

THE DEATH MASK
OF JAN PALACH
Jan Palach Square
Palachovo náměstí
No. 2
You take line A from the metro station Můstek to Staroměstská (1 stop). You come out to the left into Kaprová Street, cross Valentinská and go straight on into Náměstí Jana Palacha. You go up a few steps on the right into the arcade of the Philosophical Faculty which you go through and down the other

side. Jan Palach's death mask is on the wall of this faculty.

RUZYNĚ PRISON
You take line A from the metro station MŮSTEK to HRADČANSKÁ (3 stops), then bus No. 108 to STARÉ NÁMĚSTÍ (10 stops).

PREFAB CITY
Of the numerous possibilities to see a socialist concrete jungle, we offer this one: you take line A from the metro station MŮSTEK to MUSEUM (1 stop), change to line C and go to HÁJE (9 stops). Spreading all around you is the Southern Town, the most abominable of Prague's prefab towns.

JAN PATOČKA'S GRAVE
(Břevnovský hřbitov)
(Břevnov cemetery)
You take line A from the metro station MŮSTEK to HRADČANSKÁ (3 stops) and then tram No. 8, to BŘEVNOVSKÝ KLÁŠTER where you turn left round the Monastery and along the street U VOJTĚŠKY to the cemetery.

JOHN LENNON'S WALL
(Velkopřevorské Square)
(Velkopřevorské náměstí)
You take line A from the metro station MŮSTEK to MALOSTRANSKÁ (2 stops), from where you walk down Klárov, cross Letenská and go straight into the street U LUŽICKÉHO SEMINÁŘE to the Charles Bridge. You go down the steps to Kampa and turn right into HROZNOVÁ Street and cross the little bridge into VELKOPŘEVORSKÉ NÁMĚSTÍ. John Lennon's Wall stands beneath an enormous plane tree that is 700 years old.

THE RAISED HANDS
(Národní třída Street)
You take line B from the metro station MŮSTEK to NÁRODNÍ TŘÍDA and go round the department store Máj into NÁRODNÍ TŘÍDA (National Street), then cross Spálená Street and you will see an arcade in front of you, where the carving is.

WARNING
The names of streets are sometimes changed, and also the names of tram and bus stops.

Index

403